RAILW

RESTO

1997

Edited by Alan C. Butcher

IAN ALLAN
Publishing

Contents

Front cover: **The practice of renumbering locomotives to recall long since scrapped members of the class is increasing, usually due to events being commemorated or special charters. Here No '69521' crosses Swithland Viaduct on the Great Central Railway played by the real No 69523.** *John East*

Back cover: **More history is re-created at Cranmore on the East Somerset Railway as GWR No 1450 runs with an auto-coach and milk tanker recalling long gone days on the Hemyock branch.** *Robin Stewart-Smith*

Previous page: **Class 8F power on the Keighley & Worth Valley Railway. The 12.40 from Keighley arrives at Oxenhope.** *Michael J. Collins*

First published 1997

ISBN 0 7110 2497 9

Published by Ian Allan Publishing

an imprint of Ian Allan Ltd, Terminal House, Station Approach, Shepperton, Surrey TW17 8AS; and printed by Ian Allan Printing Ltd, Coombelands House, Coombelands Lane, Addlestone, Weybridge, Surrey KT15 1HY

Code: 9703/C1

Chairman's Foreword

April 1996 saw the final merger of the Association of Independent Railways (AIR) and Association of Railway Preservation Societies (ARPS) which became the Association of Independent & Preserved Railways (AIRPS). All a bit of a mouthful so we adopted the more easily understood sobriquet of *Heritage Railways* for everyday use. The activities of the new organisation fall into several distinct categories of which the main headings are Safety, Operating, Legislation, Marketing, Commmercial and Awards and each has an appropriate committee to digest information received and distribute details and advice to member companies. It is at once a trade association and a forum for the exchange of mutual concerns.

But this is just the umbrella body, for *Heritage Railways* is the individual companies which are indeed individual and range from 10¼in gauge lines up to 18 miles or more of standard gauge track carrying everything from the heaviest of former BR locomotives down to diminutive tank engines. Some Heritage Railways are out-and-out commercial concerns; others are non-profit-making companies whilst many are operated by charitable trusts, but all have the same aim, to provide an enjoyable, nostalgic day out to relish the smell and joys of steam — and on some lines, diesels. Whatever the ultimate aim, all have to make a profit to cover maintenance and other costs and all have a common desire to woo as many passengers per year as they possibly can and this has brought in special activities throughout the 'season' covering Christmas time Santa Specials, Mince Pie Specials, Thomas the Tank Engine attractions, Diesel galas, to name but a few. The movement is very lively

and whilst everyone looks over their shoulders to see what the next railway is doing, there is no real rivalry or competition between them for competition comes not from fellow railways but from other entertainment caterers — zoos, theme parks and the like. I say 'other entertainment' advisedly for all have realised that *Heritage Railways* is in show business and the pure railway element has to be complemented with good refreshment facilities, children's playgrounds, good toilets and souvenir shops. And our lines are doing jolly well at both railways and side shows.

To keep them up to scratch, there are several awards schemes given each year to worthy and winning projects. AIRPS has its own awards committee and of course one of the main activities is the annual *Ian Allan Heritage Awards* about which there is a separate feature in this book. But perhaps the most prestigious 'general' award is the Independent Railway of the Year Award sponsored by *Railway World*. The current holders are Llangollen Railway with runners up Swanage and Seaton Tramway, all three of which did splendidly in 1996.

The Movement continues to grow and whilst many may have thought there were too many lines being revived, it now seems that the public has an insatiable appetite for rail travel by steam or even diesel and electric power as long as it seems 'nostalgic'. Long may it continue and long may *Heritage Railways* serve the public by presenting a happy atmosphere and safe, clean and efficient train services.

Ian Allan
Chairman, AIRPS

Introduction

The last 12 months have seen the emergence of several new schemes, some of which have graduated to be included in this new edition of *Railways Restored*, along with a few sites that have been around a bit longer but not hitherto included. The same period has seen the demise of a couple of smaller sites; not due to lack of commitment by volunteers or patronage, but to a change of council policy in one case, and the vandal elsewhere. In both cases the stock, and volunteers, have moved on, joining forces with other schemes, and strengthening the Movement at the same time.

The various awards are being 'fought' for on an increasing basis, radically changing the public's conception of their day out. Stock awaiting restoration has been tidied up, toilet and catering facilities improved, and a 'day out package' put together for all the family.

New items of interest are being acquired all the time. As this issue was being prepared the privatised

rail freight company, English Welsh & Scottish Railway, was preparing to dispose of surplus locomotives and rolling stock. This will result in the acquisition of locomotives from classes 31, 33 and 47 for preservation — these will keep company with the various types of rolling stock. Whilst it may seem contary to the 'steam' railway policy it should be remembered that steam disappeared from the main line 30-odd years ago, and the majority of branch lines were being dieselised before that. Today's younger enthusiasts would never have seen steam in action, the nearest probably being Thomas the Tank!

Railways Restored is full of information enabling the reader to choose an enjoyable 'railway' day out virtually anywhere in the country. Areas once thought too far away from centres of population are being targetted by visitors and the railway preservation movement will ensure an environmentally friendly way to enable views of the countryside to be enjoyed.

Ian Allan National Railway Heritage Awards

The awards have been made annually since 1979 with the object of encouraging high standards of structural restoration and environmental care, thereby promoting public recognition and awareness of historic railway structures and their place in the environment. We aim to promote careful design and quality workmanship in restoration, modernisation and maintenance, after taking full account of all relevant factors, particularly, of course, manpower and finance. In this way, we encourage both public and private railways to present their operational premises as an attractive 'shop window' while occupiers of former railway buildings now used for other purposes are similarly encouraged to retain as much as possible of the original character.

The organisers are the Association of Railway Preservation Societies and the main sponsors are Ian Allan Ltd, together with British Rail through their Community Unit and the Railway Heritage Trust. Judging is done from the beginning of May through to the end of August and the results are notified at the beginning of October. The awards are presented in late November at a prestigious location by a well-known public figure, with full media coverage.

WHAT IS ELIGIBLE

1 Any present or former railway structure such as a station, warehouse, bridge, viaduct, tunnel or signalling installation, that has been sympathetically restored for whatever purpose.

2 A replica structure intended to re-create or augment some aspect of the railway heritage.

3 A new structure designed in traditional style in order to blend with or complement the local environment.

WHO CAN ENTER?

Any group in Great Britain and Ireland involved in railway preservation, whether as a private railway company or as a less formal organisation. British Rail, Irish Rail, Northern Ireland Railways (NIR). Other public or commercial organisation. Private individuals.

The scheme is divided into:
(a) The Volunteer Sector for organisations run wholly or largely by volunteers.
(b) The Public & Commercial Sector. In cases of doubt, the awards committee decides which sector is appropriate.

For application forms apply to:
Arthur Harding, 6 Ullswater Grove, Alresford, Hants SO24 9NP. Tel: 01826 22018.

Editor's Notes

On the following pages will be found a guide to the major preserved railways, railway museums and preservation centres in the British Isles. Information for visitors has been set out in tabular form for easy reference, together with a locomotive stocklist for most centres.

Many preservation centres and operating lines provide facilities for other groups and organisations to restore locomotives and equipment on their premises. It has not been possible to include full details of these groups, but organisations which own locomotives are shown under the centres at which they operate. In addition a full list of member societies of the AIRPS is given elsewhere. In the case of most operating lines their length is given but there is no guarantee that services are operated over the entire length.

Within the heading to each entry a reference has been incorporated for guidance as to what each site offers in the way of passenger service to visitors. These are as follows:

Timetable Service: railways providing a passenger service between two or more stations with public access; eg Mid-Hants Railway.

Steam Centre: a railway or preservation site offering a passenger service on a short length of line, on a regular basis, with public access at only one point; eg Lavender Line.

Museum: A museum or site that does not offer a passenger service on a regular basis, if at all; eg Science Museum, London. Some sites may however offer rides on miniature railways.

As well as a guide as to what to expect on each site, this year's *Railways Restored* shows what, if any, particular professional body the Companies, or Societies, belong to; these are:

AIRPS: Indicates that either the company or supporter's organisation is a member of the Association of Independent & Preserved Railways (AIRPS).

TT: Indicates that the organisation is a member of the Transport Trust.

Membership of the AIRPS and TT is open to both organisations and private individuals. Private members are able to take advantage of concessions offered to them by the organisations that subscribe to these two bodies.

Details given under **Access by public transport** should be checked beforehand to ensure services shown are operating.

Visitors wishing to see specific items of rolling stock or locomotives are advised to check before their visit that the exhibit is available for inspection. It should be stressed that not all items are usually available for inspection due to restoration, operating or other restrictions.

The AIRPS Annual Award

This, the premier award made by AIRPS, is made to a group or organisation making an outstanding contribution to railway preservation during the year of the award.

The Award takes the form of a Royal Train Headboard from the London, Brighton & South Coast Railway, which is on loan to AIRPS from the National Railway Museum. The award is held for one year and the winning group also receives a commemorative plaque. The Award is announced and presented at the Association's Annual General Meeting which is held on the last weekend of January each year.

Standard Abbreviations

Builders abbreviations

AEC	Associated Equipment Co
AEG	Allgemeine Electricitaets Gesellschaft
A/Porter	Aveling & Porter Ltd
A/Whitworth	Armstrong Whitworth
B/Drewry	Baguley/Drewry
B/Peacock	Beyer Peacock & Co
B/Hawthorn	Black, Hawthorn & Co
BRCW	Birmingham Railway, Carriage & Wagon
BTH	British Thomson Houston
Buch	23 August Locomotive Works
D/Metcalfe	Davies & Metcalfe
E/Electric	English Electric Ltd
F/Jennings	Fletcher Jennings & Co
F/Walker	Fox Walker
G/England	George England & Co
GRCW	Gloucester Railway, Carriage & Wagon
H/Clarke	Hudswell Clarke & Co Ltd
H/Leslie	Hawthorn Leslie & Co
H/Hunslet	Hudson Hunslet
K/Stuart	Kerr Stuart & Co Ltd
M/Cam	Metropolitan Cammel
M/Rail	Motor Rail Ltd
M/Vick	Metrovick (Metropolitan-Vickers)
M/Wardle	Manning Wardle & Co Ltd
N/British	North British Locomotive Co Ltd
N/Wilson	Nasmyth Wilson & Co Ltd
O&K	Orenstein & Koppel
P/Steel	Pressed Steel Co Ltd
RSH	Robert Stephenson & Hawthorn Ltd
R/Hornsby	Ruston Hornsby
R/Proctor	Ruston Proctor
S. F. Belge	Societé Franco Belge
YEC	Yorkshire Engine Co

Company abbreviations

BR	British Railways
DB	German Federal Railways
DSB	Danish State Railways
GWR	Great Western Railway
JZ	Jugoslovenske Zeleznice
LMS	London Midland & Scottish Railway
LNER	London & North Eastern Railway
MoS	Ministry of Supply
NSB	Norwegian State Railways
RR	Rhodesian Railways
SJ	Swedish Railways
SAR	South African Railways
SNCF	French National Railways
SR	Southern Railways
USA TC	United States Army Transportation Corps
WD	War Department
ZSR	Zambesi Sawmills Railway

Other abbreviations

BE	Battery electric
DE	Diesel-electric
DH	Diesel-hydraulic
DM	Diesel-mechanical
E	Overhead electric
EMU	Electric multiple-unit
F	Fireless
G	Geared
GH	Gas-hydraulic
LRO	Light Railway Order
PM	Petrol-mechanical
PH	Petrol-hydraulic
ParM	Paraffin-mechanical
PT	Pannier tank
R	Railcar
SO	Steam outline
ST	Saddle tank
T	Side tank
VB	Vertical boiler
WT	Well tank
4w	4-wheel

INVERNESS
Alford
Strathspey
Mull Rail
Caledonian Rly (Brechin)
Kerr's
Summerlee
Boness
Prestongrange
EDINBURGH
GLASGOW Museum
Scottish Ind. Rly Museum
Dalmellington
Leadhills
North Tyneside (North Shields)
CARLISLE
Bowes
Tanfield
Beamish
South Tynedale
Foyle
South Donegal
Rly Pres. Society of Ireland
Ulster Folk & Transport Museum
BELFAST
Downpatrick
Snaefell Mountain
Groudle Glen
Manx Electric
DOUGLAS
I.O.M Railway
Ravenglass & Eskdale
Lakeside & Haverthwaite
Steamtown
Darlington
Lightwater Valley (Ripon)
North Yorkshire
Embsay
Keighley & Worth Valley
National Rly Mus. YORK
Mus. of Army Transport (Beverley)
Blackpool
LEEDS
Middleton
Leeds Industrial
I R I S H
Southport
West Lancs
East Lancs (Bury)
Liverpool Mus.
Kirklees
Cleethorpes Light Rly
S E A
Great Orme
MANCHESTER Museum
South Yorkshire
DUBLIN
Penrhyn Castle
Churnet Valley
Crich (Nat. Tramway)
Peak Rail
Midland Rly
Wells & Walsingham
Irish Steam Pres. Society
Llanberis
Snowdon Mountain
Conwy Valley
Railway Age
Foxfield
Nottingham
North Norfolk Rly
Bure Valley
Ffestiniog/NGRC
Welsh Highland
Cambrian Rlys
Llangollen (Oswestry)
Chasewater
Great Central
Abbey
Rutland Rly Mus.
County School
Fairbourne
Corris
Bala
Battlefield (Shackerstone)
PETERBOROUGH
Mid-Norfolk
East Anglia Transport
Welshpool & Llanfair
Telford
Ironbridge
Nene Valley Rly
Bressingham
Talyllyn
BIRMINGHAM
Cadeby
Colne Valley
Mid-Suffolk
Vale of Rheidol
Severn Valley
Museum St. Railway Museum
Northampton Steam
Northampton Ironstone
Irchester
East Anglian Rly
Airfield Line
Leighton Buzzard
Audley End
Teifi
Glouc. & Warks Rlv
Winchcombe
Buckinghamshire
Mangapps Farm
Gwili
Brecon
Dean Forest
National Waterways
Swindon & Cricklade
Cholsey & Wallingford
Didcot
Ruislip Lido
N. Woolwich
LONDON
Pontypool
Swindon GWR Mus.
London Transport Science Museum Southall
Sittingbourne
Vale of Glamorgan
Bristol Ind.
Avon Valley
Great Cockcrow
East Kent
Swansea Vale + Maritime & Ind
East Somerset
Mid-Hants
Hollycombe
Bluebell Rly
K&ESR
Romney
West Somerset
Gartell
Amberley
Lavender Line
Bideford
Tiverton
Bicton
Moors Valley (Ringwood)
Launceston
Seaton
Swanage
Isle of Wight
Bodmin
Dobwalls
South Devon
Plymouth
Plym Valley
Paignton & Dartmouth
Alderney
Tuam – Westrail 20m NE of Galway

N O R T H
S E A

E N G L I S H
C H A N N E L

6

England

Abbey Pumping Station

Members: TT

Leicester Museum

Narrow gauge site railway (2ft gauge) formerly part of a sewage pumping station that now forms museum site. Railway relaid in concrete by MSC scheme during early 1980s to original track layout. New track layout as an extension to original laid with 35lb rail on wooden sleepers. All the railway system is now run by volunteers. Original Simplex locomotive kept on site in operational condition. A Planet petrol locomotive and a Ruston diesel are used to demonstrate the railway with typical tipper wagons and mine tubs. Line originally used for transferring solid material from screens to tip (about 100yd).
Location: Abbey Pumping Station, Corporation Road, off Abbey Lane, Leicester LE4 5XP
Operating group: Leicestershire County Council Museum, Arts & Records Service and Leicestershire Museums Technology Association (until 1 April 1997)
Telephone: 0116 266 1330
Car park: Free on site
Access by public transport: BR

Industrial locomotives
Narrow gauge:

Name	No	Builder	Type	Built
—	—	Motor Rail (5260)	4wPM	1931
—	—	Hibberd (1776)	4wPM	1931
—	—	R/Hornsby (223700)	4wDM	1944

Stock
10 skip wagons, 6 mine tubs, 2 flats, various miscellaneous

Leicester (London Road). Leicester City Bus route 54 or 54K from city centre (alight at Beaumont Leys Lane)
Length of line/gauge: About 300yd, 2ft gauge. No public riding on line
Period of public opening: Daily from 9 April, 10.00 to 17.30 Monday to Saturday and 14.00 to 17.30 Sunday (until 1 April 1997)
On site facilities: Museum/shop/toilets/car park. Refreshments only on Special Event Days
Facilities for disabled: Access to museum lower floor and grounds. Steps to Engine House and refreshments on event days
Volunteer contact: Mr N. Pell, c/o

Abbey Pumping Station
Museum contact: Mr C. Stevens, c/o Abbey Pumping Station (Tel: 0116 266 1330)
Other attractions: Museum holds various transport, steam navvy, beam engines. Some items only viewable by appointment or on Special Event Days
Special events: Please contact for details
Important note: From 1 April 1997 Abbey Pumping Station will become the responsibility of Leicester City Council Arts & Leisure Services Dept. At the time of writing no details were available of LCC's plans for the Museum. Visitors are requested to contact before planning a visit

Airfield Line

Member: AIRPS

Warwickshire Steam Centre

The railway is the only standard gauge line in Warwickshire and has been constructed on a 'greenfield' site by members of The 1857 Society, work beginning in 1983. Originally known as the Coventry Steam Railway Centre, the public were first admitted in 1988, after which time the marketing name — Airfield Line — was adopted. Development continues and the site now houses ex-MR Little Bowden Junction signalbox, and the rebuilt

Multiple units

Name	No	Origin	Class	Type	Built
—	29720	LMS	503	TSO	1938
—	28690	LMS	503	DMBSO	1938

Industrial locomotives

Name	No	Builder	Type	Built
—	N2	H/Clarke (1857)	0-6-0T	1952
—	1	A/Barclay (1772)	0-4-0F	1922
Southam	—	H/Clarke (D604)	0-4-0DM	1936
Mazda	—	R/Hornsby (268881)	0-4-0DE	1950
—	L7	R/Hornsby (349038)	4wDM	1954

Cont

118-year old LNWR North Kilworth station building, to be renamed Thistledown Halt on completion. Work is on going to convert the six acre site to an authentic railway setting. The site also contains a collection of vintage road vehicles

Location: Within the boundary of Coventry Airport, south of the city. Easily reached via Rowley Road, junction with A45/A46, Coventry eastern by-pass — M6/M69/M1 link road. Follow Coventry Airport direction signs — entrance is adjacent to Emergency Exit Gate 2

OS reference: SP 349750

Access by public transport: BR Coventry, West Midlands bus route 20/21 from City Centre to Toll Bar end

Operating Society/organisation: Coventry Steam Railway Centre Ltd, 18 Lochmore Close, Hinckley, Leics LE10 0TY in conjunction with Carrick Wardale Steam Crane Group, The 1857 Society and MATEP Co Ltd

Telephone: Hinckley (01455) 634373/635440 evenings only and/or answerphone

On site facilities: Buffet car, souvenir sales shop and picnic area

Catering facilities: Buffet

Length of line: Third of a mile (under construction)

Public opening: Every Sunday and bank holiday from Easter to October, 11.00-17.00, static display. See press for operating days and special events. Other times and party visits by prior arrangement. (No access at other times.)

Car park: On site, access off Rowley Road

Facilities for disabled: Site relatively flat. Members willing to assist if prior notice given. No access to buffet coach, no toilets

Name	No	Builder	Type	Built
C. P. May	—	Hibberd (2895)	4wPM	1944
Crabtree	—	R/Hornsby (338416)	4wDM	1953

Owners
Class 503 vehicles the Merseyside & Tyneside Electric Traction Preservation Co Ltd

Rolling stock
1 BR Mk 1 Res/buffet (TSO conversion), 2 cranes, 2 fitted vans, 1 LNER brake van, 1 SR brake van

Amberley Museum

Member: AIRPS, TT

West Sussex
Steam Centre

Narrow Gauge and Industrial Railway Collection (incorporating the Brockham Museum of Narrow Gauge Railways)

The NG&IR Collection is part of an open air industrial museum set in 36 acres of the former Pepper & Co chalk pits. A 2ft gauge line has been constructed and this is used for carrying passengers in genuine workmen's vehicles

Museum Director: Robert Taylor

Location: Houghton Bridge, Amberley, West Sussex (3 miles north of Arundel). On B2139. Adjacent to Amberley BR(SR) station

OS reference: TQ 031122

Operating society/organisation: Amberley Museum Trust, Amberley Museum, Houghton Bridge, Amberley, Arundel, West Sussex BN18 9LT

Telephone: Bury (01798) 831370 (Museum office)

Car park: Adjacent to Amberley Station

On site facilities: Shop, light refreshments, audio-visual show

Public opening: Wednesday to

Locomotives
(2ft or 60cm unless otherwise indicated)

Name	No	Builder	Type	Built
Polar Bear	—	Bagnall (1781)	2-4-0T	1905
Peter	—	Bagnall (2067)	0-4-0ST	1918
Townsend Hook	4	F/Jennings (172L)	0-4-0T	1880
			(3ft 2.25in gauge)	
Scaldwell	—	Peckett (1316)	0-6-0ST	1913
			(3ft 0in gauge)	
—	23†	Spence	0-4-0T	1921
			(1ft 10in gauge)	
—	—	Decauville (1126)	0-4-0T	1950
—**	—	Baldwin (778)	4-6-0T	1917
Monty	(6)	O&K (7269)	4wDM	1936
			(3ft 2.25in gauge)	
The Major	(7)	O&K (7741)	4wDM	1937
—	2	Ransomes & Rapier (80)	4wDM	1937
—	—	Hudson-Hunslet 4wDM (3097)		1944
—	2	R/Hornsby (166024) (3041)	4wDM	1933
—	3101	M/Rail (Simplex) 4wPM (1381) Armoured		1918
Peldon	—	John Fowler (21295)	4wDM	1936
Redland	—	O&K (6193)	4wDM	1937
—	—	Lister (35421) (LR 2593)	4wPM	1949
—	—	M/Rail (Simplex) (872)	4wPM	1918
—	27	M/Rail (Simplex) (5863)	4wDM	1934

Sunday (inclusive) each week, and Bank Holiday Mondays, (open all week in school holidays) 10.00-last entry 17.00, 20 March-3 November 1996

Special events: Railway Gala Weekend — 29/30 June. Please see press for details of further activities

Special Notes: Displays include working potter, blacksmith, boatbuilder and printer, stationary engines, historic radio collection and vintage Southdown garage and buses. A 2ft 0in gauge industrial railway system is demonstrated when possible, and a 3ft 2.25in gauge line is under construction. In addition a 2ft 0in gauge 'main line' has been constructed. The 500yd line, was officially opened by HRH Prince Michael of Kent on 5 June 1984. The railway is operated every day the museum is open (subject to mechanical availability), with steam locomotive haulage on certain days — for details contact the museum office. Wheelchairs can normally be accommodated on the train. A Narrow Gauge Industrial Railway Introductory Exhibition sets the scene for these and other set-piece display areas

Membership details: Friends of Amberley Museum, c/o above address

Membership journal: *Wheelbarrow* — bi-monthly

—	—	M/Rail (Simplex) (10161)	4wDM	1949 (2ft 11in gauge)
Ibstock	—	M/Rail (Simplex) (11001)	4wDM	1951
*Burt**	—	Simplex 9019))	4wDM	1959
CCSW	—	Hibberd (1980)	4wDM	1936
Thakeham Tiles	No 3	Hudson-Hunslet (2208)	4wDM	1941
Thakeham Tiles	No 4	Hudson-Hunslet (3653)	4wDM	1948
—	—	H/Clarke (DM686)	0-4-0DM	1948
Star Construction	—	Hudson-Hunslet	4wDM	c1941
—	18	R/Hornsby (187081)	4wDM	1937
—	—	Lister (33937)	4wDM	1949
—	—	R/Hornsby (172892)	4wDM	1934
—	WD 904	Wickham (3403)	2w 2PMR	1943
—	2	Wingrove & Rogers (5031)	4wBE	1953
—	—	Wingrove & Rogers (5034)	4wBE	1953
—	—	Wingrove & Rogers (4998)	4wBE	1953
—	—	Wingrove & Rogers (T8033)	0-4-0BE	1979

** on loan to Leighton Buzzard Railway for restoration
* standard gauge
†Includes hoist and 'haulage truck' for conversion to 5ft 3in gauge

Stock
2 Penrhyn Quarry Railway 4-wheel coaches (2ft gauge, ex-1ft 10.75in gauge); RAF Fauld bogie coach (1940) (2ft gauge); Rye & Camber Tramway bogie (incomplete) (1895) (3ft gauge); Post Office Railway unit No 808 of 1930; 4 Groudle Glen Railway 4-wheel coaches (1896 and 1905) (2ft gauge); 60 other varied pieces of rolling stock of 12 different gauges ranging from 1ft 6in to 3ft 2.25in plus numerous miscellaneous exhibits including track, signals etc

---

Amerton Railway
Member: AIRPS

Staffordshire
Steam Centre

Construction of the Amerton Railway started in June 1990. Over the following two tyears volunteers of the Staffordshire Narrow Gauge Railway Society Ltd constructed a new 2ft gauge railway on a greenfield site. Work undertaken in this period consisted of building a track bed, laying a quarter mile of track and building a stock shed and station facilities. The railway opened to the public on 14 July 1992. There are plans to extend the railway and construct a museum dedicated to Staffordshire narrow gauge railway history

Location: Amerton Railway, Amerton Working Farm, Stowe-by-Chartley, Stafford ST18 0LA

Industrial locomotives

Name	No	Builder	Type	Built
Isabel	–	Bagnall (1491)	0-4-0ST	1897
–	746	M/Rail (40SD501)	4wDM	1975
Dreadnought	–	Baguley (3024)	0-4-0DM/SO	1939
–	Yard No 70	R/Hornsby (221623)	4wDM	1943
–	–	Hunslet (8561)	4wDH	1978

Rolling stock
3 Baguley toastrack coaches (2 converted to semi-enclosed, 1 being rebuilt into balcony-ended coach). Various wagons and SNGRS built brake van

(situated between Stafford and Uttoxeter, signposted off A51 at Weston)
Operating company: Staffordshire Narrow Gauge Railway Society Ltd, c/o above address
Telephone: 01785 284388

(railway only); 01889 270294 (Working Farm)
OS reference: SJ 993278
On site facilities: Car park at Working Farm. Museum under construction; licensed tea room and bakery (not operated by railway).

Souvenir shop in railway booking hall. The railway is one of the main attractions at the Working Farm, admission to most attractions is free
Access by public transport: By rail to Stafford, then Stevenson's of Uttoxeter Ltd bus to Weston, then a mile walk to Amerton (no Sunday service)
Period of public operation:

Sundays from mid-March to beginning of October. Saturdays from Easter until August Bank Holiday. Bank Holiday Mondays. Trains run 12.00 until 17.00. Subject to availability *Isabel* will be in steam Sundays and Bank Holidays. Diesel haulage on Saturdays
Special events: *Isabel* will be celebrating its 100th birthday on

17/18 May, visiting locomotives will be in attendance. Santa Specials in December. Footplate experience courses (contact for details)
Membership details: Membership Secretary, c/o above address
Membership journal: *Isabel Gazette,* quarterly

Avon Valley Railway

Member: AIRPS

Avon
Timetable Service

Following the granting of their Light Railway Order in 1990 the Avon Valley Railway has progressed well, with the opening of the extension to Oldland. Work on a three-road engine shed has also begun.
Headquarters: Bitton Railway Company Limited, Bitton Station, Willsbridge, Bristol BS15 6ED
Telephone: (0117) 932796 for timetable information. (0117) 325538 weekends
Main station: Bitton
OS reference: ST 670705
Car park: Bitton
Access by public transport: Badgerline service No 332 (Bristol-Bath), No 558 (Bristol-North Common). 5.5 miles
Catering facilities: Buffet is able to provide hot and cold snacks, confectionery, hot and cold drinks and ice creams
On-site facilities: Toilets, picnic area, children's play area close-by
Public opening: Open every weekend for static viewing. Please contact for operating dates
Special events: Please contact for details
Facilities for disabled: Coach converted for disabled use (no toilet facilities)
Membership details: Membership Secretary, c/o Bitton station
Membership journal: *Semaphore* — quarterly

Locomotives

Name	No	Origin	Class	Type	Built
Sir Frederick Pile	34058	SR	BB	4-6-2	1947
—	44123	LMS	4F	0-6-0	1925
—	45379	LMS	5MT	4-6-0	1937
—	48173	LMS	8F	2-8-0	1943
—	9600	GWR	5700	0-6-0PT	1945
—	D2994	BR	07	0-6-0DE	1962
—	51909	BR	108	DMBS	1958
—	54271	BR	108	DTC	1958

Locomotive notes: All steam locomotives undergoing restoration.

Industrial locomotives

Name	No	Builder	Type	Built
Edwin Hulse	2	Avonside (1798)	0-6-0ST	1918
Littleton No 5	—	M/Wardle (2018)	0-6-0ST	1922
—	—	RSH (7151)	0-6-0T	1944
—	—	R/Hornsby (235519)	4wDM	1945
—	—	Baguley/Drewry (2153)	0-4-0	1941
—	2*	Bagnall (2842)	0-4-0ST	1946
General Lord Robertson	610	Sentinel (10143)	0-8-0DH	1961
Kingswood	—	Barclay (446)	0-4-0DM	1959
—	D1171	H/Clarke (D1171)	0-6-0DM	1959

*On display at Warmley station, Bristol

Locomotive notes: R/Hornsby (235519) and Bagnall (2842) undergoing restoration. D1171 undergoing overhaul off-site.

Stock
16 ex-BR Mk1 coaches (9 stored off-site); 1 ex-BR Mk 1 Restaurant Coach; 1 ex-BR Mk 1 sleeper; 1 ex-LMS brake composite corridor; 2 cranes; 2 Wickham trolleys; numerous assorted wagons

Owners
44123 the London Midland Society
48173 the Bitton 8F Locomotive Group
9600 on loan from the Birmingham Railway Museum

England

The Battlefield Steam Railway

Leicestershire
Timetable Service

A quiet country railway operated by the Shackerstone Railway Society Ltd
Headquarters: Shackerstone station (3 miles north of Market Bosworth in Leicestershire)
Address: Shackerstone Station, Shackerstone, Nuneaton CV13 6NW
Telephone: (01827) 880754
Main station: Shackerstone
Other public station: Market Bosworth, Shenton*
OS reference: SK 379066
Car park: Shackerstone (free), Shenton (council car park), no facilities at Market Bosworth
Access by public transport: Midland Fox, service 153 (tel: 01162 511411). Leicester to Market Bosworth (square) weekdays and Sundays
Refreshment facilities: Tea rooms on Shackerstone station. Buffet/bar on most trains
Souvenir shop: Shackerstone
Museum: Shackerstone
Depot: Shackerstone
Length of line: 4.5 miles (8km)
Passenger trains: Shackerstone-Market Bosworth-Shenton
Period of public operation: Passenger steam service: Sundays and bank holiday Mondays Easter-October. Diesel service: Saturdays May-September (possibly steam-hauled on Bank Holidays). Diesel service: Wednesdays June-August
Special events: Easter Eggstras — 29-30 March; Teddy Bear's Picnic — 4/5 May; Spring Bank Holiday (intensive service)— 25/26 May; Friends of Thomas the Tank Engine — 21/22, 25, 27-29 June, 15-17 August; August Bank Holiday (intensive service)— 23-25 August; Shackerstone '97 Steam & Canal Weekend — 6/7 September; Postman Pat — 26 October; Diesel Gala — 1/2 November. See press for details of Bank Holiday weekend and Diesel Gala)
Special notes: Family tickets available. 'Tudor Rose' dining train

Locomotives and multiple-units

Name	No	Origin	Class	Type	Built
—	20048	BR	20	Bo-Bo	1959
—	D5217	BR	25	Bo-Bo	1963
Harlech Castle	25265	BR	25	Bo-Bo	1963
—	D5518	BR	31	A1A-A1A	1958
—	D2245	BR	04	0-6-0DM	1956
—	D3429	BR	08	0-6-0DE	1958
—	51131	BR	116	DMBS	1958
—	54289	P/Steel	121	DTS	1960
—	55005	GRCW	122	DMBS	1958
—	59496	P/Steel	117	TCL	1959
—	59508	P/Steel	117	TCL	1959
—	59522	P/Steel	117	TSL	1959
—	59791†	P/Steel	107	TSL	1960

†Converted to locomotive-hauled vehicles
Two ex-BR locomotives are expected to pay a visit during 1997

Industrial locomotives

Name	No	Builder	Type	Built
Linda	—	Bagnall (2648)	0-4-0ST	1941
Waleswood	—	H/Clarke (750)	0-4-0ST	1906
—	11	Hunslet (1493)	0-4-0ST	1925
Dunlop No 7	—	Peckett (2130)	0-4-0ST	1951
—	3	RSH (7537)	0-6-0T	1949
Lamport No 3	—	Bagnall (2670)	0-6-0ST	1942
Florence	2	Bagnall (3059)	0-6-0ST	1953
—	—	R/Hornsby (235513)	4wDM	1945
—	—	R/Hornsby (263001)	4wDM	1949
—	—	R/Hornsby (347747)	0-6-0DM	1957
—	—	R/Hornsby (393304)	4wDM	1956
—	—	R/Hornsby (423657)	0-4-0DE	1958
—	—	R/Hornsby (420142)	0-4-0DE	1958
—	—	S/Crossley (7697)	0-6-0DM	1953
—	RS/140	Planet (3892)	4wDM	1958
—	9118	B/Drewry (3707)	4wDHRC	1975

Stock
7 ex-BR Mk 1 coaches (including Griddle Car); 5 passenger-rated vans; 2 rail mounted steam cranes; 2 rail mounted diesel cranes; 35 wagons (inc 3 goods brake vans SR, MR, BR); 2 LNER ballast brakes

3rd Sunday in each month. School Special Days Wednesdays in June. Must book for dining and schools. Scenic countryside views including Ashby Canal. Shenton station is adjacent to Bosworth Battlefield (1485) Country Park. 20 minute walk along 'Battlefield Trail' to visitor centre, return by later train
Operating Manager: B. Warwick
Operating Company/ Preservation Society contact: The

Secretary, Shackerstone Railway Society, Shackerstone Station, Shackerstone, Nuneaton CV13 6NW
Membership journal: *Shackerstone News* — 3/4 times/year
Marketing name: The Battlefield Line

The railway station, signalbox and goods shed have been completely recreated along with the other exhibits to show a way of life long past. There are some very old locomotives in the collection.

Museum Director: Peter Lewis
Location: The North of England Open Air Museum, Beamish, County Durham DH9 0RG.
OS reference: NZ214548
Telephone: Stanley (01207) 231811
Fax: 01207 290933
Car park: At museum
Access by public transport: Bus service from Eldon Square, Newcastle upon Tyne; Bus service Nos 775 and 778 from Sunderland via Chester-le-Street; Bus service 720 from Milburngate, Durham City
On site facilities: This 200-acre open air museum vividly recreates life in the North of England in the early 1800s and 1900s. The Town with dentist's surgery, solicitor's office, Co-op shops, garage, sweetshop and sweet factory. The Colliery Village with pit cottages, village school and chapel, 'drift' mine and pithead. Home Farm with farm house, livestock and exhibitions. Railway station complete with goods yard and signalbox, locomotives and rolling stock on static display. Pockerley Manor and Horse Yard illustrates the lifestyle of a yeoman farming family in the early 1800s
Public opening: Summer (April-October) daily 10.00-17.00, last admission 15.00. Extended summer opening (20 July-1 September) –

daily 10.00-18.00, last admission 16.00. Winter (November-March) 10.00-16.00, last admission 15.00, closed Mondays and Fridays. Please check for Christmas opening times
  NB: A winter visit to Beamish is centered on the Town and Tramway, other areas of the museum are closed and admission charges are, consequently, reduced

Special events: A full programme of events is planned for 1997
Length of line: Rebuilt NER station, colliery sidings
Facilities for disabled: Not ideal for wheelchairs. Rolling stock not converted. Advanced notice for parties to Bookings Officer preferred

Locomotives

Name	No	Origin	Class	Type	Built
—	876	NER	C1	0-6-0	1889
Locomotion	1*	—	—	0-4-0	1975

*Replica, and may be out on loan

Industrial locomotives

Name	No	Builder	Type	Built
Twizell†	3	Stephenson (2730)	0-6-0T	1891
—	14	H/Leslie (3056)	0-4-0ST	1914
South Durham Malleable*	No 5	Stockton Ironworks	0-4-0ST	c1880
Coffee Pot	—	Head Wrightson	0-4-0VB	1871
—*	E1	Black, Hawthorn (897)	2-4-0CT	1883
Hetton Loco	—	G. Stephenson	0-4-0	1822
—	—	R/Hornsby (476140)	0-4-0DM	1963
Jacob	680	McEwan Pratt	0-4-0P	1916
—**	18	Lewin	0-4-0WT	1877

†Currently running in at Tanfield
*In store for long-term restoration
** Undergoing major rebuild

Locomotive notes: Nos 3 and *Coffee Pot* in working order. R/Hornsby not usually on display. Others usually on display

Owner
Hetton Loco on loan from National Railway Museum
Locomotion the Locomotion Trust

Note
Not all exhibits on display

A passenger-carrying line of 18in gauge with stock mainly from the Woolwich Arsenal Railway and of World War 1 vintage
Location: Bicton Park, near Budleigh Salterton
OS reference: SY 074862
Operating society/organisation:

Locomotives

Name	No	Builder	Type	Built
Woolwich	1	Avonside (1748)	0-4-0T	1916
Bicton	2	R/Hornsby (213839)	4wDM	1942
Carnegie	3	Hunslet (4524)	0-4-4-0DM	1954
Clinton	4	H/Hunslet (2290)	0-4-0	1941
Budley*	—	R/Hornsby (235624)	4wDM	1945

*Static exhibit

Bicton Woodland Railway, Bicton Gardens, East Budleigh, Budleigh Salterton, Devon
Telephone: Colaton Raleigh (01395) 568465
Car park: On site
Access by public transport: Buses pass half-hourly from Exeter, Exmouth, Sidmouth in season

Stock
4 open bogie coaches; 5 closed bogie coaches

On site facilities: Refreshments, shop, one museum, toilets, 18in gauge railway, Grade 1 gardens
Length of line: 3,250yd
Public opening: Open March to

October, 10.00-18.00. Please enquire for winter opening.
Facilities for disabled: Toilets, wheelchairs available. Special carriage for wheelchairs

Bideford Railway Museum

Devon
Museum

Based at the former LSWR/SR station on the now closed Barnstaple-Torrington line, the site is undergoing restoration. The former signalbox has been rebuilt, double track laid throughout and signals erected. A growing collection of rolling stock is being gathered.
Headquarters: Bideford Station, Railway Terrace, East-the-Water, Bideford, Devon EX39 4BB
OS reference: 456263 (sheet 180)
Operating Society: Bideford & Instow Railway Group

Rolling stock
BR Mk 1 TSO No 4489, ex-SR Parcels Van No S2142, ex-BR brake van, ex-LMS closed box van, platelayer's trolley

Access by public transport: By train — Barnstaple 9 miles. Station is within walking distance from the town of Bideford and its bus stops
On site facilities: Museum, souvenir shop, book shop, refreshments, visitor centre, rolling stock under restoration
Period of public opening: Sundays, Tuesdays and bank

hoildays 14.00-17.00, Easter to end October
Special events: Annual open day — Sunday 10 August
Membership details: Mr Taylor, 7 Myrtle Gardens, Bideford, Devon EX39 3HU
Membership journal: *Atlantic Coast Express* (quarterly)

The BR Mark 1 coach being craned into position. *B&IRG*

Birmingham Museum of Science & Industry

West Midlands
Museum

Member: TT

Location: Newhall Street, Birmingham B3 1RZ
OS reference: SP 064874
Organisation: Birmingham City Council
Telephone: 0121-235 1661
Car park: Public multi-storey nearby in Newhall Street
Access by public transport: Birmingham New Street or Snow Hill stations, then short walk following signs
Admission: Free, but donations welcomed
Facilities: Shop, cafe
Opening times: Monday-Saturday 10.00-17.00; Sunday 12.30-17.00

Locomotives

Name	No	Origin	Class	Type	Built
City of Birmingham	46235	LMS	8P	4-6-2	1939

Industrial locomotives

Name	No	Builder	Type	Built
Secundus	—	B/Seekings	0-6-0WT	1874*
Leonard	1	Bagnall (2087)	0-4-0ST	1919†
Lorna Doone	56	K/Stuart (4250)	0-4-0ST	1922†

*2ft 8in gauge
†2ft gauge

Special notes: Some facilities for the disabled (toilet and lifts). Special parking facility (prior notice required)

Birmingham Railway Museum

West Midlands
Steam Centre

Location: 670 Warwick Road (A41), Tyseley, Birmingham B11 2HL
OS reference: SP 105841
Operating society/organisation: Birmingham Railway Museum Trust
Telephone: 0121-707 4696
Car park: Site
Access by public transport: West Midlands Travel bus routes No 37 from city centre. BR service to Tyseley station
On site facilities: The Museum is on the site of a former GWR/BR steam shed and has been equipped with specialised railway engineering machinery. Souvenir shop, restaurant, passenger demonstration line and station, viewing gallery, schools education service
Refreshment facilities: Available in 'Chuffs' restaurant
Length of line: Third-mile
Public opening: Static display daily 10.00-17.00 except Christmas and New Year. Steam days most Saturdays, Sundays, Bank Holidays and some weekdays
Special events: Santa and Thomas (see press for details)
Special notes: Tyseley is a centre

Locomotives

Name	No	Origin	Class	Type	Built
Albert Hall	4983	GWR	'Hall'	4-6-0	1931
Earl of Mount Edgcumbe	5043	GWR	'Castle	4-6-0	1936
Defiant	5080	GWR	'Castle'	4-6-0	1939
Clun Castle	7029	GWR	'Castle'	4-6-0	1950
—	7752	GWR	5700	0-6-0PT	1930
—	7760	GWR	5700	0-6-0PT	1930
—	9600	GWR	5700	0-6-0PT	1945
Kolhapur	5593	LMS	'Jubilee'	4-6-0	1934
Galatea	5699	LMS	'Jubilee'	4-6-0	1936
Scots Guardsman	6115	LMS	'Royal Scot'	4-6-0	1927
—	13029	BR	08	0-6-0DE	1953
—	40118	BR	40	1Co-Co1	1961

Note: Not all locomotives are on site, and some are undergoing restoration

Industrial locomotives

Name	No	Builder	Type	Built
Cadbury No 1	—	Avonside (1977)	0-4-0T	1925
—	1	Peckett (2004)	0-4-0ST	1942
—	—	Baguley (800)	0-4-0PE	1920
Henry	—	H/Leslie (2491)	0-4-0ST	1901
Victor	—	Bagnall(2996)	0-6-0ST	1950

Stock
Various passenger, goods and departmental vehicles, including buffet car, engineer's saloon and steam crane

for 'Steam on BR' railtours over the BR lines to Stratford upon Avon and Didcot (via Oxford). Full education service providing guided tours, work sheets and live presentation. The Museum is noted for its driving experience courses where members of the public can

14

actually drive and fire a steam locomotive. These courses mainly feature *Clun Castle* and range from four hours to all day. Please contact for prices

Membership details: Membership is available to the public providing free entry to site events, newsletters, members' evenings etc, details from the museum office

Note: All attractions and facilities are advertised subject to availability

Blackpool & Fleetwood Tramway
Lancashire
Timetable Service

Operating organisation: Blackpool Transport Services Ltd, Rigby Road, Blackpool, Lancashire FY1 5DD
Telephone: (01253) 23931
Length of line: 11.5 miles, standard gauge
Period of public operation: Daily throughout the year
Number of trams: 86 double and single-deck Trams the Blackpool & Fleetwood Tramway is the sole surviving traditional street tramway system in the United Kingdom and attracts visitors from all over the country. During the autumn the streets are illuminated and several specially decorated trams are used
Managing Director: Anthony Depledge
Commercial Director: David Eaves

Bluebell Railway
Member: AIRPS, TT
West Sussex
Timetable Service

This famous steam railway was the first standard gauge passenger line to be taken over by enthusiasts. It derives its name from bluebells which proliferate in the woodlands adjoining the line. A strong Victorian atmosphere pervades this branch line which has a large collection of Southern and pre-Grouping locomotives and coaches.
Contact: Mr John Potter
Headquarters: Bluebell Railway Preservation Society, Sheffield Park station, Uckfield, East Sussex TN22 3QL
Telephone: Newick (01825) 722370 for travel information (24hr talking timetable); 01825 723777 for general enquiries etc during office hours. 01825 722008 – Golden Arrow Pullman, and catering reservations
Main station: Sheffield Park
Other public stations: Horsted Keynes and Kingscote
Car parks: Sheffield Park, Horsted Keynes
OS reference: Sheffield Park TQ 403238, Horsted Keynes TQ 372293
Access by public transport: Bus service between BR East Grinstead and Kingscote (2 miles) with all Bluebell trains
Refreshment facilities: Sheffield Park restaurant/bar/self-service; Horsted Keynes – 'Brief

Locomotives

Name	No	Origin	Class	Type	Built
Stepney	55	LBSCR	A1X	0-6-0T	1875
Fenchurch	72	LBSCR	A1X	0-6-0T	1872
Birch Grove	473	LBSCR	E4	0-6-2T	1898
—	27	SECR	P	0-6-0T	1910
—	263	SECR	H	0-4-4T	1905
Bluebell	323	SECR	P	0-6-0T	1910
—	592	SECR	C	0-6-0	1901
—	1178	SECR	P	0-6-0T	1910
—	96	LSWR	B4	0-4-0T	1905
—	120	LSWR	T9	4-4-0	1899
—	488	LSWR	0415	4-4-2T	1885
—	58850	NLR	2F	0-6-0T	1880
Earl of Berkeley	3217	GWR	9000	4-4-0	1938
—	541	SR	Q	0-6-0	1939
—	830*	SR	S15	4-6-0	1927
—	847	SR	S15	4-6-0	1937
Stowe	928	SR	V	4-4-0	1934
—	1618	SR	U	2-6-0	1928
—	1638	SR	U	2-6-0	1931
—	30064	SR	USA	0-6-0T	1943
—	C1	SR	Q1	0-6-0	1942
Sir Archibald Sinclair	34059	SR	BB	4-6-2	1947
Port Line	35027	SR	MN	4-6-2	1948
Camelot	73082	BR	5MT	4-6-0	1955
—	75027	BR	4MT	4-6-0	1954
—	78059†	BR	2MT	2-6-0	1956
—	80100	BR	4MT	2-6-4T	1954
—	92240	BR	9F	2-10-0	1959
Blackmore Vale	21C123	SR	WC	4-6-2	1946

Industrial locomotives

Name	No	Builder	Type	Built
¶Blue Circle	—	A/Porter (9449)	2-2-0TG	1926
Baxter	—	F/Jennings (158)	0-4-0T	1877
Stamford	—	Avonside (1972)	0-6-0ST	1927

Cont

England

encounters'-style buffet. The line's 'Golden Arrow' Pullman operates a dinner service most Saturday evenings and Pullman luncheon service most Sundays.

Telephone 0825 722008 during normal office hours for details.

Souvenir shops: Sheffield Park, Horsted Keynes

Museum: Sheffield Park

Depots: Sheffield Park (locomotives), Horsted Keynes (stock)

Length of line: 9 miles

Passenger trains: Sheffield Park-Horsted Keynes-Kingscote

Period of public operation: Weekends all year round; daily May-September; additional trains run in school half-term weeks and in the lead up to Christmas. Museum and locomotive sheds at Sheffield Park open daily except Christmas Day

Special events: Programme of events held during the year and detailed in advance (send SAE for details)

Name	No	Builder	Type	Built
Sharpthorn	—	M/Wardle (641)	0-6-0ST	1877

*Purchased without tender, in store
†Purchased without tender, for conversion to tank engine, work in hand
¶On long term loan to Northamptonshire Ironstone Railway

Stock

Substantial collection of pre-Nationalisation coaches including SECR, LSWR, Bulleid, Maunsell and Chesham vehicles. Also freight stock and engineers' vehicles plus 45ton steam crane

Owners

592 the Wainwright C Class Preservation Society
541, 830, 847 and 1618 the Maunsell Locomotive Society Ltd
96 and 21C123 the Bulleid Society Ltd
263 the H Class Trust
73082 the Camelot Locomotive Society
C1, T9 on loan from the National Railway Museum
928 on loan from Montagu Venturers Ltd
35027, 1178 the Southern Locomotives Ltd

Facilities for disabled: All station facilities are on the level and ramps available for placing wheelchair visitors into trains. Special toilet in Buffet at Sheffield Park

Membership details: Membership Secretary c/o above address
Membership journal: Bluebell News — quarterly

Bodmin & Wenford Railway

Member: AIRPS

Cornwall
Timetable Service

The Bodmin & Wenford Railway typifies the bygone branch railways of Cornwall. The terminus, close to Bodmin town centre, has an interesting collection of small standard gauge locomotives and rolling stock; and the operating line winds down to a junction with British Rail at Bodmin Parkway. Passengers can alight at the intermediate Colesleggett Halt from where a footpath leads to Cardinham Woods (FC) with waymarked trails, picnic areas, a café and cycle hire facilities. From the track there are scenic views across the beautiful valley of the River Fowey. A second line circles Bodmin to Boscarne junction where it meets the Camel Trail, a recreational path for cyclists and walkers. The Borough Arms public house is about 10 min walk from Boscarne and a visit can be made to the nearby Camel Valley Vineyard. Most trains are steam-hauled except Saturday

Location: Bodmin General station, on B3268

General Manager: Mr R. Webster

Locomotives and multiple-units

Name	No	Origin	Class	Type	Built
—	3802	GWR	2884	2-8-0	1938
—	5552	GWR	4575	2-6-2T	1928
Wadebridge	34007	SR	WC	4-6-2	1945
Triumph	50042	BR	50	Co-Co	1968
River Fowey	20166	BR	20	Bo-Bo	1966
—	20197	BR	20	Bo-Bo	1967
—	31286	BR	31	A1A-A1A	1961
—	33110	BR	33	Bo-Bo	1960
—	D3452	BR	10	0-6-0DE	1957
—	D3559	BR	08	0-6-0DE	1958
—	51947	BR	108	DMBS	1960
—	52054	BR	108	DMC	1960
—	53645	BR	108	DMC	1958
—	53988	BR	108	DMBS	1960

Industrial locomotives

Name	No	Builder	Type	Built
—	—	Bagnall (2766)	0-6-0ST	1944
—	19	Bagnall (2962)	0-4-0ST	1950
Alfred	—	Bagnall (3058)	0-4-0ST	1953
—	—	Bagnall (3121)	0-4-0F	1957
Peter	—	Fowler (22928)	0-4-0DM	1940
Progress	—	Fowler (4000001)	0-4-0DM	1945
Swiftsure	—	Hunslet (2857)	0-6-0ST	1943
Progress	—	Peckett (1611)	0-4-0ST	1923
Lec	—	R/Hornsby (443642)	4wDM	1960
—	—	RSH (7597)	0-6-0ST	1949
Ugly	62	RSH (7673)	0-6-0ST	1950

16

Operating society/organisation:
Bodmin & Wenford Railway,
Bodmin General Station, Bodmin,
Cornwall PL31 1AQ
Telephone: All enquiries (01208)
73666
Car park: Bodmin General only,
no parking permitted at BR's
Bodmin Parkway station
Access by public transport:
Interchange with BR at Bodmin
Parkway (arrivals by BR train
only). Local bus services to
Bodmin
Refreshment facilities: Light
refreshments at Bodmin General
and on most trains
On site facilities: Souvenir shop,
limited display of historic artefacts,
toilets
Length of lines: 3.5 miles General-
Parkway; 3 miles General-
Boscarne
Passenger trains: 23-31 March; 1-
6, 9, 13, 20, 23, 27, 30 April; 4-11,

Stock
9 BR Mk 1 coaches; 3 BR Mk 2 coaches; 1 Mk 3 Sleeper, 6-wheel 10-ton
steam crane, 4 GWR coaches; 2 GWR Siphon G; Various freight wagons

Owners
34007 the Wadebridge 34007 Ltd
3802 the GW 3802 Ltd
7597 the Railway Vehicle Preservations Ltd

14, 18, 21, 24-31 May; daily June-
28 September; 1, 5, 8, 12, 15, 19,
22, 26-31 October; 6/7, 13/14, 20-
24, 26-28, 31 December, 1 January
1998.
Service will be steam hauled
except on the following dates: All
Saturdays (except 29 March, 24,
May, 28 June, 30 August, 6
September); 21 September.
Special events: Friends of Thomas
the Tank — 28-31 March, 28/29
June, 30/31 August; Steam &
Diesel Gala — 24/25 May; Steam
Gala — 6/7 September; Diesel

Weekend — 20/21 September
Driving experience courses:
Courses held in spring and autumn.
Please apply for details
Facilities for disabled: Yes
Membership details: Mr J.
Tizzard, Bodmin Railway
Preservation Society, c/o above
address
Special notes: Reduced fares for
family groups and for passengers
arriving at Bodmin Parkway in
possession of a valid BR ticket
Membership journal: *Bodmin &
Wenford News* — 3 issues/year

Bowes Railway

Members: AIRPS

Tyne & Wear
Steam Centre

The railway includes the only
preserved rope-hauled standard
gauge inclines, whose operation
requires considerable skill and
sleight of hand. You should not
miss the opportunity of inspecting
the inclines and cable house and
haulage engine when you can
Chairman: Phillip Dawe
Location: Bowes Railway,
Springwell Village, near
Gateshead, Tyne & Wear (on
B1288)
OS reference: NZ 285589
Operating society/organisation:
Bowes Railway Co Ltd
Telephone: Tyneside (0191)
4161847
Car park: Springwell
Access by public transport:
Northern Buses services Nos 184
Washington/Birtley, 187/188
Gateshead Metro/Sunderland, 189
Washington (Brady Sq)-Gateshead
638 Ryton/Sunderland
On site facilities: Exhibition of
Railway's history, wagon
exhibition, workshop displays. On
operating days — shop,
refreshments and guided tours.
Steam hauled brake van rides.
Rope haulage demonstration trains

Industrial locomotives

Name	No	Builder	Type	Built
WST	—	Barclay (2361)	0-4-0ST	1954
—	22	Barclay (2274)	0-4-0ST	1949
—	20/110/709	Barclay (613)	0-6-0DH	1977
—	—	Hunslet (6263)	0-4-0DH	1964
-	503	Hunslet (6614)	0-6-0DH	1965
Norwood	77	RSH (7412)	0-6-0ST	1948
—	101	Planet (3922)	4wDM	1959
—	2207/456†	E/Electric (2476)	4wBE	1958
Victoria	2216/286†	H/Clarke (DM842)	0-6-0DMF	1954
BO3	20/122/514*	Hunslet (8515)	Bo-BoDMF	1981
—	—*	EIMCO (LD2163)	Rockershovel	1959

†2ft gauge
*2ft 6in gauge

Owners
WST on loan from British Gypsum Ltd
Barclay 0-6-0DH on loan from Mr P. Dawe

Stock
20 Ordinary 10-ton wooden hopper wagons (Springwell built); 16 other
wooden hopper wagons (of various pedigrees); 3 steel 14-ton hopper, 2
steel 16ton hopper wagons; 7 wagons; 7 steel 21-ton hopper wagons; 1 reel
bogie (for rope replacement); 1 drift bogie (for shunting by rope); 1 loco
coal wagon; 7 material wagons; 2 tool vans; 4 brake vans; 4 flat wagons; 1
17-ton wooden hopper (ex-NER); 1 18-ton wooden hopper (ex-Ashington);
1 21-ton wooden hopper (ex-Seaham); 2 steel ballast Hopper Wagons; 1
tank wagon; 1 wooden side door coal wagon; Londonderry Chaldron
wagons, 2ft gauge 4-wheel manrider, 2ft 6in gauge R. B. Bolton-type bogie
manrider, Easington Colliery weights wagon

Cont

Public opening: Bank Holidays, also second and fourth Sunday in each month, Easter-September. Santa specials week prior to Christmas. Disabled Children's Day — mid July. Guided tours midweek/out of season can be accommodated with prior notice (not trains)
Length of line: 1.25 miles total length; 1.25 miles of rope haulage; three quarter-mile used for passenger trains (extension in hand)
Special notes: Preserved section of the Pontop & Jarrow Railway; designed G. Stephenson; opened 1826; largest collection of colliery wagons in country, the only standard gauge rope-hauled incline railway in the world; Railway's own historic workshops preserved, with examples of all of the Railway's wagon types
Facilities for disabled: Toilet and refreshment room
Membership details: Dr Peter Norman, Railway Secretary, c/o above address or telephone 0191 4877548

Stationary haulage
Met-Vick/Wild, 300bhp electric (Blackham's Hill) 1950
BTH/Robey, 500bhp electric (Black Fell) 1950
Clarke Chapman, 22hp electric (Springwell Yard)
14ft Diam, Gravity Dilly Wheel (Springwell)

Membership journal: *The Incline* — quarterly
Disclaimer: The Bowes Railway Co Ltd wish to point out that all advertised facilities are subject to alteration without prior notice. The company can therefore not be held responsible for any loss or expense incurred

---

Bressingham Steam Museum

Norfolk
Steam Centre

Five miles of various gauges of railway running through extensive gardens and a collection of well maintained and impressive main line locomotives. All the fun of the fair, with something for everyone including the mother who never wants to see another steam engine
Location: Two miles west of Diss on the A1066
OS reference: TM 080806
Operating society/organisation: Bressingham Steam Preservation Co Ltd, Bressingham Hall, Diss, Norfolk IP22 2AB
Telephone: Bressingham (0137 988) 386. 24hr hotline (0137 988) 382
Car park: Steam Centre (free)
Access by public transport: Diss BR station (3 miles)
On site facilities: 10.25/15/24in and standard gauge lines, totalling nearly 5 miles. Museum, steam roundabout, fire museum, souvenir shop and restaurant, extensive gardens and plant centre
Public opening: Open daily from April to September, reduced schedule in October. Special steam days every Sunday and Thursday, plus Wednesdays in July and August, and bank holiday Mondays, 10.00-17.30 on all open days. Christmas events in December (dates to be confirmed).
  Education services for schools are available with pre-booking in March-October period

Locomotives

Name	No	Origin	Class	Type	Built
Martello	662	LBSCR	A1X	0-6-0T	1875
Thundersley	80	LTSR	3P	4-4-2T	1909
Granville	102	LSWR	B4	0-4-0T	1893
—	490	GER	E4	2-4-0	1894
—	2500	LMS	4P	2-6-4T	1934
Royal Scot	6100	LMS	7P	4-6-0	1927
Oliver Cromwell	70013	BR	7MT	4-6-2	1951
Peer Gynt	5865	NSB	52	2-10-0	1944
King Haakon VII	377	NSB	21c	2-6-0	1919

Industrial locomotives

Name	No	Builder	Type	Built
Beckton	1	Neilson (4444)	0-4-0ST	1892
Beckton	25	Neilson (5087)	0-4-0ST	1896
William Francis	6841	B/Peacock (6841)	0-4-0+0-4-0T	1937
Millfield	—	RSH (7070)	0-4-0CT	1942
Bluebottle	—	Barclay (1472)	0-4-0F	1916

Narrow gauge locomotives

Name	No	Builder	Type	Built
Gwynedd	—	Hunslet (316)	0-4-0ST	1883
George Sholto	—	Hunslet (994)	0-4-0ST	1909
Bronllwyd	—	H/Clarke (1643)	0-6-0WT	1930
Toby	—	M/Rail (22120)	4wDM	1964

15in gauge locomotives

Name	No	Builder	Type	Built
Rosenkavalier	—	Krupp (1662)	4-6-2	1937
Mannertreu	—	Krupp (1663)	4-6-2	1937
Flying Scotsman	4472	W. Stewart (4472)	4-6-2	1976
Works Loco	—	Diss	0-4-0DM	1992

10.25in gauge locomotives

Name	No	Builder	Type	Built
Alan Bloom	1	BSM	0-4-0ST	1995

Owners
80, 490, 2500, 70013 on loan from the National Railway Museum

Special events: Please contact for details
Facilities for disabled: Toilets, wheelchairs available. Able to take wheelchairs on Nursery Line Railway
Special notes: Reduced rates for coach parties. Prices on application

Bristol Industrial Museum
Bristol Steam Centre

The Museum houses machinery and vehicles associated with Bristol's industrial past, from horse-drawn vehicles to aircraft
Location: Princes Wharf, Bristol
OS reference: ST 585722
Operating society/organisation: Bristol Industrial Museum, Princes Wharf, Bristol BS1 4RN
Telephone: Bristol (0117) 9251470
Fax: 0117 9297318
Car parks: Available nearby
Access by public transport: Buses to centre of town, 1km from Temple Meads station

Industrial locomotives

Name	No	Builder	Type	Built
Portbury	—	Avonside (1764)	0-6-0ST	1917
Henbury	—	Peckett (1940)	0-6-0ST	1937
—	3	F/Walker (242)	0-6-0ST	1874
—	—	R/Hornsby (418792)	0-4-0DM	1958

On site facilities: Shop
Length of line: Half-mile, extension of one-mile open, special occassions only
Public opening: Open Tuesday-Sunday 10.00-17.00. Closed Mondays
Facilities for disabled:

Reasonable access
Special notes: Operation of railway on advertised weekends only, 12.00-17.30
Membership details: Officer in charge D. Martin, Bristol Harbour Railway c/o above address

Buckinghamshire Railway Centre
Buckinghamshire Steam Centre
Member: AIRPS

The Buckinghamshire Railway Centre is situated at Quainton Road on the freight only Aylesbury-Calvert line, once part of the Metropolitan and Great Central line from London to Verney junction. Quainton Road station is also the old junction for the Brill Tramway closed in 1935.
Location: Adjacent to BR goods only line to Aylesbury. Turn off A41 at Waddesdon 6 miles NW of Aylesbury, Bucks
OS reference: SP 738190
Operating society/organisation: Quainton Railway Society Ltd, The Railway Station, Quainton, near Aylesbury, Bucks HP22 4BY
Telephone: Quainton (01296) 655450
Car park: Quainton Road — Free parking
Access by public transport: BR Aylesbury station. Local bus Monday-Saturday only
On site facilities: Souvenir bookshop, light refreshments, toilets, steam-hauled train rides. Museum of small relics, secondhand bookshop, miniature railway

Locomotives and multiple-units

Name	No	Origin	Class	Type	Built
—	1	Met Rly	E	0-4-4T	1898
—	0314	LSWR	0298	2-4-0WT	1874
Wightwick Hall	6989	GWR	'Hall'	4-6-0	1948
—	7200	GWR	7200	2-8-2T	1934
—	7715	GWR	5700	0-6-0PT	1930
—	9466	GWR	9400	0-6-0PT	1952
—	41298	LMS	2MT	2-6-2T	1951
—	41313	LMS	2MT	2-6-2T	1952
—	46447	LMS	2MT	2-6-0	1950
—	D2298	BR	04	0-6-0DM	1960
—	3405*	SAR	25NC	4-8-4	1958
—	51886	BR	115	DMBS	1960
—	51899	BR	115	DMBS	1960
—	59761	BR	115	TC	1960

*3ft 6in gauge

Industrial locomotives

Name	No	Builder	Type	Built
Sydenham	—	A/Porter (3567)	4wTG	1895
Scott	—	Bagnall (2469)	0-4-0ST	1932
—	—	Baguley (2161)	0-4-0DM	1941
Swanscombe	—	Barclay (699)	0-4-0ST	1891
—	—	GF3 Barclay (1477)	0-4-0F	1916
Tom Parry	—	Barclay (2015)	0-4-0ST	1935
—	—	Barclay (2243)	0-4-0F	1948
Osram	—	Fowler (20067)	0-4-0DM	1933
—	3	H/Leslie (3717)	0-4-0ST	1928
Sir Thomas	—	H/Clarke (1334)	0-6-0T	1918
—	—	H/Clarke (1742)	0-4-0ST	1946

Cont

England

19

Catering facilities: Hot snacks and light refreshments available

Length of line: Two half-mile demonstration lines

Public opening: Sundays and Bank Holidays: Easter-end October. Wednesdays in June, July and August. Limited opening (no engines in steam) daily

Special events: A series of special events is held throughout the year including Thomas the Tank Engine weekends on 14/15 June and 6/7 September. At Easter circus performers will visit the Centre. Transport Art Festival — 25/26 May; Bus Rally — 26 May; Rover Car Rally — 24 August; Vintage Car Rally — 25 August. Half day steam locomotive driving courses are held throughout the year. Full details are available on application

Facilities for disabled: Access to most of site including special toilets

Special notes: One of the largest collection of standard gauge locomotives, together with a most interesting collection of vintage coaching stock, much of which was built in the last century

General: The public area of the centre covers some 25 acres of land with views across the Buckinghamshire countryside. A picnic area is available at the miniature railway

Name	No	Builder	Type	Built
—	—	Hunslet (2067)	0-4-0DM	1940
Arthur	—	Hunslet (3782)	0-6-0ST	1953
Juno	—	Hunslet (3850)	0-6-0ST	1958
—	65	Hunslet (3889)	0-6-0ST	1964
—	66	Hunslet (3890)	0-6-0ST	1964
—	26	Hunslet (7016)	0-6-0DH	1971
Redland	—	K/Stuart (K4428)	0-4-0DM	1929
Coventry No 1	—	NBL (24564)	0-6-0ST	1939
—	—	Peckett (1900)	0-4-0T	1936
Gibraltar	—	Peckett (2087)	0-4-0ST	1948
—	—	Peckett (2104)	0-4-0ST	1948
—	—	Peckett (2105)	0-4-0ST	1948
—	T1	Hibberd (2102)	4wD	1937
Tarmac	—	Hibberd (3765)	0-4-0DM	1955
—	—	Sentinel (6515)	4wVBTG	1926
—	11	Sentinel (9366)	4wVBTG	1945
—	7	Sentinel (9376)	4wVBTG	1947
—	—	Sentinel (9537)	4wVBTG	1947
Chislet	9	Yorkshire (2498)	0-6-0ST	1951

Stock: *Coaches* —
1 LCDR 1st Class 4 wheeler; 1 MSLR 3rd Class 6 wheeler; 4 LNWR coach bodies; 2 GNR 6 wheelers; 3 LNWR; 3 LMSR; 1 BR(W) Hawksworth brake 3rd; 2 BR Mk 1; 1 BR Mk 2; 1 BR Suburban brake; 3 LNER; 1 LNWR full brake 6 wheeler; 1 LMSR passenger brake van; 1 GWR passenger brake van

Wagons —
A large and varied collection including 1 LNWR combination truck; 1 LSWR ventilated fruit van; 1 SR PMV; 1 BR(W) 'Siphon G'; 1 BR horse box; 1 BR CCT

3 ex-London Underground coaches
1 2ft gauge post office mailbag car 803
Sentinel/Cammell 3-car steam railcar unit 5208 (ex-Egyptian National)
Numerous goods vehicles/wagons/vans

Owners
41298, 41313, 46447 and *Juno* the Ivatt Locomotive Trust)
9466 the 9466 Group)

Bure Valley Railway
Member: AIRPS, TT

Norfolk
Timetable Service

Opened in 1990 the BVR runs over the old Great Eastern Wroxham-Aylsham line. It is paralleled throughout the entire 9 miles by the Bure Valley Walk which offers excellent photographic opportunities

Headquarters: Bure Valley Railway (1991) Ltd, Aylsham Station, Norwich Road, Aylsham, Norwich NR11 6BW

Managing Director: Paul Conibeare

Telephone: (01263) 733858

Fax: (01263) 733814

Main public station: Aylsham (Norwich Road); Wroxham

Locomotives

Name	No	Class	Type	Built
Wroxham Broad	1	G&S/Winson	2-6-4T	1992
Volunteer†	2	H/Hunslet	0-4-0DH	1996
Buxton Mill	3	BVR	4w-4wDH	1989
—	4	Fairbourne	2-6-2	1989
—	5	Lister	4wDM	
Blickling Hall	6	Winson*	2-6-2	1994
—	7	Winson*	2-6-2	1994
—	8	BVR/Winson*	2-6-2T	1997
Little Titan	9	Cheeseman	Steam crane	1975

*Based on Indian Railways 2ft 6in gauge 'ZB' class
†Rebuilt by EAGIT

Stock
19 fully enclosed saloons, 1 fully enclosed brake saloon, 2 guards van, generator car, miscellaneous wagons

(Coltishall Road)
Other public stations: Coltishall, Brampton and Buxton
Car and coach parks: Aylsham and Wroxham
OS reference: Aylsham — TG619540326456; Wroxham — TG630300318646
Access by public transport: By rail – Wroxham station is adjacent to BR Hoveton & Wroxham station (Norwich-Cromer/Sheringham line). By bus – Eastern Counties buses run between Norwich and Aylsham
Refreshment facilities: Restaurant at Aylsham, with picnic area and light refreshments at Wroxham
Souvenir shops: Aylsham and Wroxham
Journey time: Approximately 45min each way plus turnround time
Length of line: 9 miles; 15in gauge
Passenger trains: Frequency depends on time of year, maximum frequency one hour
Period of public operation: Open from Easter to end of September – trains run most days, telephone for details
Facilities for disabled: Toilets at Aylsham and Wroxham, no special rolling stock but each train can carry one wheelchair, advance notice would be appreciated
Special events: Please contact for details
Special notes: Steam locomotive driving courses. Party discounts available. Private charters by arrangement. Special combined train and Broads boat excursions run most days during the summer
Membership details: Friends of the Bure Valley Railway, Membership Secretary, c/o above address

---

Cadeby Light Railway

Members: AIRPS, TT

Warwickshire Steam Centre

A new museum was opened in 1990, 'The Boston Collection', encompassing the lifetime collection of Teddy Boston and his family. The narrow gauge railway running in the grounds of the old rectory has been saved by Teddy Boston's enterprising widow and a small band of dedicated supporters in the face of considerable odds. Echoes of the *Titfield Thunderbolt* and Ancient and Modern. Their endeavours deserve your support
Location: One mile south of Market Bosworth on A447
OS reference: SK 426024
Operating society/organisation: Mrs J. A. Boston, The Old Rectory, Cadeby, Nuneaton, Warwicks CU13 0AS
Telephone: Market Bosworth (01455) 290462
Car park: In local side roads
Access by public transport: Midland Fox/Stevenson 178 from Hinckley. 153 Leicester City Bus from Leicester to Market Bosworth (1.25-miles away)
On site facilities: 2ft gauge railway, also traction engines, model railway, and a museum housing the 'Boston Collection'. Brass rubbing centre in church with over 70 replica brasses
Refreshment facilities: Light refreshments available

Narrow gauge locomotives

Name	No	Builder	Type	Built
Pixie	—	Bagnall (2090)	0-4-0ST	1919
—	2	O&K (7529)	0-4-0WT	1914
—	—	Baguley (1695)	0-4-0PM	1928
—	—	Deutz(10050)	0-4-0DM	1931
—	—	H/Clarke (D558)	4wDM	1930
—	—	Lister (4088)	4wPM	1931
—	—	M/Rail(1320)	4wDM	1918
—	87004	M/Rail (2197)	4wDM	1922
—	87009	M/Rail (4572)	4wDM	1929
—	—	M/Rail (5853)	4wDM	1934
—	—	M/Rail (7512)	4wDM	1938
—	42	M/Rail (7710)	4wDM	1939
—	20	M/Rail (8748)	4wDM	1942
Delta	—	O&K (4588)	4wPM	c1931
—	87008	R/Hornsby (179870)	4wDM	1936
—	87051	R/Hornsby (404967)	4wDM	1957
—	—	SMH(104063G)	4wDM	1976
—	—	Thakeham(4TH)	4wDM	c1946

Standard gauge

—	—	Peckett (2012)	0-4-0ST	1942

Stock

Penrhyn Quarrymans' coach; 2 flat trucks; 7 open trucks; 2 platelayers trolleys

Public opening: 2nd Saturday of every month, plus 1st Saturday in November (Steam & Bonfire Party), Father Christmas Specials in December and Boxing Day. From 13.00 or by arrangement. Admission free (donations requested)
Special events: Please contact for details
Special notes: Party bookings by prior arrangement

Cambrian Railways Society

Location: Oswestry station yard, Oswald Road, Oswestry, Shropshire
OS reference: SJ 294297
Operating society/organisation: Cambrian Railways Society Ltd, C. W. Mottram, 'Delamere', Old Chirk Road, Gobowen, Oswestry, Shropshire SY11 3LH
Telephone: (01691) 671749
Car park: In Society's depot
Length of line: 400yd, opened 7 December 1996, the Light Railway Order having been granted
Public opening: Daily 10.00-16.00
On site facilities: Refreshment room — the 'Whistle Stop' (open on special days in former Llansantffraid signalbox) and picnic area
Special notes: Railwayana, artefacts and 15 bicycles on display. Normally B/Peacock 1827, Peckett 2131 and Hunslet 3770 are on display inside the building. Group discount available. Also known as Oswestry Transport Museum

Diesel Multiple-Units

Name	No	Origin	Class	Type	Built
—	53531	BRCW	104	DMC	1957
—	53479	BRCW	104	DMBS	1957

Industrial locomotives

Name	No	Builder	Type	Built
—	1872	B/Peacock (1827)	0-4-0ST	1879
—	1	H/Clarke (D843)	0-4-0DM	1954
Adam	1	Peckett (1430)	0-4-0ST	1916
—	3	Hunslet (D3526)	0-6-0DM	1954
Oliver Velton	6	Peckett (2131)	0-4-0ST	1951
—	8	Barclay (885)	0-6-0ST	1900
—	322	Planet (3541)	4wDM	1952
Norma	3770	Hunslet (3770)	0-6-0ST	1952
—	—	Sentinel (9374)	4wVBT	1947
—	—	Hibberd (3057)	4wDM	1946
—	—	Planet	4wDM	1960

Locomotive notes

Barclay (885) is now on static display by the old Cambrian Railways locomotive works

Stock

1 GWR auto-trailer; 1 GWR brake van; 1 LMS brakevan; 2 tank wagons; 1 open wagon, 1 box van

Chasewater Railway

Member: AIRPS, TT

Founded in 1959 as the Railway Preservation Society (West Midlands District), the Chasewater Railway was reformed in 1985 as a Registered Charity. The railway operates as 'The Colliery Line' to reflect its origins and location in the heart of the Cannock Chase coalfield. The railway extended its running line in October 1995 and now runs a regular timetabled service between Brownhills West Station and the newly-opened Norton Lakeside Station (which adjoins Chasewater's Wildfowl Reserve).
Location: Chasewater Park, Brownhills (off A5 southbound, nr jct A452 Chester Road).
OS Reference: SK 034070.
Operating society/organisation: Chasewater Light Railway & Museum Co.

Diesel Multiple Units

Name	No	Builder	Class	Type	Built
—	W51370	P/Steel	117	DMBS	1960
—	W51372	P/Steel	117	DMBS	1960
—	W51412	P/Steel	117	DMS	1960
—	W59444	BR	116	TS	1958
—	W59603	P/Steel	127	TSL	1959

Industrial Locomotives

Name	No	Builder	Type	Built
Alfred Paget	11	Neilson (2937)	0-4-0ST	1882
Sheepbridge No.15	—	H/Clarke (431)	0-6-0T	1885
—	6	Peckett (917)	0-4-0ST	1902
Asbestos	4	H/Leslie (2780)	0-4-0ST	1909
Colin McAndrew	3	Barclay (1223)	0-4-0ST	1911
Little Lady	—	Peckett (1903)	0-4-0ST	1936
Invicta	8	Barclay (2220)	0-4-0ST	1946
Whit No.4	—	H/Clarke (1822)	0-6-0T	1949
Sentinel	5	Sentinel (9632)	4wVBT	1957
—	1	M/Rail (1947)	4wPM	1919
—	21	Kent Constr (1612)	4wDM	1929
—	—	Fowler (4100013)	0-4-0DM	1948
—	—	R/Hornsby (305306)	0-4-0DM	1952

Telephone: 01543 452623.
Car park: within Chasewater Park.
Access by public transport: By rail – Walsall (no Sunday service) and Birmingham New Street. Bus (Sunday services) – Midland Red North 156A from Birmingham (Dale End); 362 from Walsall (Bridge Street). For timetable information and details of midweek/Saturday services, contact Centro Hotline 0121-200 2700.
On site facilities: Refreshments. Shop. Lakeside walks and large grassed areas.
Catering facilities: Hot and cold buffet.
Length of line: 1.25 miles (Standard Gauge).

Name	No	Builder	Type	Built
Toad	37	Fowler (4220015)	0-4-0DH	1962
Fleet	7	R/Hornsby (458641)	0-4-0DE	1963

Rolling Stock
A variety of passenger and freight vehicles are housed on site, including a number of considerable historical importance

Public opening: Sundays and Bank Holiday Mondays from Easter to end of October. Trains run at 45 min. intervals from 12 noon until 5.15pm.
Special events: 15 June (Transport Festival); 10 August (Military Tattoo); 11/12 October (Vintage Vehicle Rally). Santa Specials 14, 21 December.

Facilities for disabled: Disabled access to stations, trains and buffet.
Membership details: Membership Secretary, Brownhills West Station, Hednesford Road, Brownhills West, Walsall WS8 7LT.

Chinnor & Princes Risborough Railway — 'The Icknield Line'
Member: AIRPS

Oxfordshire
Timetable Service

The Chinnor & Princes Risborough Railway Association was formed in 1989 with the aim of restoring the disused line from Princes Risborough to Chinnor, part of the former Watlington branch
Location: Chinnor, Oxon, 10 miles SW of Aylesbury. J6 on M40, station signposted from B4009, which passes through village
OS reference: TL 774362
Operating society/organisation: Chinnor & Princes Risborough Railway Co, Chinnor Station, Station Road, Chinnor, Oxon OX9 4ER
Access by public transport: BR Princes Risborough then Wycombe Bus Nos 232/331/332 to Chinnor (Sats only)
Length of line: 4 miles. First 3.5 miles miles opened for 1995 season
Passenger trains: Chinnor-Thame Junction-Chinnor
Public opening: Weekends from Easter-end October. Thomas

Locomotives and multiple-units

Name	No	Origin	Class	Type	Built
Haversham	D3018	BR	08	0-6-0DE	1953
—	D8568	BR	17	Bo-Bo	1963
—	55003	BR	122	DMBS	1958
—	4247	GWR	4200	2-8-0T	1916

Industrial locomotives

Name	No	Builder	Type	Built
Sir Robert Peel	8	Hunslet (3776)	0-6-0ST	1952
Iris	459515	R/Hornsby (459515)	0-6-0DH	1952

Stock - coaches
1 ex-LNWR Mess coach, 1 ex-BR Mk 1 NDV, 1 ex-BR Mk 1 RMB, 1 ex-BR Mk 1 CK, 1 ex-BR Mk 1 BSK, 1 ex-BR Mk 2 FK, 12 various wagons, 1 Coles self-propelled crane

visiting in May and August. Santa & Mince Pie Specials in December. Up to date information on Talking Timetable 01844 353535
On site facilities: Souvenir shop, buffet plus on train buffet. Toilets. Free car park. Picnic area
Special note: Visiting locomotives

during the season, please 'phone for details or see railway press
Membership details: Mr Peter Harris, 12 Ann's Close, Aylesbury, Bucks
Membership journal: *The Watlington Flyer* — bi-monthly

Cholsey & Wallingford Railway
Member: AIRPS

Oxfordshire
Steam Centre

Location: Hithercroft Industrial Estate, St Johns Road, Wallingford, Oxfordshire
Traffic Manager: David

Goodenough
Operating Society: Cholsey & Wallingford Railway Preservation Society, PO Box 16, Wallingford,

Oxon OX10 0NF
Telephone: 01491 835067 (24hr information line)
Access by public transport:

Thames Transit (390) from Oxford-London, BR Cholsey (2 miles)
Public Opening: Please contact for details
Length of line: 1.25 miles from Wallingford
Journey time: Approximately 20min
On site facilities: Souvenir and coffee shop, museum, model railway
Special events: Please contact for details
Special notes: Light Railway Order now granted. Railway crosses new bypass (A4130) at a

level crossing. The Society has completed track into Cholsey bay platform. Train services are currently based on Wallingford
Membership details: Ian Bowyer,

at above address
Membership journal: *The Bunk* — 3 issues/year

Locomotives

Name	No	Origin	Class	Type	Built
George Mason	08123	BR	08	0-6-0	1955

Industrial locomotives

Name	No	Builder		Type	Built
Carpenter	3271	Planet (3271)		0-4-0	1949

Rolling stock — coaches: 2 BR Mk 1 coaches, 1 BR Mk 2 brake coach

---

Churnet Valley Railway

Member: AIRPS

Staffordshire
Steam Centre

Easter 1996 saw the re-opening of the first mile of the Churnet Valley Railway from Cheddleton to Leekbrook. Cheddleton is a Victorian country station set in the attractive Staffordshire moorlands, situated adjacent to the River Churnet. Pleasant walks can be taken alongside the Caldon Canal, and the Flint Mill Museum is only 1,200yd away. Please ring to confirm timetable and events.
Location: Cheddleton station, near Leek, Staffordshire
OS reference: SJ 983519
Operating society/organisation: Churnet Valley Railway (1992) plc
Telephone: Churnetside (01538) 360522
Car park: Riverside car park and picnic area opposite the station
Access by public transport: BR Stoke-on-trent (10 miles). A regular bus service operated by Proctors, PMT and Stevensons from Hanley, Longton and Leek to Cheddleton village
On site facilities: The station contains a refreshment room, souvenir shop and small relics museum. On open days visitors are allowed to visit the yard, signalbox and new locomotive display hall. Modern toilets and picnic area on site
Length of line: 1-mile, Cheddleton-Leekbrook
Public opening: Easter-September inclusive — Sundays and bank holiday Mondays, 11.00-17.30. Sundays October-March 12.00-

Locomotives and Multiple-units

Name	No	Origin	Class	Type	Built
—	4422	LMS	4F	0-6-0	1927
—	2	NSR	New L	0-6-2T	1923
—	80136	BR	4MT	2-6-4T	1956
—	D2070	BR	03	0-6-0DM	1959
—	D2334	BR	04	0-6-0DM	1961
—	D3420	BR	08	0-6-0DE	1957
Tamworth Castle	D7672	BR	25	Bo-Bo	1967
Burma Star	33056	BR	33	Bo-Bo	1961
—	33102	BR	33	Bo-Bo	1960
—	53455	BRCW	104	DMBS	1957
—	53517	BRCW	104	DMCL	1957

Industrial locomotives

Name	No	Builder		Type	Built
Josiah Wedgwood	52	Hunslet (3777)		0-6-0ST	1952

Locomotive notes: Locos expected to be in service: 4422, D2070, D2334, D3420, D7672, 33102 and Class 104 DMU

Owners
4422 the 4422 Locomotive Fund
D3420, 33056, 33102 and D7672 the NSR Diesel Group
NSR 2 the National Railway Museum

Stock
2 ex-BR Mk 1 CK coaches; 2 ex- BR Mk 1 BSK coaches; 1 ex-BR Mk 1 SO coach; 2 ex-BR Mk 1 TSO coaches; 2 ex-BR Mk 1 FK coaches; 1 ex-BR Mk 1 RMB coach; 2 ex-BR brake suburban coaches; 1 ex-NSR coach body; 1 ex-LMS 6-wheel full brake; 1 ex-LMS goods brake van; 1 ex-LMS 6-wheel CCT; 2 ex-LMS box vans; 3 ex-BR box vans; 2 ex-LMS 5-plank wagons; 1 ex-LMS hopper wagon; 1 Esso tank wagon; 1 7ton diesel rail-mounted crane; 1 ex-BR standard 20ton brake van

17.00.
Refreshment room only April-September, 13.00-17.00 daily excluding Thursdays
Special Events: Please contact for details

Facilities for disabled: Access to most of the site is possible by wheelchair. Train rides by arrangement
Membership details: North Staffordshire Railway Co,

Membership Secretary c/o above address

Special notes: Coach parties catered for by prior arrangement. Guided tours available for parties on request. The sale of track and trackbed between Leekbrook Junction and Oakamoor sand sidings (7 miles) has been agreed. A share issue of £400,000 is the target and the public are invited to buy shares in the Churnet Valley Railway (1992) plc to help develope the railway. The first stage of the CVR opened at Easter 1996 and will be extended progressively over the next few years.

Cleethorpes Coast Light Railway
Member: AIRPS

NE Lincolnshire
Timetable Service

One of the country's latest 15in gauge recruits. Previously a 14.25in gauge railway it was converted to 15in in time for the 1994 Steam Gala. The railway is gaining a reputation for good events and galas, as well as now being the chosen site for a Museum of Seaside Miniature Railways. Planning for this major new project is well underway with the completion planned over the next four years.

1997 will again feature steam haulage on the line with visiting locomotives planned for the main season to assist the resident stock. The railway operating company is lucky to be able to call upon the Cleethorpes Coast Light Railway supporters association to provide the majority of operating staff. This small group are always looking for new helpers, and membership is free. Details are available from the company

Operating society/organisation: Cleethorpes Coast Light Railway Ltd, Lakeside Station, Kings Road, Cleethorpes, NE Lincolnshire DN35 0AG
Telephone/Fax: 01472 604657
Access by public transport: BR Cleethorpes, Stagecoach service 17

Locomotives

Name	No	Built/rebuilt	Type	Date
Konigswinter	1	CCLR	2-8-0GH	1992
Arnold J Rimmer	2	Lister	4wDH Tram	—
The Cub	3	CCLR	4w4DM	1993
Sian*	4	Guest	2-4-2	1963
Haigh Hall/Katie†	5	Guest	2-4-2	1954
—	6	Stanhope/CCLR	0-4-0VBT	1995
King George	—	B/Lowke	4-4-2	—

Also on site

Blue Pacific	—	Guiness	4-6-2VBT	1935

Rolling stock
4 Severn Lamb semi-open saloons (one converted to brake coach by CCLR); 5 Alan Keef toast racks (one includes guard's compartment); 1 JMA open coach; 2 4-wheel tub wagons; 14-wheel box van; 14-wheel five plank wagon; 1 4-wheel ballast hopper, 1 bogie passenger brake van;

Owners/notes
*On loan from *Sian* Project Group, currently undergoing overhaul off site
†On loan from Wigan Council
Flying Scotsman currently away at Cumbrian Steam Miniatures being rebuilt as a steam locomotive to be named *Seabreeze*

from Sea Road passes the line. By car, Kings Road is the main resort road. Follow Lakeside brown tourist signs
On site facilities: Large 500 space car park (pay & display – April to October). Station gift shop at Kingsway station. Teapot tearoom for refreshments at Lakeside station. Lakeside picnic area
Period of public opening: Daily during main season. Railway open from 10.00. *Winter weekends —* November-Good Friday.
Special events: Please contact for details

Colne Valley Railway
Member: AIRPS, TT

Essex
Steam Centre

An completely reconstructed country station and railway within sight of the 12th century castle and specialising in entertainment and education
Location: Castle Hedingham Station, Yeldham Road, Castle Hedingham, Halstead, Essex CO9 3DZ
OS reference: TL 774362

Operating society/organisation: Colne Valley Railway Preservation Society Ltd
Telephone: Hedingham (01787) 461174
Car park: At the site (access from A604 road) between Castle Hedingham and Great Yeldham
Access by public transport: Eastern National bus services No

88 Colchester-Halstead, 89 Halstead-Hedingham and Hedingham Omnibuses No 4 Braintree-Hedingham, No 5 Sudbury-Hedingham. Nearest station — Braintree (7 miles)
On site facilities: Depot, museum, souvenir shop buffet, 4-acre riverside wooded picnic area (suitable for nature studies

by visiting school children), toilets, video carriage, information centre

Catering facilities: Buffet carriage when trains operating. Pullman on train service on selected days for Sunday lunch, private hire and evening wine and dine (pre-booking essential for all Pullman services)

Length of line: Approx 1-mile

Public opening: Daily for static displays except 24 December to 31 january. Steam trains operate every Sunday from 16 March to 26 October, also Tuesdays Wednesdays and Thursdays during school summer holidays, and every Bank Holiday (except Christmas & New Year), Wednesdays during other school hoildays (except February). Heritage diesel trains operate Saturdays 24 May to 30 August, Fridays during school holidays, Sundays 2/9 March and every Sunday in November

Special events... Gala Days, Friends of Thomas weekends, Santa Specials

Educational events: Diesel trains available every day for school visits. Learning with Thomas in June, Victorian Special in October. All educational events must be pre-booked

Family tickets: Available — 2 Adults + 4 Children, giving unlimited train rides except on special events

Facilities for disabled: Access to most areas. Ramps to trains, staff will help. No toilets suitable for disabled

Special notes: The railway has been completely rebuilt on part of the original Colne Valley &

Halstead Railway track-bed. The railway offers much of educational value specialising in school party visits by appointment at any time

of the year

Membership details: Membership Secretary, c/o Castle Hedingham Station

Locomotives and Multiple-units

Name	No	Origin	Class	Type	Built
Blue Star	35010	SR	MN	4-6-2	1942
—	45163	LMS	5	4-6-0	1935
—	45293	LMS	5	4-6-0	1936
—	D2041	BR	03	0-6-0DM	1959
—	D2184	BR	03	0-6-0DM	1962
—	D5634	BR	31	A1A-A1A	1960
—	51138	BR	108	DMBS	1958
—	51151	BR	108	DMS	1958
—	51347	BR	117	DMBS	1959
—	55033	P/Steel	121	DTC	1960
—	W79976	AC Cars	—	Railbus	1958
—	E79978	AC Cars	—	Railbus	1958

Industrial locomotives

Name	No	Builder	Type	Built
Victory	8	Barclay (2199)	0-4-0ST	1945
—	190	Hunslet (3790)	0-6-0ST	1952
—	68072	Vulcan (5309)	0-6-0ST	1945
Jupiter	60	RSH (7671)	0-6-0ST	1950
—	40	RSH (7765)	0-6-0T	1954
Barrington	—	Avonside (1875)	0-4-0ST	1921
—	1	H/Leslie (3715)	0-4-0ST	1928
—	—	Barclay (349)	0-4-0DM	1941
—	YD43	R/Hornsby (221639)	4wDM	1943
—	—	Hibbard (3147)	4wDM	1947
—	—	Unilok (2109)	4wDM R/R	1982
—	—	Lake & Elliot (1)	4wPM	1924

Stock
9 ex-BR Mk 1 coaches (2xTSO, SO, 3xCK, SK, 2xBSK); 1 ex-Norwegian State Railway 18803 Balcony; Open Second; 2 ex-Pullman cars, *Aquila* and *Hermione*; 1 ex-BR Mk 3 SLEP; 9 BR NPCCS, 2 ex-LNER — 1xBTO (16551) 1xTK (42240); Sundry items of freight stock

Owners
35010 and 45293 the British Enginemans Steam Preservation Society

County School

A preserved station on the former Great Eastern Railway line at the northern end of the East Dereham branch

Operating society/organisation: At the time of writing the site is closed pending renegotiation of the lease. The stock shown here was still on site at the end of January 1997. The railway press will carry details of the situation once clarified, in the meantime

Diesel Multiple-units

Name	No	Origin	Class	Type	Built
—	51669	BR	115	DMBS	1960
—	51894	BR	115	DMBS	1960
—	59701	BR	115	TS	1960

Industrial locomotives

Name	No	Builder	Type	Built
Pony	—	H/Leslie (2918)	0-4-0ST	1912
County School	—	R/Hornsby (497753)	0-4-0DH	1963
—	—	RSH (8368)	0-4-0DH	1963

prospective visitors are warned that the site is guarded by security staff
OS reference: TF 990227
On site facilities: Refreshments and souvenir shop. Toilets, parking, picnic area and country walks
Length of line: 1-mile towards North Elmham

Name	No	Builder	Type	Built
—	12	RSH (7845)	0-6-0T	1955
Edmundsons	—	Barclay (2168)	0-4-0ST	1940

Stock-wagons
1 oil tank, LMS, GWR and SCCR brake vans, 1 ironstone hopper, 1 covered van. Plus Jones diesel shunting crane and Wickham trolley

Darlington Railway Centre & Museum

County Durham
Museum

Located on the original 1825 route of the Stockton & Darlington Railway, the restored North Road station, dating from 1842, is now a museum which forms the centrepiece of an area devoted to railway history and preservation.

The Museum is administered by Darlington Borough Council. The collection includes locomotives, rolling stock and many small exhibits. The site also includes two other historic buildings of the S&DR — the former Goods Shed and the Hopetown Carriage Works. Steam train rides over a short length of line are available on selected dates, and there are plans for future extension of the line.

The Ken Hoole Study Centre houses a collection of reference material on the railways of north-east England including the library of the North Eastern Railway Association (access by appointment).

Regional Railways North East provides a link to Darlington's main line station and to Shildon, for the Timothy Hackworth Museum
Museum Curator: Steven Dyke
Location: North Road station, Darlington, County Durham DL3 6ST. Approximately three quarter-mile north of town centre, off North Road (A167)
OS reference: NZ 289157
Telephone: 01325 460532
Car park: At museum site
Access by public transport: Rail services to Darlington North Road station. Local bus services along North Road
Catering facilities: Refreshment area open Spring Bank Holiday to mid-September. Confectionery and drinks at other times
On site facilities: Souvenir and book shop. Toilets

Locomotives

Name	No	Origin	Class	Type	Built
Locomotion	1	S&DR	—	0-4-0	1825
Derwent	25	S&DR	—	0-6-0	1845
—	1463	NER	1463	2-4-0	1885
—	910	NER	901	2-4-0	1875

Industrial locomotives

Name	No	Builder	Type	Built
Met	—	H/Leslie (2800)	0-4-0ST	1909
—	17	Head Wrightson (33)	0-4-0VB	1873
—	—	Bagnall (2898)	0-4-0F	1948
—	39	RSH (6947)	0-6-0T	1938

Stock
1 Stockton & Darlington Rly passenger coach (1846)
1 North Eastern Railway Coach body (c1860)
1 NER 20-ton mineral wagon
1 Chaldron wagon

Owners
Locomotion, Derwent, 1463 and 910 are all on loan from the National Railway Museum
Met is on loan from Messrs D. & R. Branch

Darlington Railway Preservation Society
Member: AIRPS

Locomotive

Name	No	Origin	Class	Type	Built
—	78018	BR	2MT	2-6-0	1954

Industrial locomotives

Name	No	Builder	Type	Built
—	2	RSH (7925)	0-4-0DM	1959
—	1	Peckett (2142)	0-4-0ST	1953
David Payne	185	Fowler (4110006)	0-4-0DM	1950
Smiths Dock Co Ltd	—	Fowler (4200018)	0-4-0DM	1947
—	—	GEC	4wE	1928
—	—	R/Hornsby (279591)	0-4-0DM	1949
—	—	R/Hornsby*	4wDM	
—	—	R/Hornsby*	4wDM	
—	—	R/Hornsby*	4wDM	

*1ft 6in gauge

Stock
Various wagons, steam and diesel cranes

Cont

Public opening: Daily throughout the year 10.00-17.00 (except Christmas/New Year holidays). Days and times may be subject to amendment
Special events: Railway Carnival — September; steam days (contact for details)
Facilities for disabled: Access to main museum building for wheelchairs. Disabled persons toilet. Guide tape for visually handicapped
Membership details: Friends of Darlington Railway Museum, Darlington Railway Preservation Society and A1 Steam Locomotive Trust, all c/o above address
Note: Some locomotives are located in the former goods shed, where restoration work is being undertaken by the Darlington Railway Preservation Society (limited opening to visitors — times vary; groups by arrangement). The former carriage works is being renovated for use by the A1 Steam Locomotive Trust

---

Dean Forest Railway
Member: AIRPS, TT

Passenger services have been extended beyond St Mary's Halt to terminate at Lydney Junction (Severn & Wye Joint)
Location: Norchard Railway Centre on the B4234, three quarter-mile off A48 at Lydney, Glos
OS reference: SO 629044
Operations Manager: Vacant
Operating society/organisation: Dean Forest Railway Society in conjunction with owning company, Forest of Dean Railway Ltd
Telephone: (01594) 843423 information line; 01594 845840 (daytime); 01452 840625 (general info and evenings)
Car park: Adequate for cars and coaches — no charge
Access by public transport: BR Lydney
On site facilities: A shop and refreshments are available at Norchard along with a museum, riverside walk, forest trail and picnic area
Catering facilities: Hot and cold snacks on steam days. Parties catered for by appointment
Length of line: 2 miles
Public opening: Daily for static display — shop, museum, refreshments open every Saturday and Sunday 11.00-17.00 and weekdays Easter to December. Train rides: Good Friday, Easter Saturday and all Bank Holidays Sundays and Mondays (Christmas/New Year excepted). All Sundays Easter-September.

Locomotives and mutliple-units

Name	No	Origin	Class	Type	Built
—	28	TVR	O1	0-6-2T	1897
—	5541	GWR	4575	2-6-2T	1928
—	9681	GWR	5700	0-6-0PT	1949
—	08238	BR	08	0-6-0DE	1956
—	51914	BR	108	DMS	1960
—	50619	BR	108	DMBS	1958
—	56492	BR	108	DMC	1960

Industrial locomotives

Name	No	Builder	Type	Built
—	—	Barclay (2221)	0-4-0ST	1946
Jessie	—	Hunslet (1873)	0-6-0ST	1937
Uskmouth No 1	—	Peckett (2147)	0-4-0ST	1952
Wilbert	—	Hunslet (3806)	0-6-0ST	1953
Warrior	—	Hunslet (3823)	0-6-0ST	1954
—	—	Hunslet (2145)	0-4-0DM	1940
—	—	Fowler (4210127)	0-4-0DM	1957
—	—	Hibberd (3947)	4wPM	1960
Cabot	39	R/Royce (10218)	0-6-0DH	1965

Owners
28 the National Railway Museum, on loan from the Museum of Wales

Stock
8 ex-GWR coaches; 16 ex-BR coaches; 3 Wickham trolleys; 1 steam crane Thos Smith (Rodley) TS 5027 (10ton); 90+ wagons

Wednesdays in June and July. Wednesdays, Thursdays and Saturdays in August
Special events: Friends of Thomas the Tank Engine — 27 May-1 June, 13/14 September; Transport Gala — 19 October; Santa Specials in December; December/January — *Wilbert's* New Year Party

Facilities for disabled: Access to museum, shop, toilets and train rides
Membership details: Mr R. Bramwell, 4 Poole Ground, Highnam, Gloucester GL2 8DJ
Membership journal: *Forest Venturer* — half yearly
Marketing name: The Friendly Forest Line

Derby Industrial Museum

Member: TT

Derbyshire
Museum

As would be expected of a railway town the museum has an extensive collection of railway material including locomotives and rolling stock (most on display at the Midland Railway Centre). The railway gallery relates the stories of railway industries in Derby, especially as they relate to the Midland Railway and its successors. Replica Midland Railway signalbox and model railway. The story is brought up to date by the Railway Research Gallery which looks at the rolew of the Railway Technical Centre
Location: Silk Mill Lane, Derby
Operating society/organisation:

Industrial locomotives

Name	No	Builder	Type	Built
Victory	—	Peckett (1547)	0-4-0ST	1919
—	—	Motor Rail (6155)	4wPM	1919

Derby Industrial Museum, Silk Mill Lane, off Full Street, Derby DE1 3AR
Telephone: 01332 255308
Fax: 01332 255804
Car park: Local car parks around town
Access by public transport: Bus station quarter mile, railway station three-quarter mile.
On site facilities: Shop. Baby changing facilities

Opening times: Admission free. Mondays 11.00-17.00, Tuesdays to Saturdays 10.00-17.00, Sundays 14.00-17.00, Bank Holidays 14.00-17.00
Facilities for disabled: Parking by arrangement. Level access to building, lifts and ramps to all gallery areas, toilets, sign language and sub-titles in Rolls-Royce gallery

Derwent Valley Light Railway

North Yorkshire
Steam Centre

Location: Murton Park, Murton Lane, Murton, Nr York YO1 3UF
Operating society/organisation: Great Yorkshire Railway Preservation Society
Telephone: 01904 489966
OS Reference: SE 651537
On site facilities: Refreshments, souvenir shop (Yorkshire Museum of Farming)
Car park: Free, on site
Length of line: Half-mile
Access by public transport: York-Stamford Bridge bus service from BR York station
Facilities for disabled: Toilets, ramped ways etc
Public opening: Open daily mid February-end October, for the Yorkshire Museum of Farming, Houlgate (Viking) Village and the

Industrial locomotives

Name	No	Builder	Type	Built
—	—	A/Barclay (2369)	0-4-0ST	1955
—*	—	Peckett (2103)	0-4-0ST	1948
—	—	Fowler (22077)	0-4-0DM	1937
—	ED6	Fowler (4200022)	0-4-0DM	1948
Churchill	—	Fowler (410005)	0-4-0DM	1947
Jim	—	R/Hornsby (417892)	4wDM	1959
Octavius Atkinson	—	R/Hornsby (466630)	4wDM	1962
—	—	R/Hornsby (327964)	4wDM	1953

*May not be on site for all of 1996

Rolling stock
1 ex-LNER coach, 1 NER coach, 1 NER coach body, 10 various freight wagons, and 1 rail crane

Derwent Valley Light Railway. Trains operate Sundays and Bank Holidays Easter-end September and for Santa Specials
Membership details: Andy Bell,

45 Maryland Avenue, Willerby Road, Hull HU5 5JA
Society journal: *DVLR News* (quarterly)

Didcot Railway Centre

Member: AIRPS, TT

Oxfordshire
Steam Centre

Based around the GWR engine shed and depot, the Centre now has a typical GWR small country station with signalboxes (from Radstock and Frome), re-creation of Brunel's broad gauge railway,

two demonstration lines, and a small relics museum
General Manager: Michael Dean
Location: Adjacent to BR station, Didcot, Oxfordshire. Access via station subway

OS reference: SU 525907
Operating society/organisation: Great Western Society Ltd, Didcot Railway Centre, Didcot, Oxon OX11 7NJ
Telephone: Didcot (01235)

Cont 29

817200

Car park: Didcot BR station access by public transport: Didcot Parkway BR station

Refreshment facilities: Refreshment room open all days centre is open (lunches, snacks). Picnic area

On site facilities: GWR locomotive depot, replica GWR station, museum and broad gauge demonstration. Souvenir sales. Rides are available on the demonstration lines on Steamdays. Admission price on Steamdays includes train rides

Length of line: 1,000yd

Public opening: Saturdays and Sundays all year. Daily 28 March-28 September, 25 October to 2 November, 27 December to 3 January. Steamdays first and last Sunday each month from March, Bank Holidays, all Sundays June-August, all Wednesdays in July and August, all Saturdays in August. Open 10.00-17.00 (dusk in winter)

Train rides: On Steamdays there is normally continuous operation of the passenger train, interrupted by Travelling Post Office demonstrations and turning of the locomotives on some days

Special events: Friends of Thomas the Tank Engine — 7-9 March, 3-5 October; Freight Weekend — 27/28 September; Photographers Evening (to 9pm) — 31 October/1 November; Santa Steamings — 10, 13/14, 20/21 December; New Year Steamings — 28 December/1 January 1998

Facilities for disabled: Steps at access from BR subway may cause problems but assistance can normally be provided (advance notification is useful)

Membership details: Richard Bullock, at above address

Membership journals: *Great*

Locomotives

Name	No	Origin	Class/builder	Type	Built
—	22	GWR	Diesel Railcar	1A-A1	1940
—	1338	GWR	Kitson (3799) (Cardiff Rly)	0-4-0ST	1898
Trojan	1340	GWR	Avonside (1380)	0-4-0ST	1897
—	1363	GWR	1361	0-6-0ST	1910
—	1466	GWR	1400	0-4-2T	1936
—	3650	GWR	5700	0-6-0PT	1939
—	3738	GWR	5700	0-6-0PT	1937
—	3822	GWR	2884	2-8-0	1940
—	4144	GWR	5101	2-6-2T	1946
Maindy Hall	4942	GWR	'Hall'	4-6-0	1929
Caerphilly Castle	4073	GWR	'Castle'	4-6-0	1923
Earl Bathurst	5051	GWR	'Castle'	4-6-0	1936
—	5322	GWR	4300	2-6-0	1917
—	5572	GWR	4575	2-6-2T	1927
Hinderton Hall	5900	GWR	'Hall'	4-6-0	1931
King Edward II	6023	GWR	'King'	4-6-0	1930
—	6106	GWR	6100	2-6-2T	1931
—	6697	GWR	5600	0-6-2T	1928
Burton Agnes Hall	6998	GWR	'Hall'	4-6-0	1949
—	7202	GWR	7200	2-8-2T	1934
Cookham Manor	7808	GWR	'Manor'	4-6-0	1938
—	D3771	BR	08	0-6-0DE	1959
Pontyberem	2	Burry Port & Gwendraeth Valley Rly		0-6-0ST	1900
Shannon	5	Wantage Tramway		0-4-0WT	1857

Industrial locomotives

Name	No	Builder	Type	Built
Bonnie Prince Charlie	1	RSH (7544)	0-4-0ST	1949
—	26	Hunslet (5238)	0-6-0DH	1962

Locomotive notes: Locomotives available in 1997 should be: 22, 1466, 3738, 5051. Locomotives under restoration include: 1340, 3650, 4144, 5322, 6023, 7202. Construction of the Firefly Trust's reproduction broad gauge locomotive *Firefly* is being undertaken

Stock
Over 40 ex-GWR coaches are preserved along with numerous ex-GWR freight wagons

Owners
5 and 4073 on loan from the National Railway and ScienceMuseums

Western Echo — quarterly;
National Newsletter — seven times annually

East Anglia Transport Museum

Member: TT

Suffolk
Operating Museum

The East Suffolk Light Railway is the title given to the 2ft gauge railway, which winds its way some 300yd or so along the northern perimeter of the museum site, between the stations of Chapel Road and Woodside. The railway commenced operation in 1973 and aims to re-create a typical passenger-carrying light railway of years gone by. Many aspects of railway interest can be found along its length. The track came from Leziate sand-quarry and Canvey Island, as well as from the Southwold Railway. There is also a signalbox from the Lowestoft-Great Yarmouth line, and signals from various local locations; all of which help to set the overall scene

Location: Carlton Colville, three

miles south-west of Lowestoft in Suffolk
OS reference: TM 505903
Operating society/organisation: East Anglia Transport Museum Society Ltd, Chapel Road, Carlton Colville, Lowestoft, Suffolk NR33 8BL
Telephone: (01502) 518459
Car park: Adjacent
Access by public transport: Eastern Counties L11, L12 & 171 (Monday-Saturday); Flying Banana 171 and Eastern Counties L18 & L19 (Sundays and bank holidays) from Lowestoft. BR, Oulton Broad South (1.5 miles)
On site facilities: Refreshments, picnic area, souvenir and bookshop, toilets, working transport museum,

Industrial locomotives

Name	No	Builder	Type	Built
—	2	M/Rail (5912)	4wDM	1934
—	4	R/Hornsby (177604)	4wDM	1936

Stock
Locally designed and built covered coach and brake van
Small selection of wagons
Van body ex-Southwold Railway

including trams, narrow-gauge railway, trolleybuses, steam-rollers and other commercial and public transport vehicles. Unlimited free rides
Period of public opening: Easter, and Sundays from beginning of May to end of September, also other Bank Holidays in this period; open from 11.00. Wednesdays and

Saturdays from the beginning of June to the end of September, and every weekday from 21 July-5 September; open from 14.00
Special notes: Limited facilities for the disabled. Pre-booked party rates
Membership details: From the above address

East Anglian Railway Museum
Member: AIRPS, TT

Essex
Steam Centre

Adjacent to Chappel Viaduct which is the most spectacular railway structure in East Anglia
Location: Chappel & Wakes Colne station, near Colchester CO6 2DS
OS reference: TL 898289
Chairman: Hon Gordon V. Adams
Operating society/organisation: East Anglian Railway Museum, Chappel & Wakes Colne Station, Station Road, Wakes Colne, Essex CO6 2DS. Registered charity No 1001579
Telephone: Colchester (01206) 242524
Car park: On site
Access by public transport: Great Eastern Chappel & Wakes Colne station. Also Eastern National/Hedingham Omnibus service No 88 Colchester-Halstead. Sundays Eastern National No 188 Colchester-Halstead
On site facilities: Refreshments, comprehensive bookshop, museum, signalboxes, souvenir shop, picnic area, miniature railway, heritage centre and toilets
Public opening: Daily 10.00-1630
Special events: Thomas the Tank Engine — 28-31 March; Diesel Day & Bus Rally — 20 July; 11th Annual Beer Festival — 10-13 September; Photographic evening — 4 October; Santa Specials 7, 20/21 December; Friends of Thomas the Tank Engine — 13/14

Locomotives and multiple-units

Name	No	Origin	Class	Type	Built
A. J. Hill	69621	GER	N7	0-6-2T	1924
—	80151	BR	4MT	2-6-4T	1956
—	D2279	BR	04	0-6-0DM	1960
—	D3940	BR	08	0-6-0DE	1960
—	50599	BR	108	DMBS	1958
—	56491	BR	108	DTC	1960
—	51568	BR	108	DMCL	1959
—	52053	BR	108	DMCL	1960

Industrial locomotives

Name	No	Builder	Type	Built
Jubilee	—	Bagnall (2542)	0-4-0ST	1936
—	1074	Barclay (1047)	0-4-0ST	1905
Belvoir	—	Barclay (2350)	0-6-0ST	1954
—	2	M/Vick	0-4-0E	1912
Jeffery	2039	Peckett (2039)	0-4-0ST	1943
Penn Green	54	RSH (7031)	0-6-0ST	1941
—	AMW144	Barclay (333)	0-4-0DM	1938
—	23	Fowler (4220039)	0-4-0DH	1965
—	2029	Simplex (2029)	0-4-0PM	1920

Locomotive notes: 69621 is operational, 80151 approaching completion

Stock
4 ex-BR Mk 1s; 1 ex-BR sleeping coach; 1 ex-BR Mk 1 full brake; 1 ex-LNER Buffet car; 1 ex-LNER pigeon van; 1 ex-LNER TSO coach; 1 fully restored GER 6-wheel full brake; 1 GER 6-wheel family saloon; 1 GER fully restored 4-wheel coach; 1 ex-GER bogie coach; 1 MSL 6-wheel coach; 1 SR PMV; 1 ex-BR CCT; 1 ex-BR 13-ton open wagon; 2 ex-BR 16-ton mineral wagons; 1 Lomac wagon; 1 ex-LMS 12-ton open wagon; 3 Wickham Trolleys; 1 GWR Toad Brakevan; 1 ex-BR brake van; Somersham 'pump' trolley, 1 Grafton steam crane

Cont

December
Family tickets: Available on all days (unlimited rides on steam days)
Special notes: Special steam days are held first Sunday of month March-August inclusive and October, plus Bank Holidays,
Wednesdays and Sundays in August. Three restored signalboxes, large goods shed and restoration shed. Original Victorian country junction station. Schools days and Santa steamings. Disabled visitors welcome — prior advice appreciated. Guided tours by prior
arrangement. Buffet open daily May-October
Membership details: Membership Secretary, 50 Ayr Way, Rise Park, Romford, Essex RM1 4UH
Membership journal: *Stour Valley Steam* — 3 times/year

East Kent Railway

Member: AIRPS

Kent
Timetable Service

The East Kent Light Railway Society was formed in 1985 with the aim of preserving the remaining 3-mile section of the Colonel Stephens' light railway which originally ran from Shepherdswell to Wingham. Passenger carrying operations between Shepherdswell and Eythorne started during 1995 and 1996 saw the first steam on the line for over 30 years
Location: Shepherdswell (EKLR) Station, Shepherdswell, Dover, Kent
Operating society/organisation: East Kent Light Railway Society
Car park: At both Shepherdswell and Eythorne stations
Access by public transport: South Eastern trains to Shepherdswell station (adjacent). Bus — Stagecoach East Kent (limited service, not Sundays), Tel: 01843 581333
On site facilities: Light refreshments, souvenirs, small museum, plus 3.5/5in gauge steam railway. Picnic area and toilets
Public opening: Weekends and Bank Holidays Easter-Christmas (Sundays only during low season)
Special events: Easter Bunny Specials; Teddy Bear Picnic — 28-31 May; Teddy Bears' Picnic – 26 May; Gala Weekend — 26/27

Locomotives and Multiple-units

Name	No	Origin	Class	Type	Built
Merlin	33046	BR	33	B0-B0	1960

Expected to arrive during 1997

Industrial locomotives

Name	No	Builder	Type	Built
—	—	Barclay (2248)	0-4-0ST	1948
Richborough Castle	—	E/Electric (D1197)	0-6-0D	1967
Snowdon	—	Fowler (416002)	0-4-0DM	1952
—	—	V/Foundry (D297)/ Drewry (2583)	0-4-0DM	1951
St Dunstan	—	Avonside (2004)	0-6-0ST	1927
Dougal	—	V/Foundry (D77)/ Drewry (2251)	0-4-0DM	1947

Rolling stock
Leyland Experimental coach, BR Mk1 coach, LMS brake third, 2 x LMS full brake (BG), SR scenery van, BR Mk 2A first brake and a selection of freight vehicles.

Owners
St Dunstan on long-term loan from British Coal
33046 and LMS BG the 33046 Fund
Leyland Experimental Coach the Nene Valley Railway

July; Ghost Trains — 1/2 November; Santa Specials weekends 29 November-21 December; Mince Pie Specials – 27/28 December, 3/4 January 1998. All events subject to confirmation
Facilities for disabled: Limited access to buffet, and platforms at
both stations
Membership details: Mr B. Hancock, 33 Beaufield, Whitfield, Dover, Kent CT16 3JW
Membership journal: *EKRLS Newsletter*

East Lancashire Railway

Member: AIRPS

Lancashire
Timetable Service

A very popular yet newly opened railway by the East Lancs Railway Society in close co-operation with local authorities, the line won the 1987 ARPS award. Visit the line to find out the cause of the line's popularity and success
Location: Bolton Street Station,
Bury, Lancashire BL9 0EY
OS reference: SD 803109
Publicity Director: Graham Vevers
Operating society/organisation: East Lancashire Railway Preservation Society
Telephone: 0161 764 7790
Access by public transport: BR to Manchester, Bolton, Rochdale and Burnley. Metro-Link from central Manchester to Bury Interchange. Various bus services also operate to Bury, Ramsbottom or Rawtenstall from the BR stations listed.

Cont

England

No 71000 *Duke of Gloucester* **powers along the Irwell Valley on the East Lancashire Railway.**
Melvyn Hopwood

The 'new' railway at Elsecar with *Earl Fitzwilliam* steaming slowly through the platform. *Melvyn Hopwood*

England

On site facilities: Refreshments normally available when trains are running. Buffet car service on most trains. Souvenir shop, transport museum

Length of line: Approximately 8 miles

Public opening: Steam and diesel-hauled services operate on Saturdays, Sundays and Bank Holidays throughout the year. Santa Specials (advanced booking only) in December

Special events: August — Teddy Bear's Picnic; Santa Specials — weekends in December; Diesel Enthusiasts' Weekend and Friends of Thomas the Tank Engine Days — please apply for details; Irwell Valley Diner, Wine & Dine Trains (advance booking only — please apply for details)

Special Notes: The Society re-opened the Bury-Summerseat-Ramsbottom section in 1987 and the Ramsbottom-Irwell-Rawtenstall section in 1991. Since 1987 over 500,000 passengers have been carried

Membership details: D. Flood

Membership journal: *The East Lancashire Railway News* — twice yearly

Marketing name: East Lancs

Stock
29 BR Mk 1 coaches; 1 L&YR coach; 3 Bogie Guards coaches; 3 Newspaper vans; Cravens 50-ton steam crane RS1013/50 (1930), NER 5-ton hand crane DB915390 (1880) and Smiths 5-ton diesel crane (1939) plus a small number of other goods vehicles

Owners
40145 the Class 40 Preservation Society
Battery-electric MU on loan from Transperience

Locomotives and multiple-units

Name	No	Origin	Class	Type	Built
—	7229	GWR	7200	2-8-2T	1935
—	52322	L&Y	27	0-6-0	1896
—	2700	LMS	5P4F	2-6-0	1927
—	42765	LMS	5P4F	2-6-0	1927
—	45337	LMS	5MT	4-6-0	1937
—	5407	LMS	5MT	4-6-0	1937
Leander	5690	LMS	'Jubilee'	4-6-0	1936
—	46441	LMS	2MT	2-6-0	1950
—	46428	LMS	2MT	2-6-0	1948
—	47324	LMS	3F	0-6-0T	1926
Sir Nigel Gresley	60007	LNER	8P	4-6-2	1937
Duke of Gloucester	71000	BR	8P	4-6-2	1954
—	73156	BR	5MT	4-6-0	1956
—	80097	BR	4MT	2-6-4T	1954
Morning Star	92207	BR	9F	2-10-0	1959
—	45160	WD/TCCD	8F	2-8-0	1941
—	388	USATC	S160	2-8-0	1942
Royal Army Ordnance Corps	45112	BR	45	1Co-Co1	1962
—	D335	BR	40	1Co-Co1	1961
—	D345	BR	40	1Co-Co1	1961
Valiant	50015	BR	50	Co-Co	1967
Onslaught	D832	BR	42	B-B	1961
Western Prince	D1041	BR	52	C-C	1962
—	D2767	BR	—	0-4-0DH	1960
—	D2774	BR	—	0-4-0DH	1960
—	D2956	BR	01	0-4-0DM	1956
—	D5054	BR	24	Bo-Bo	1960
—	55002	BR	55	Co-Co	1961
—	D9019	BR	55	Co-Co	1961
—	D7076	BR	35	B-B	1963
—	25901	BR	25	Bo-Bo	1966
—	D9531	BR	14	0-6-0DH	1965
Gateshead	D1501	BR	47	Co-Co	1962
—	08479	BR	08	0-6-0DE	1958
—	08868	BR	08	0-6-0DE	1960
—	7069	LMS	—	0-6-0DE	1936
—	51285	Cravens	105	DMBC	1958
—	51813	BRCW	110	DMBC	1961
—	51842	BRCW	110	DMCL	1961
—	56121	Cravens	105	DTC	1956
—	59701	BRCW	110	DMCL	1961
—	65451	BR	504	DMBS	1958
—	77172	BR	504	DTS	1958
—	79998*	BR	—	DMBS	1958
—	79999*	BR	—	DTCL	1958

*Battery-electric multiple-unit

Industrial locomotives

Name	No	Builder	Type	Built
Gothenburg	32	H/Clarke (680)	0-6-0T	1903
Phoenix	70	H/Clarke (1464)	0-6-0T	1921
—	1	Barclay (1927)	0-4-0ST	1927
—	DH16	Sentinel (10175)	4wDH	1964
—	—	Sentinel (10204)	4wDH	1964
MR Mercury	1	Hibberd (3438)	4wDM	1950
Winfield	—	M/Rail (9009)	4wDM	1948
—	E2	H/Clark (D1199)	6wDM	1960
—	4002	H/Clarke (D1076)	6wDM	1959

East Somerset Railway

Member: AIRPS, TT

Set up by the artist, David Shepherd, 'the man who loves giants', the railway line is home to *Black Prince* and *The Green Knight* housed in their 'traditional' shed. As one might expect, Cranmore station is well laid out and aesthetically pleasing. An art gallery is situated at Cranmore station where prints of his, and other artist's, paintings can be bought. One of only two remaining all steam railways in the country

General Manager: Mr S. McColl

Headquarters: East Somerset Railway, (Cranmore Railway Station) Shepton Mallet, Somerset BA4 4QP

OS reference: ST 664429

Telephone: Cranmore 01749 880417

Fax: 01749 880764

Main station: Cranmore

Car park: Cranmore — free

Refreshment facilities: Restaurant 'Whistle Stop' situated in car park offering lunches, snacks, teas, etc. Group catering by arrangement. Picnic areas at Cranmore, Merryfield Lane stations and depot. On train catering by arrangement. Private saloon trips

Souvenir shop: Cranmore

On site facilities: Museum, Victorian style engine shed and workshops, children's play area. Railway and wildlife prints for sale in art gallery

Depot: Cranmore West

Length of line: 2.75 miles

Passenger trains: Cranmore to Mendip Vale. Stations at Cranmore West, Merryfield Lane and Mendip Vale, unlimited train travel

Period of public operation: Open daily with trains running on Sundays in January, February, March and November. Wednesdays to Sundays in June and September. Daily in July and August. Saturdays and Sundays in April, May, October, (and December for Santa Trains only) plus all bank holidays and Wednesdays to Sundays during half term weeks. Also New Years Day
Last admission 30min before closing time. Each day ticket

Locomotives

Name	No	Origin	Class	Type	Built
—	1450	GWR	1400	0-4-2T	1935
Nunney Castle	5029	GWR	'Castle'	4-6-0	1934
—	6634	GWR	5600	0-6-2T	1928
—	B110	LBSCR	E1	0-6-0T	1877
—	47493	LMS	3F	0-6-0T	1927
—	68846	GNR	J52	0-6-0ST	1899
The Green Knight†	75029	BR	4MT	4-6-0	1954
Black Prince†	92203	BR	9F	2-10-0	1959
—	D3998	BR	08	0-6-0DE	1960
—*	390	ZSR	7	4-8-0	1896

*3ft 6in gauge
†On loan to Great Central Railway

Industrial locomotives

Name	No	Builder	Type	Built
Lord Fisher	1398	Barclay (1398)	0-4-0ST	1915
—	705	Barclay (2047)	0-4-0ST	1937
Lady Nan	1719	Barclay (1719)	0-4-0ST	1920
—	4101	Dubs (4101)	0-4-0CT	1901

Stock

10 ex-BR Mk 1 coaches; 25 assorted wagons, mostly LMS and SR; Rhodesian Railways sleeping car 1808. Home to the 'Riviera' main line vehicles. Frequent main line visitors

Owners

D3998 on loan from Prism Rail

allows unlimited travel on all timetabled trains

Special events: Freight charters, Steam Dream, Music in the Engine Shed, dirty weekend

Facilities for disabled: Yes

Special Notes: Santa special steam trains weekends, and other days, in December. Footplate experience courses

Membership details: Please apply to above address, SAE for brochure

Membership journal: *East Somerset Railway Journal* — quarterly

Marketing name: The Strawberry Line

No 7822 *Foxcote Manor* (Llangollen Railway) and 75029 *The Green Knight* double-head a train away from Cranmore.

Elsecar at Barnsley

The Elsecar Railway runs between Elescar Workshop site and the canal basin at Hemingfield, through a scenic conservation area alongside the Elescar branch of the Deane & Dove Canal.

Location/headquarters: Elsecar Discovery Centre, Wath Road, Elsecar, Barnsley, South Yorkshire S7 8HJ

Telephone number: 01226 740203

Fax number: 01226 350239

Main station: Elsecar

Length of line: 1 miles, 20min journey

Car park location: On site

Access by public transport: BR Elsecar from Sheffield, Huddersfield, Leeds.

Refreshment facilities: On site

Souvenir shops: On site

On site facilities: Refreshments, souvenir shop, toilets

Museum: Attractions include 'The Power House' science centre, Science Track, Educational Workshops, 'Elsecar People' history exhibition, Bottle Collection, Hot Metal Press, Newcomen Beam Engine, working crafts people

Facilities for disabled: There are four disabled persons toilets at different locations on the site. All buildings are fully wheelchair accessible at ground floor level

Period of public opening: Daily (except 25/26 December) 10.00-17.00

Special events: Include Friends of Thomas the Tank Engine and Victorian Christmas Fayre — contact for details

Special notes: Entrance to site is free. Charges made for some attractions ('passport' and family tickets available). Santa specials run during December.

Industrial locomotives

Name	No	Builder	Type	Built
Countess Fitzwilliam	—	R/Hornsby(382808)	4wDM	1955
Earl Fitzwilliam	—	Avonside (1917)	0-6-0ST	1923

Stock
3 ex-BR Mk 1 coaches

Embsay & Bolton Abbey Steam Railway

Member: AIRPS, TT

Yorkshire's 'Friendly Line' operates from Embsay station built in 1888. The railway is very family oriented with many events for children. The enthusiast is not forgotten with one of the finest collections of ex-industrial tank engines in Britain. The railway is currently constructing a new museum and workshop complex and the line's extension to Bolton Abbey will open in spring 1997. Bolton Abbey station has been built to Midland Railway style. An atmosphere of the rural branch line prevails, which is operated by a fine collection of ex-industrial locomotives

Operating Committee: Stuart Bell

Business & Marketing Manager: Stephen Walker (tel: 01756 794727 ext 21). Fax: 01756 795189

Location: Embsay station, Embsay, Skipton, Yorkshire BD23 6AX

OS reference: SE 007533

Locomotives and multiple-units

Name	No	Origin	Class	Type	Built
—	D2203	BR	04	0-6-0DM	1952
—	NCB 38 (D9513)	BR	14	0-6-0DH	1964
—	LEV2	Derby	—	Railbus	1984

Industrial locomotives

Name	No	Builder	Type	Built
Annie	9	Peckett (1159)	0-4-0ST	1908
Gladiator	8	H/Clarke (1450)	0-6-0ST	1922
Slough Estates No 5	—	H/Clarke (1709)	0-6-0ST	1939
Primrose No 2	S121	Hunslet (3715)	0-6-0ST	1952
Ann	—	Sentinel (7232)	4wVB	1927
Beatrice	7	Hunslet (2705)	0-6-0ST	1945
Airedale	3	Hunslet (1440)	0-6-0ST	1923
York No 1	—	Yorkshire (2474)	0-4-0ST	1949
—	140	H/Clarke (1821)	0-6-0T	1948
Spitfire	S112	Hunslet (2414)	0-6-0ST	1942
Wheldale	S134	Hunslet (3168)	0-6-0ST	1944
—	69	Hunslet (3785)	0-6-0ST	1953
Monkton No 1	—	Hunslet (3788)	0-6-0ST	1953
—†	22	Barclay (2320)	0-4-0ST	1952
—	68005	RSH (7169)	0-6-0ST	1945
Thomas	4	RSH (7661)	0-4-0ST	1950
H. W. Robinson	—	Fowler (4100003)	0-4-0DM	1946

Operating society/organisation:
Yorkshire Dales Railway Museum Trust
Telephone: Skipton (01756) 794727. 24hr Talking Timetable (01756) 795189
Car parks: Embsay and Bolton Abbey
Access by public transport: Pennine bus from Skipton
On site facilities: Souvenir shop — specialising in children's gifts, transport and industrial archaeological titles, plus model railway supplies
Catering facilities: Buffet and bar on most trains. Buffet on Embsay station, a tea room will open at Bolton Abbey during 1997. Evening catering trains will serve meals on selected dates. Special charters can be arranged. Meals for parties can be arranged on normal service trains (subject to advance booking). Please write for further details
Length of line: 4.5 miles (with Bolton Abbey extension)
Public opening: Steam trains run every Sunday throughout the year, plus Saturdays in June and

Name	No	Builder	Type	Built
—	MDE15	Baguley/ Drewry (2136)	4wDM	1938
—	887	R/Hornsby (394009)	4wDM	1955
—	—	Wickham (7610)	2w-2PMR	1957
—	—	Lister (9993)*	4wPM	1938
—	—	Lister (10225)*	4wPM	1938
—	—	R/Hornsby (175418)*	4wDM	1936
—	—	R/Hornsby*	4wDM	—
—	—	M/Rail (8979)*	4wDM	1946
—	—	M/Rail (5213)*	4wDM	1930
—	—	R/Hornsby	4wDM	1957
Meaford	—	Barclay (440)	0-4-0DH	1958
—	36	H/Clarke (D1037)	0-6-0DM	1958

† on loan to Swindon & Cricklade Railway during 1997
*2ft gauge

Stock
18 ex-BR Mk 1 coaches (SK, CK, 2xBCK, 5xTSO, 2xRMB, 1xBSO(T), 1xRBR and 1xSLS) 4 ex-LNER coaches; 2 SR parcels vans; Freight stock and service vehicles, SR and GW brakes

September then daily from late July until the end of August (except for Mondays and Fridays). Trains run regularly between 11.00 and late afternoon
Special events: Friends of Thomas the Tank at Easter, Spring and August Bank Holidays and Santa

Trains from mid-November until December
Membership details: Membership Secretary at above address
Membership journal: *Dales Steam, YDR News* — 4 times/year

The new station at Bolton Abbey nearing completion. *E&BASR*

The railway, built in 1893 to connect a colliery to the national system, closed in 1965, has been re-opened.

Chairman: Ian A. Rutherford
Headquarters: Foxfield Steam Railway, Blythe Bridge, Stoke on Trent
Telephone: (01782) 396210 (weekends), (01270) 874959 (weekdays)
Fax: 01270 874959
Main station: Blythe Bridge (Caverswall Road)
OS reference: SJ 957421
Car park: Blythe Bridge
Access by public transport: BR Blythe Bridge (400yd). PMT bus service to Blythe Bridge
Refreshment facilities: Blythe Bridge
Souvenir shop: Blythe Bridge
Passenger trains: Steam-hauled trains operate from Blythe Bridge (Caverswall Road) to Dilhorne Park and return
Family ticket: Available (2 adults + 2 children or 1 adult + 4 children)
Length of line: 2.75 miles
Period of public operation: Steam trains operate Sundays and Bank Holidays Mondays only, April–September inclusive between Blythe Bridge and Dilhorne Park.
Special events: Please contact for details. Santa Specials, weekends in December (advanced booking essential)
Facilities for disabled: Access to majority of facilities is on the level. For special requirements prior

Industrial locomotives

Name	No	Builder	Type	Built
Whiston	—	Hunslet (3694)	0-6-0ST	1950
Wimblebury	—	Hunslet (3839)	0-6-0ST	1956
Roker	—	RSH (7006)	0-4-0CT	1940
Meaford No 2	2	RSH	0-6-0T	1951
Cranford	—	Avonside (1919)	0-6-0ST	1924
Lewisham	—	Bagnall (2221)	0-6-0ST	1927
Hawarden	—	Bagnall (2623)	0-4-0ST	1940
Wolstanton No 3	—	Bagnall (3150)	0-6-0DM	1960
Bagnall	—	Bagnall (3207)	0-4-0DH	1961
—	—	B/Peacock (1827)	0-4-0ST	1879
—	—	E/Electric (788)	4wBE	1930
Spondon No 2	—	E/Electric (1130)	4wBE	1939
—	6	R/Heath	0-4-0ST	1886
Henry Cort	—	Peckett (933)	0-4-0ST	1903
Lion	—	Peckett (1351)	0-4-0ST	1914
Ironbridge No 1	—	Peckett (1803)	0-4-0ST	1933
—	11	Peckett (2081)	0-4-0ST	1947
C.P.C./Spitfire	—	Barclay (1964)	0-4-0ST	1929
Moss Bay	—	K/Stuart (4167)	0-4-0ST	1920
Rom River	—	K/Stuart (4421)	6wDM	1929
—	1	Barclay (1984)	0-4-0F	1930
Meaford No 4	—	Barclay (486)	0-6-0DH	1964
Helen	—	Simplex (2262)	4wDM	1924
—	820	Drewry (2157)	4wDM	1941
Amoco	—	R/Hornsby (395305)	0-4-0DM	1956
Gas-oil	—	R/Hornsby (408496)	0-4-0DM	1957
Hercules	—	Ruston (242915)	4wDM	1946
—	—	R/Hornsby	0-4-0DE	—
Megan	—	Thomas Hill (103C)	0-4-0DH	1957
Marston	3	H/Leslie (3581)	0-6-0ST	1924

Thorntwaite & Everard

Stock
5 coaches; 4 scenery vans (some converted for other uses); 29 assorted wagons, 16ton mineral wagons; 1 rail-mounted self-propelled diesel-electric crane

notice is desirable
Membership journal: *Foxfield News* — quarterly

The line is fully signalled using a variety of upper and lower quadrant, colour light and shunting signals controlled by two full size signalboxes. From Pinesway Junction to Park Lane the line runs along a half-mile section of the former Somerset & Dorset Railway trackbed. An extension northwards is underway along the trackbed

which will involve a flyover and the reopening of the old S&D level crossing north of Pinesway Junction. The line's first steam locomotive is expected to enter service early in the 1997 season
Location/headquarters: Gartell Light Railway, Common Lane, Yenston, Nr Templecombe, Somerset BA8 0NB

Telephone: 01963 370752
General Manager: John Gartell
Main station: Common Lane
Other stations: Pinesway Junction, Park Lane (southern terminus)
Car park: Common Lane
OS reference: Sheet 183, 718218
Access by public transport: 1.5 miles south east of Templecombe

railway station

Refreshment facilities: Trackside refreshment room adjacent to the station at Common Lane serving range of hot and cold snacks and drinks. Lakeside picnic area at Pinesway Junction

Souvenir shop: Common Lane

Museum: Common Lane — Templecombe Railway Museum (collection of artefacts, photographs, documents, models etc recording the history of Templecombe station)

Depot: Common Lane (not open to public)

Facilities for disabled: Enclosed passenger coach with accommodation for one wheelchair now in service. Wheelchair access to refreshment room via ramp

Period of public operation: 5, 26

Industrial locomotives

2ft gauge:

Name	No	Builder	Type	Built
Amanda	1	Lister (55070)	4wDH	1966
Andrew	2	R/Hornsby	4wDH	—
Alan	3	Lister (42494)	4wDM	1956
Alistair	4	R/Hornsby (201790)	4wDM	1950
Alison	5	A/Kief (10)	4wDH	1983

Rolling stock — coaches: 3 fully enclosed bogie coaches, 3 covered open-sided bogie coaches (scheduled for replacement by fully enclosed coaches during 1997)

Rolling stock — wagons: goods guards van, tool van, open wagon, bogie hopper, bogie open 2 bogie flats

May; 29 June; 27 July; 24/25 August; 28 September. 10.30-16.30
Special events: Family Day — 6 May; S&D Day — 26 May; Traction engine display — 29 June; Teddy Bears Picnic — 28 July;

Enthusiasts Day — 24/25 August; Senoir Citizen's Day — 28 September; Santa Specials — 14/21 December

Gloucestershire Warwickshire Railway

Member: AIRPS

Part of an ambitious project to link Cheltenham racecourse with Stratford racecourse, much has been done to recreate the railway and buildings that made up this cross-country route. The railway is home to many owners of private locomotives and rolling stock, so from time to time the items on display may vary

Location: Toddington Station, Toddington

OS reference: SO 050322

Operating society/organisation: Gloucestershire Warwickshire Steam Railway PLC, The Station, Toddington, Cheltenham, Glos GL54 5DT

Telephone: Toddington (01242) 621405

Main station: Toddington

Other public stations: Winchcombe

Access by public transport: Public transport is very limited with occasional buses from Cheltenham, Stratford on Avon and Evesham only. Local bus service Castleways will answer timetable queries on (01242) 602949

Car park: On site

On site facilities: Sales, catering, narrow gauge rides, toilets

Length of line: 5 miles

Locomotives and multiple-units

Name	No	Origin	Class	Type	Built
—	2807	GWR	2800	2-8-0	1905
Raveningham Hall	6960	GWR	6959	4-6-0	1944
Owsden Hall	6984	GWR	6959	4-6-0	1948
Peninsular and Oriental SNCo	35006	SR	MN	4-6-2	1941
—	76077	BR	4MT	2-6-0	1956
—	03069	BR	03	0-6-0DM	1959
—	D2182	BR	03	0-6-0DM	1952
—	D9537	BR	14	0-6-0DH	1965
—	D9539	BR	14	0-6-0DH	1965
—	D9553	BR	14	0-6-0DH	1965
—	20137	BR	20	Bo-Bo	1966
—	26043	BR	26	Bo-Bo	1959
—	D5541	BR	31	A1A-A1A	1959
—	37215	BR	37	Co-Co	1964
—	45149	BR	45	1Co-Co1	1961
Goldcrest	47105	BR	47	Co-Co	1963
—	51950	BR	108	DMBS	1960
—	52062	BR	108	DMC	1960

Industrial locomotives

Name	No	Builder	Type	Built
Byfield No 2	—	Bagnall (2655)	0-6-0ST	1941
King George	—	Hunslet (2409)	0-6-0ST	1942
—	19	Fowler (4240016)	0-6-0DH	1964
—	21	Fowler (4210130)	0-4-0DM	1957
—	—	H/Clarke (D615)	0-6-0DM	1938
—	—	Hibberd (2893)	4wPM	1943
John	—	Peckett (1976)	0-4-0ST	1939

Stock

3 ex-GWR coaches; 23 ex-BR coaches; 1 ex-LMS coach; plus numerous wagons

Public opening: On non-operating days the station is unmanned but visitors are welcome. Public services Weekends, Bank Holiday Mondays, between March and October. Some summer weekdays and Sundays in November

Special events: Please contact for details

Special notes: The site is being developed as the headquarters of the railway between Cheltenham and Stratford. The GWR owns the railway land between Cheltenham and Broadway and operates over 5 miles from Toddington to Far Stanley with an intermediate station at Winchcombe.

Guest locomotives will be operating during the year.

Family tickets available. Railway postal service

Membership details: From above address

Membership journal: *The Cornishman* — quarterly

Owners

2807 the Cotswold Steam Preservation Ltd
35006, 76077 the P & O Locomotive Society
26043 the Cotswold Mainline Diesel Group
D9537, D9539, 40149 and D9553 Cotswold Diesel Preservation Group
37215 the Brush Type 4 Fund, the Growler Group & GWR Diesel Dept

North Gloucestershire Railway

Industrial narrow gauge locomotives (2ft gauge)

Name	No	Builder	Type	Built
Isibutu	5	Bagnall (2820)	4-4-0T	1946
George B	—	Hunslet (680)	0-4-0ST	1898
Chaka	—	Hunslet (2075)	0-4-2T	1940
Justine	—	Jung (939)	0-4-0WT	1906
Brigadelok	—	Henschel (15968)	0-8-0T	1918
—	2	Lister (34523)	4wDM	1949
—	3	M/Rail (4565)	4wPM	1928
Spitfire	—	M/Rail (7053)	4wPM	1937
—	1	R/Hornsby (166010)	4wDM	1932
—	L5	R/Hornsby (181820)	4wDM	1936
—	—	R/Hornsby (354028)	4wDM	1953

Stock

3 coaches; 11 wagons

Great Central Railway
Member: AIRPS, TT

Leicestershire
Timetable Service

The original Great Central Railway's extension to London in 1899 was the last main line to be built in this country, most of which was closed in the 1960s. Steam-hauled services operate through attractive rolling Leicestershire countryside, crossing the picturesque Swithland reservoir. The railway's aim is to re-create the experience of British main line railway operation in the days of steam. The images of a main line are backed up by a double track line with long trains hauled by large locomotives

Headquarters: Great Central Railway PLC, Loughborough Central Station, Great Central Road, Loughborough, Leicestershire LE11 1RW

Telephone: Loughborough (01509) 230726

Main stations: Loughborough Central, Leicester North

Other public stations: Quorn & Woodhouse, Rothley

OS reference: SK 543194

Car park: Quorn, Rothley

Access by public transport: Loughborough BR station (3/4-

Locomotives and multiple-units

Name	No	Origin	Class	Type	Built
—	5224	GWR	5205	2-8-0T	1924
Witherslack Hall	6990	GWR	'Hall'	4-6-0	1948
—	5231	LMS	5MT	4-6-0	1936
—	5305	LMS	5MT	4-6-0	1936
—	47406	LMS	3F	0-6-0T	1926
—	48305	LMS	8F	2-8-0	1943
—	1264	LNER	B1	4-6-0	1947
—	69523	LNER	N2	0-6-2T	1921
—	63601	GCR	8K	2-8-0	1919
Bittern	4464	LNER	A4	4-6-2	1937
Boscastle	34039	SR	WC	4-6-2	1946
Canadian Pacific	35005	SR	MN	4-6-2	1941
Brocklebank Line	35025	SR	MN	4-6-2	1948
The Green Knight	75029	BR	4MT	4-6-0	1954
Black Prince	92203	BR	9F	2-10-0	1959
—	92212	BR	9F	2-10-0	1959
—	13180	BR	08	0-6-0DE	1955
—	D3101	BR	08	0-6-0DE	1955
—	08788	BR	08	0-6-0DE	1960
—	D4067	BR	10	0-6-0DE	1961
—	D8098	BR	20	Bo-Bo	1961
—	31418	BR	31	A1A-A1A	1958
Great Gable	D4	BR	44	1Co-Co1	1957
—	D1572	BR	47	Co-Co	1965
—	51616	BR	127	DMBS	1959
—	51622	BR	127	DMBS	1959
—	59276	BR	120	TS	1958

mile). Trent, South Notts, and Midland Fox bus services to Loughborough bus station (3/4-mile). Some Midland Fox services pass bottom Great Central Road, 300yd

Refreshment facilities: Licensed buffet car and light refreshments on all trains and at all stations. Saturday and Sunday lunches on mid-day train; evening dining trains on most Saturday nights, please contact railway for dates and reservations (advance booking recommended). Picnic areas at Quorn and Rothley stations. Most trains carry griddle car serving all day Great Central breakfast and other hot food. Private charter trains available on request

Souvenir shop: Loughborough
Museum: Loughborough
Depot: Loughborough
Length of line: 8 miles
Passenger trains: Loughborough-Leicester North
Period of public operation: Weekends throughout the year and Bank Holiday Mondays. Daily Easter week, May-August inclusive.

Guided tours available by prior arrangement. School/party visits a speciality — Tel: 01509 230726 for details

Industrial locomotives

Name	No	Builder	Type	Built
Arthur Wright	D4279	Fowler (4210079)	0-4-0DE	1952
—	28	A/Barclay (400)	0-4-0DM	1956

Owners

Bittern on loan from North Eastern Locomotive Preservation Group
69523 the Gresley Society
5305 the Humberside Locomotive Preservation Group
6990 the Witherslack Hall Locomotive Society
61264 the Thompson B1 Locomotive Society
92212 the 92212 Holdings Ltd
63601 on loan from the National Railway Museum
75029 and 92203 on loan from the East Somerset Railway
D8098, 31418 and D1572 the Type 1 Locomotive Association

Special events: Easter Gala — 28-31 March, 1-6 April; Diesel Weekend — 18-20 April; 1940s Weekend — 3-5 May; Members & Shareholders Day — 11 May; Toy & Model Fair/Swapmeet — 1 June, Summer Gala — 7 to 15 June; Friends of Thomas the Tank — 26 July-3 August — 18/19 October; Toy & Model Fair and Hornby Dublo Weekend 9/10 August; Swapmeet — 31 August; Autumn Gala — 13/14 September; Members & Shareholders Day — 25 October; Bonfire Night — 5 November; Santa Trains 29/30 November, 6/7, 13/14, 17 to 24 December

Facilities for disabled: Special carriage for wheelchair/disabled persons (advance notice required). Wheelchair access good at Quorn and Rothley, can be arranged at Loughborough with advance notification. Boarding ramps at all stations

Membership & share details: Share enquiries: Company Secretary, Great Central Railway (1976) PLC
Membership: Membership Secretary, Main Line Steam Trust Ltd. Both c/o above address

No 45231 at speed, bound for Loughborough. *Michael Collins*

Great Whipsnade Railway

Member: AIRPS

Bedfordshire
Steam Centre

Location: Whipsnade Wild Animal
Park, Dunstable, Bedfordshire
LU6 2LF
Telephone: 01582 872171
(extension 2270)
Fax: 01582 872649
General Manager: Ian Gordon
Main station: Whipsnade Central
On site facilities: Car park
(100yds), Souvenir shop,
refreshments (30yds)
Period of public operation:
January — no trains; February —
half term; March — weekends
only, April to July — daily
(Weekdays diesels only/steam at

Locomotives

Name	No	Builder	Type	Built
Chevalier	1	M/Wardle(1877)	0-6-2T	1915
Excelsior	2	K/Stuart(1049)	0-6-2T	1908
Superior	4	K/Stuart(4034)	0-6-2T	1920
Victor	—	Fowler(4160004)	0-6-0DM	1951
Hector	—	Fowler(4160005)	0-6-0DM	1951
Mr Bill	10	R/Hornsby(221625)	0-4-0DM	1944

Rolling stock: 10 carriages, 9 wagons

weekends); August daily steam
trains; September/October — daily
(Weekdays diesels only/steam at
weekends); November — no trains;

December — steam, weekends &
school holidays
Facilities for disabled: Carriage
designed for wheelchairs

Hollycombe Steam Collection

Member: TT

West Sussex
Steam Centre

An extensive collection of
railways, traction engines, steam
fairground rides, Bioscope, organs,
the oldest Burrell Showman's
engine *Emperor*, sawmill and
engine from the paddle steamer
Caledonia, set in woodlands and
gardens
Location: Iron Hill, Hollycombe,
near Liphook, Hants
OS reference: SU 852295
Operating society/organisation:
Hollycombe Steam & Woodland
Garden Society, Iron Hill, Midhurst
Road, Liphook, Hants GU30 7LP
Telephone: Liphook (01428)
724900 (24hr answerphone)
Car park: On site

Industrial locomotives

Name	No	Builder	Type	Built
Caledonia	70	Barclay (1995)	0-4-0WT	1931*
Jerry M	38	Hunslet (638)	0-4-0ST	1895*
Commander B	—	H/Leslie (2450)	0-4-0ST	1899
—	16	R/Hornsby	4wDM	1941*
Excelsior	—	A/Porter (1607)	2-2-0WT	1880†

*2ft gauge
†3ft gauge

Access by public transport:
Liphook BR station (1.5 miles)
On site facilities: Shop and
refreshments. Toilets, car park,
dogs allowed in car park only
Length of lines: Standard gauge –
quarter mile

2ft gauge 'Quarry Railway' – 1.5
miles
7.25in gauge – quarter mile
Public opening: Easter then
Sundays and bank holidays only
until 12 October. Daily 28 July-
1 August; 10-25 August only

Irchester Narrow Gauge Railway Museum

Member: AIRPS

Northants
Steam Centre

The aims of the controlling trust
are to acquire and preserve narrow
gauge railway locomotives, rolling
stock and exhibits associated with
Northamptonshire and the east
Midlands. To display the collection
for the benefit of the public and to
restore exhibits to working order so

they may be demonstrated in a
proper manner
Location: Within Irchester
Country Park, 2 miles south of
Wellingborough
Operating society/organisation:
The Irchester Narrow Gauge
Railway Trust, 71 Bedford Road,

Cranfield, Bedford MK43 0EX
On site facilities: Shop, museum,
demonstration line, picnic area
Access by public transport: BR
Wellingborough (Midland Road)
station, buses to Irchester and Little
Irchester
Car Parks: Main park car parks

England

Toilets: Main park complex
Public opening: Every Sunday (summer 10.00-17.30, winter 10.00-16.00), at other times by arrangement. Steam and demonstration weekends are held on last full weekend of the month — March-October
Facilities for disabled: Museum and site on level, staff available if required
Membership details: Membership Secretary, 1 Wilby Street, Northampton NN1 5JX

Industrial locomotives

Name	No	Builder	Type	Built
—	85*	Peckett (1870	0-6-0ST	1934
—	86*	Peckett (1871)	0-6-0ST	1934
—	87*	Peckett (2029)	0-6-0ST	1942
Cambrai	—*	Corpet (493)	0-6-0T	1888
—	ND3645*	R/Hornsby (211679)	4wDM	1941
—	—†	R/Hornsby (281290)	0-6-0DM	1949
—	ED10*	R/Hornsby (411322)	4wDM	1958
—	—†	M/Rail (1363)	4wPM	1918
The Rock	—*	Hunslet (2419)	0-4-0DM	1941

* Metre gauge
† 3ft Gauge

Ironbridge Gorge Museum — Shropshire Museum

The railway items form only a small part of the displays on two of the museum's main sites, Blists Hill and Coalbrookdale. The Blists Hill site offers an opportunity to see a number of industrial and other activities being operated in meticulously reconstructed period buildings. A working foundry and ironworks are just two of the exciting exhibits. The Ironbridge Gorge was designated a World Heritage Site in 1987
Location: Ironbridge, Shropshire
OS reference: SJ 694033
Operating society/organisation: Ironbridge Gorge Museum Trust, Ironbridge, Telford, Shropshire TF8 7AW
Telephone: Telford (01952) 433522
Car park: At the sites
Access by public transport: Various private bus companies,

Industrial locomotives

Name	No	Builder	Type	Built
—	—	Sentinel/Coalbrookdale (6185)	0-4-0VBT	1925
—	—	Sentinel/M/Wardle (6155)	0-4-0VBT	1925
—	5	Coalbrookdale	0-4-0ST	1865

All locomotives are at the Museum of Iron & Iron Mighty, Coalbrookdale

including Midland Red, Williamson's Shearings, Elcocks, Boultons. Please telephone (01952) 433522 for further details
Catering facilities: Licensed Victorian pub, sweet shop and tea rooms at the Blists Hill site, serving drinks and mainly cold snacks. Tea, coffee and light refreshments at the Museum of Iron and Rosehill House, Coalbrookdale
Public opening: Main sites including Museum of Iron and on Blists Hill, daily (except Christmas Eve and Christmas Day) 10.00-

17.00, 10.00-18.00 during British Summer Time
Special notes: Tickets for all the sites or just for single sites available.
  A full size working replica of Richard Trevithick's 1802 steam locomotive built by the Coalbrookdale Company, will be operating at the Ironbridge Power Station on certain wekends throughout the year. For further details please telephone 01952 432141

Isle of Wight Steam Railway — Isle of Wight Timetable Service
Member: AIRPS, TT

Separated from the mainland by the Solent, the line's isolation encouraged the maintenance and retention of Victorian locomotives and coaching stock which still operate the line today. Its rural charm enhances its attraction for the island's holidaymakers during the summer season
Traffic manager: Terry Hastings
Headquarters: Isle of Wight Steam Railway, Haven Street

station, Ryde, Isle of Wight PO33 4DS
Telephone: Station: Isle of Wight (01983) 882204
Main station: Haven Street
OS reference: SZ 556898
Other public stations: Wootton, Ashey and Smallbrook Junction
Car park: Haven Street
Access by public transport: 'Island Line' service from Ryde or Shanklin to Smallbrook Jct

Refreshment facilities: Light refreshments available
Souvenir shop: Haven Street
Museum: Small exhibits museum at Haven Street
Depot: Haven Street
Length of line: 5 miles
Passenger trains: Wootton-Smallbrook Jct
Period of public operation: 27 March to 27 April: Sundays, Thursdays and Bank Holidays;

May: Sundays, Wednesdays, Thursdays and Bank Holidays. 27 May to 24 July: Sundays, Tuesdays, Wednesdays and Thursdays. 27 July to 31 August daily. 2-30 September: Sundays, Tuesdays, Wednesdays and Thursdays. October: Sundays and Thursdays

Special events: Steam Extravaganza — 22-25 August. Santa Specials, in December until Xmas (please write for details)

Facilities for disabled: Limited facilities but can be catered for singly, or in groups (by prior arrangement), toilets available

Membership details: Membership Secretary at above address

Membership journal: *Wight Report* — quarterly

Locomotives

Name	No	Origin	Class	Type	Built
Freshwater	W8 (32646)	LBSCR	A1X	0-6-0T	1876
—	32640	LBSCR	A1X	0-6-0T	1878
Calbourne	W24	LSWR	O2	0-4-4T	1891
—	D2554	BR	05	0-6-0DM	1956
—	D2059	BR	03	0-6-0DM	1959

Industrial locomotives

Name	No	Builder	Type	Built
Invincible	37	H/Leslie (3135)	0-4-0ST	1915
Ajax	38	Barclay (1605)	0-6-0T	1918
Royal Engineer	198	Hunslet (3798)	0-6-0ST	1953

Locomotive notes: *Ajax* is not on public display.

Owners
Royal Engineer on loan from Royal Corps of Transport Museum Trust

Stock
1 IWR coach; 4 LBSCR coaches; 3 SECR coaches; 2 LCDR coaches; 5 IWR coaches (bodies only); 5 LCDR coaches (bodies only); 1 LBSCR coach (body only); 1 crane; 1 ex-BR ballast tamper; 1 Wickham trolley; 30 wagons; 6 parcels vans; 2 ex-LT hoppers; 1 ex-BR Lowmac

Keighley & Worth Valley Railway
Member: AIRPS

West Yorkshire
Timetable Service

The epitome of a volunteer-run railway, the only *complete* branch line railway under independent control, which serves six stations (one oil lit and four gas lit) and which is host to an extensive and varied collection of locomotives where everything continues to provide the atmosphere of the days of the steam railway. Immaculate stations, exceptionally strong 'house style' — totems, A5 leaflets and period posters all reflecting the late 1950s/early 1960s, with uniformed staff red ties and clean trains. Very friendly and very much part of the community celebrating 29 years of continuous operation under society ownership and management in 1997

Chairman, Joint Management Committee: Brian A. Baker

Headquarters: Haworth station, Keighley, West Yorkshire, BD22 8NJ

Telephone: Haworth (01535) 647777 24hr recorded timetable and information service, Haworth (01535) 645214 (other calls)

Main stations: Keighley, Ingrow (West), Haworth, Oxenhope

Other public stations: Damems, Oakworth

Locomotives and multiple-units

Name	No	Origin	Class	Type	Built
—	41241	LMS	2MT	2-6-2T	1949
—	43924	MR	4F	0-6-0	1920
—	45212	LMS	5MT	4-6-0	1935
Bahamas	45596	LMS	'Jubilee'	4-6-0	1935
—	48431	LMS	8F	2-8-0	1944
—	47279	LMS	3F	0-6-0T	1925
—	1054	LNWR	—	0-6-2T	1888
City of Wells	34092	SR	WC	4-6-2	1949
—	80002	BR	4MT	2-6-4T	1952
—	75078	BR	4MT	4-6-0	1956
—	78022	BR	2MT	2-6-0	1953
—	30072	SR	USA	0-6-0T	1943
—	5775	GWR	5700	0-6-0PT	1929
—	52044	L&Y	2F	0-6-0	1887
—	19*	L&Y	Pug	0-4-0ST	1910
—	51218	L&Y	Pug	0-4-0ST	1901
—	752	L&Y	—	0-6-0ST	1881
—	85	TVR	O2	0-6-2T	1899
—	5820	USA TC	S160	2-8-0	1945
—	90733	MoS	WD	2-8-0	1945
—	68077	LNER	J94	0-6-0ST	1947
—	D226	BR	—	0-6-0DE	1956
—	D2511	BR	—	0-6-0DM	1961
—	D3336	BR	08	0-6-0DE	1954
—	D5209	BR	25/1	Bo-Bo	1963
—	D8031	BR	20	Bo-Bo	1960
—	50928	BR	108	DMBS	1959
—	51565	BR	108	DMC	1959
—	79962	W&M	—	Railbus	1958
—	79964	W&M	—	Railbus	1958

OS reference: SE 034371
Car parks: Free at Keighley, Ingrow West, Oakworth, Oxenhope. Limited parking at Haworth (pay). Coaches at Ingrow West and Oxenhope only
Access by public transport: Fast and frequent electric Metro trains from Leeds, Bradford and Skipton to Keighley (joint station with K&WVR) 2 adults and up to 3 half fares with a Metro Family Day Rover and the children travel free on K&WVR trains. Regional Railways through services from Carlisle, Morecambe, Lancaster to Keighley station. Through bookings to 'Oxenhope KWVR' are available from any travel centre throughout Britain and allow one day's unlimited travel on KWVR. Regional Railways from Blackpool, Preston, Blackburn, Accrington, Burnley, Manchester to Hebden Bridge for connection via bus service 500 to Oxenhope (tel 01535 603284 for days of operation and timings). A large number of bus services, including National Express operate to Keighley
Refreshment facilities: Buffet Restaurant at Oxenhope. Buffet Bar at Keighley (open when train service in operation). The only CAMRA-approved 'Real Ale' Bar operates on most steam trains (March-October). Wine and Dine by prior booking only — the 'White Rose Pullman' and 'West Riding Ltd'
Picnic areas: Keighley station, Haworth Locomotive Depot, Oxenhope station
Viewing areas: Keighley (Garsdale) Turntable, Haworth Locomotive Depot
Souvenir shops: Keighley, Haworth and Oxenhope stations; Ingrow Vintage Carriage Museum
Museums: KWVR Museum at Oxenhope, Vintage Carriage Trust's carriage and locomotive museum at Ingrow Railway Centre. Both open when KWVR train services are in operation

Industrial locomotives

Name	No	Builder	Type	Built
Hamburg	31	H/Clarke (697)	0-6-0T	1903
Nunlow	—	H/Clarke (1704)	0-6-0T	1938
Brussels	118	H/Clarke (1782)	0-6-0ST	1945
Southwick	—	RSH (7069)	0-4-0CT	1942
Fred	—	RSH (7289)	0-6-0ST	1945
—	63	RSH (7761)	0-6-0ST	1954
Tiny	—	Barclay (2258)	0-4-0ST	1949
Merlin	231	H/Clarke (D761)	0-6-0DM	1951
—	1999*	Peckett (1999)	0-4-0	1941
Austins No1	—	Peckett (5003)	0-4-0DM	1961
—	MDHB No 32	Hunslet (2699)	0-6-0DM	1944

*On loan to Southport Railway Museum

Stock
30 coaches including examples of pre-Grouping types; BR Mk 1 stock including the oldest vehicle in existence, part of the prototype batch; a Pullman car, NER and L&Y observation cars

Owners
19, 752 and 51218 the L&Y Saddletanks
75078 and 78022 the Standard 4 Preservation Society
Bahamas, Nunlow, Tiny the Bahamas Locomotive Society
1054 the National Trust
52055 the Bowers 957 Trust
34092 the *City of Wells* Syndicate

Depots: Carriage and wagon — Oxenhope; Motive power/loco works — Haworth, 'Bahamas Locomotive Society' workshops at Ingrow Railway Centre
Length of line: 4.75 miles
Passenger trains: Early morning local shoppers' services worked by diesel railbus/diesel multiple-unit, otherwise all steam-hauled
  Frequent bus service between Haworth station and Haworth village top on Sundays (May-September) and Bank Holidays, 11.00-17.00
Period of public operation: Steam-hauled passenger services every weekend and Bank Holiday throughout the year (in December diesel-hauled). Daily from mid-June to early September
Special events: Railway Children — 3-5 May; Friends of Thomas the Tank Engine — 7/8, 14/15 June; Vintage Trains — 11, 18 May and 12, 19 October; Keighley 150 Celebrations — 23-25 August;

Wheels in Motion — 4/5 October; Santa Steam Specials — 29/30 November, 6/7, 13/14, 20/21 December; White Rose Pullman (Evening Wine & Dine) — 19 April, 24 May, 28 June, 20 September; West Riding Ltd (Sunday Diner) — 9 March, 3-5 May, 13, 27 July, 10 August, 4/5 Octobe
Facilities for disabled: Wheelchairs accommodated in guard's compartments on trains. Please advise before visit to the Advanced Bookings Officer c/o Haworth station
Special notes: Accompanied children under 5 years of age free. Children 5-15 and Senior Citizens at 50% discount. Family ticket available (2 adults + 3 children/senior citizen)
Membership details: Membership Secretary c/o above address
Membership journal: *Push & Pull* — quarterly
Marketing name: *Worth Valley*

The Kent & East Sussex Railway owes much of its charm to its origin as the world's first light railway. The tightly-curved line with steep graidents is typical of these country railways that were developed on shoestring budgets to bring the 'ironhorse' to sparsely populated areas. Services operate over seven miles of line from the picturesque town of Tenterden to Northiam and the company has plans to extend to Bodiam in the future.

Pride of the line's coach fleet is the magnificently restored train of Victorian carriages built between 1860 and 1901

Company Secretary: Philip Clark-Monks

Headquarters: Tenterden Railway Co Ltd, Tenterden Town Station, Tenterden, Kent TN30 6HE

Telephone: Tenterden (01580) 762943 (24 hour talking timetable); Tenterden (01580) 765155 (office)

Main station: Tenterden Town

Other public stations: Rolvenden, Wittersham Road, Northiam

Car parks: Tenterden, Northiam

OS reference:
Tenterden TQ 882336,
Rolvenden TQ 865328,
Northiam TQ 834266

Access by public transport: Maidstone & District bus service No 400 from Ashford (Kent) BR station

Refreshment facilities: Tenterden Town and Northiam. Also on many trains. Lunch and afternoon teas on Sunday trains. Picnic areas at Tenterden, Wittersham Road and Northiam

Souvenir shop: Tenterden Town station

Museum: Colonel Stephens' Railway Museum

Depot: Rolvenden

Length of line: 7 miles

Passenger trains: Tenterden-Northiam. Trains run: Sundays — March; Weekends, Bank Holidays and School Holidays — April to October; Tuesdays, Wednesdays & Thursdays — June & September; Daily — July & August; Santa Specials at weekends in December

Locomotives and multiple-units

Name	No	Origin	Class	Type	Built
Bodiam	3	LBSCR	A1X	0-6-0T	1872
Sutton	32650	LBSCR	A1X	0-6-0T	1876
Knowle	2678	LBSCR	A1X	0-6-0T	1880†
—	1556	SECR	P	0-6-0T	1909*
Wainwright	DS238	SR	USA	0-6-0T	1943*
Maunsell	65	SR	USA	0-6-0T	1943†
—	1638	GWR	1600	0-6-0PT	1951*
—	20	GWR	AEC	diesel railcar	1940
—	376	NSB	21c	2-6-0	1919*
—	D2023	BR	03	0-6-0DM	1958*
—	D2024	BR	03	0-6-0DM	1958
—	11223	BR	04	0-6-0DM	1957
—	08108	BR	08	0-6-0DE	1955*
—	D9504	BR	14	0-6-0DH	1964
—	D9525	BR	14	0-6-0DH	1965*
—	51571	BR	108	DMC	1959*
—	53971	BR	108	DMBS	1959*
—	20	GWR	—	B0-B0	1940

Industrial locomotives

Name	No	Builder	Type	Built
Marcia	12	Peckett (1631)	0-4-0T	1923
Charwelton	14	M/Wardle (1955)	0-6-0ST	1917*
Holman F. Stephens	23	Hunslet (3791)	0-6-0ST	1952*
Rolvenden	24	Hunslet (3800)	0-6-0ST	1953*
Northiam	25	Hunslet (3797)	0-6-0ST	1953
—	40	BTH	Bo-Bo	1932
—	42	Hunslet (4208)	0-6-0DM	1948
Titan	—	R/Hornsby (423661)	0-4-0DM	1958*

*in traffic
†due to enter traffic during 1997

Passenger stock in service
SECR family saloon; LNWR 6-wheel director's saloon; SECR 4-wheel full third; SR Maunsell CK; GER 6-wheel composite; District Railway 4-wheel full first; SR Maunsell non-descript brake-open; BR Mk 1 RU and 5 other BR Mk 1 coaches; Metro-Cammell Pullman Parlour Car

Stock
2 ex-SECR 'Birdcage' coaches; 2 ex-LSWR coaches; 1 GER observation car; 2 Pullman cars; 5 ex-SR Maunsell coaches; 3 steam cranes; large interesting collection of freight vehicles, totalling 51 vehicles

Facilities for disabled: A special coach for disabled people, 'Petros', is conveyed in many trains (telephone for confirmation of availability), reserved parking at Northiam.
Toilets with disabled access at Tenterden and Northiam, and in 'Petros'

Special notes: Dining car service operates on most Saturday evenings April to October and selected Wednesdays in the summer. Roast lunch served most Sundays. Advance booking is essential for these trains. Santa special services operate on each Saturday and Sunday in December. Advanced booking recommended

Membership details: New Members Secretary c/o above address

Membership journal: *The Tenterden Terrier* — 3 times/year

A contrast in style at Tenterden Town station on the Kent & East Sussex Railway with 'Austerity' No 23 and Norwegian State Railway's No 376. *Robert Berry*

Kidderminster Railway Museum
Worcestershire
Museum

Established in an 1878 GWR warehouse, the museum houses an enormous collection of railway relics, photographs and documents, with a number of 'hands-on' exhibits.
Contact address: Station Drive, Comberton Hill, Kidderminster, Worcestershire DY10 1QX
General Manager: David Postle

Telephone: Kidderminster (01562) 825316
OS reference: SO 837763
Location: Adjacent to SVR station
Car park: SVR car park
Access by public transport: Kidderminster BR station, Midland Red bus service X92 to Kidderminster
Facilities for disabled: Ramp

access for wheelchairs to ground level
Special events: Practical signalling courses using Museum and SVR resources
On site facilities: Souvenirs, refreshments
Period of public opening: Open on SVR operating days

Kirklees Light Railway
West Yorkshire
Timetable Service

Member: AIRPS

Location/headquarters: Clayton West, A636 Wakefield-Denby Dale road
Operating Society/organisation: Kirklees Light Railway, Park Mill Way, Clayton West, Nr Huddersfield HP8 9XJ
Telephone: 01484 865727
Main station: Clayton West
Other station: Cuckoos Nest, Skelmanthorpe
Length of line: 2 miles, 15in gauge (extension proposed for 1997 opening)
Car park: Clayton West — free
Access by public transport: Bus

Locomotives

Name	No	Builder	Type	Built
Fox	—	Taylor	2-6-2T	1987
Badger	—	Taylor	0-6-4T	1991
Toby the Tram Engine	7	Taylor	0-4-0	1995
Jay	—	Taylor	4wD	1992

Rolling stock
2 rakes of four heated carriages, 4-wheel tool van, 4-wheel ballast/stone wagon, heavy bogie flat car for rail carrying

Cont

No 235 from Huddersfield & Barnsley; 484 from Wakefield. Rail to Huddersfield, Wakefield or Denby Dale stations
Refreshment facilities: Clayton West
Souvenir shop: Clayton West
On site facilities: Toilets, swings, half scale roundabouts, lake. HQ of

Barnsley Society of Model Engineers
Facilities for disabled: Limited
Period of public operation: Winter— weekends & most school holidays. Summer — daily from Spring Bank Holiday to end August
Special events: Miniature Traction

Engine Rally — 27/28 April; Friends of Thomas the Tank — 28/29 June, 26/27 July; Halloween Ghost Trains (evenings) (date to be advised); Santa Specials — 29/30 November, 6/7, 13/14, 20/21 December

---

Lakeside & Haverthwaite Railway
Member: AIRPS, TT

Cumbria
Timetable Service

Originally this Furness Railway branch line carried passengers and freight from Ulverston to Lakeside but now the only part remaining is the 3.5-mile section from Haverthwaite to the terminus at Lakeside where connections are made with the lakeside steamers which ply the 10-mile length of Windermere
General Manager: M. A. Maher
Headquarters: Lakeside & Haverthwaite Railway Co Ltd, Haverthwaite Station, near Ulverston, Cumbria LA12 8AL
Telephone: Newby Bridge (015395) 31594
Main station: Haverthwaite
Other public stations: Intermediate station at Newby Bridge. Terminus at Lakeside
OS reference: SD 349843
Car parks: Haverthwaite, Lakeside
Access by public transport: Lakeside steamers on Windermere call at Lakeside. CMS bus to Haverthwaite
Refreshment facilities: Haverthwaite
Souvenir shop: Haverthwaite
On-site facilities: Picnic area at Haverthwaite
Depot: All rolling stock at Haverthwaite
Length of line: 3.5 miles
Passenger trains: Steam-hauled Haverthwaite-Lakeside
Period of public operation: Easter then daily from early-May to end of October.
Special events: Santa Specials (advance booking essential) please

Locomotives and multiple-units

Name	No	Origin	Class	Type	Built
—	42073	LMS	4MT	2-6-4T	1950
—	42085	LMS	4MT	2-6-4T	1951
—	8(D2117)	BR	03	0-6-0DM	1959
—	17(AD601)	LMS	—	0-6-0DE	1945
—	D2072	BR	03	0-6-0DM	1959
—	5643	GWR	5600	0-6-2T	1925
—	20214	BR	20	Bo-Bo	1967
—	D5301	BR	26	Bo-Bo	1958
—	52029	BR	107	DMS	1960
—	52071	BRCW	110	DMBC	1961
—	52077	BRCW	110	DMBC	1961

Industrial locomotives

Name	No	Builder	Type	Built
Caliban*	1	Peckett (1925)	0-4-0ST	1937
Rachel	9	M/Rail (2098)	4wDM	1924
Repulse	11	Hunslet (3698)	0-6-0ST	1950
Princess	14	Bagnall (2682)	0-6-0ST	1942
Askam Hall	15	Avonside (1772)	0-4-0ST	1935
Alexandra	12	Barclay (929)	0-4-0ST	1902
David	13	Barclay (2333)	0-4-0ST	1953
Cumbria	10	Hunslet (3794)	0-6-0ST	1953
—	7	Fowler (22919)	0-4-0DM	1940
Fluff	16	Hunslet/Fowler	0-4-0DM	1937
—	20	Jones crane	0-4-0DM	1952
Sir James	21	Barclay (1550)	0-6-0F	1917
—	22	Fowler (4220045)	0-4-0DM	1967

*Under restoration at Steamtown, Carnforth

Stock

10 ex-BR Mk 1 coaches; 1 ex-LNER BG; 1 ex-BR Mk 1 miniature buffet coach, Royal saloon No 5 (built GER, Stratford 1898); Small selection of freight vehicles

contact for details
Special notes: Combined railway/lake steamer tickets available, from the station at Haverthwaite and Lakeside steamers piers at Bowness and

Ambleside. Lakeside steamers are operated by Windermere Iron Steamboat Co Ltd
Membership journal: *The Iron Horse* — quarterly

Lappa Valley Railway

Cornwall
Steam Centre

Location/headquarters: Benny Halt, St Newlyn East, Nr Newquay, Cornwall TR8 5HZ
Telephone: 01782 510317
General Manager: Miss Amanda Booth
Main station: Benny Halt
Other station: East Wheal Rose, Newlyn Downs Halt
Car park: Benny Halt and Newlyn Downs Halt
Access by public transport: Bus service, Newquay to Truro and return. Western National and The Cornishman Coaches to St Newlyn East. Signposted, half-mile walk from bus stop to railway. July and August – bus from Newquay to railway (3 times daily)
Refreshment facilities: Cafe at East Wheal Rose serving hot and cold food, snacks, hot & cold drinks; licensed with food
Souvenir shop: East Wheal Rose and Benny Halt

Locomotives

Name	No	Builder	Type	Built
Muffin	2	Berwyn	0-6-0	1967
		rebuilt Tambling		1991
Zebedee	1	S/Lamb	0-6-4T	1974
		rebuilt Tambling		1990
Lappa Lady	3	Minirail	4w-4wDH	c1960
Dougal	—	Booth	4w-4wPM	1975

(all 15in gauge)
Also one 10.25in gauge diesel

Rolling stock
15in gauge — 10 passenger coaches
10.25in gauge — 4 passenger coaches, 2 wagons
7.25in gauge — 1 Mardyle APT set

On site facilities: 15in, 10.25in and 7.25in gauge railways. Canoes, paddle boats, crazy golf, trikes, electric motorbikes, children's play area, brick path maze, listed engine house, walks and a video
Depot: Benny Halt
Facilities for disabled: Yes
Period of public operation: Easter to end of October, usually daily but ring for early and late season opening days
Special Notes: Entry is one all in price, except for motorbikes. Family tickets and reduced afternoon saver fares are available all days. Under 3s free

Launceston Steam Railway

Cornwall
Timetable Service

The railway runs through the beautiful Kensey Valley on a track gauge of 1ft 11.5in, following the trackbed of the old North Cornwall line. The locomotives formerly worked on the Dinorwic and Penrhyn railways in North Wales. Launceston station contains a museum of vintage cars and motorcycles and there is also a collection of stationary steam engines which are demonstrated at work. There are catering, gift shop and bookshop facilities. At the far end of the line there are pleasant walks and a picnic area. The covered rolling stock ensures an enjoyable visit whatever the weather
Location: Newport Industrial Estate, Launceston, Cornwall
OS reference: SX 328850
Operating Society/organisation: The Spice Settlement Trust Co Ltd, trading as the Launceston Steam Railway, Newport, Launceston

Industrial locomotives

Name	No	Builder	Type	Built
Lilian	—	Hunslet (317)	0-4-0ST	1883
Velinheli	—	Hunslet (409)	0-4-0ST	1886
Covertcoat	—	Hunslet (679)	0-4-0ST	1898
Sybil	—	Bagnall (1760)	0-4-0ST	1906
Dorothea	—	Hunslet (763)	0-4-0ST	1901
—	—	M/Rail (5646)	4wDM	1933
—	—	M/Rail (9546)	4wDM	1950

Locomotive notes: The three Hunslet locomotives (317/409/679) are expected to be in use during 1997.

Stock
1 electric inspection trolley; 4 bogie carriages and 1 4-wheel carriage

Telephone: (01566) 775665
Stations: Launceston-Hunts Crossing-New Mills
Car park: Newport Industrial Estate, Launceston
Length of line: 2.5 miles
Gauge: 1ft 11.5in
Access by public transport: BR Gunnislake 13 miles, Plymouth or Bodmin 25 miles
On site facilities: Cafe and restaurant, transport museum, workshop tours, gift and bookshop, all situated at Launceston
Period of public operation: Easter holiday, then Tuesdays and Sundays until Whitsun. Daily (not Saturdays) Whitsun until end of

Cont 49

September. Tuesdays and Sundays in October, also daily (except Saturday) during half term week. Santa Specials every Saturday and Sunday in December, also Christmas Eve and Boxing Day **Public opening:** Trains run from 11.00-16.30. Departures every 40min and more frequently if required. Unlimited riding on date of issue of ticket
Family ticket: Available, 2 Adults + 4 children
Journey time: Return 35min
Facilities for disabled: Easy access to all areas except bookshop and motorcycle museum. No toilet facilities for disabled. However, public toilets are reasonably accessible
Special events: Double-headed trains on Wednesdays in July and August (whenever possible). Demonstration freight trains (contact for details)

Lavender Line

Member: AIRPS

East Sussex Steam Centre

The Lavender Line is centred around a typical country station, which unusually is situated in the village it was built to serve. The emphasis is on steam for passenger trains, although diesel power, including the unique Class 12, is represented. The next stretch of trackbed has just been purchased, whilst the present operating length will become double track. This will enable the popular footplate experience courses to operate at weekends. The running line is currently being extended. Planned works for the coming year include new shed roads, extra sidings and return to operation of Barclay 945. Additional rolling stock is expected.
Location: Isfield Station, Isfield, near Uckfield, East Sussex TN22 5XB. (Just off the A26)
OS reference: TQ 452171
Operating society/organisation: The Lavender Line Preservation Society

Locomotives and multiple-units

Name	No	Origin	Class	Type	Built
—	15224	BR	12	0-6-0DE	1949
Sir Herbert Walker	73003	BR	73	Bo-Bo	1962
—	51656	BR	115	DMBS	1960
—	51677	BR	115	DMBS	1960

Industrial locomotives

Name	No	Builder	Type	Built
Annie	945	Barclay (945)	0-4-0ST	1904
Lady Ingrid	3	Barclay (2315)	0-4-0ST	1951
Blackie	68012	Hunslet (3193)	0-6-0ST	1944
—	15	Barclay	0-4-0DM	1945
—	16	Barclay	0-4-0DM	1945

Stock

3 ex-BR Mk 1 coaches; 1 ex-GWR 'Toad' brake van, 3 box vans, 2 coal trucks, 1 BR standard brake van, 1 LT hopper, 1 Lowmac, 1 dorm coach, 1 Sturgeon, 1 Conflat A, 1 Pipefit

Telephone: Isfield (01825) 750515
Car park: On site
Access by public transport: Train to Uckfield or Lewes, then bus to Isfield
On site facilities: Professional

Lady Ingrid in action giving brake van rides at Isfield station on the Lavender Line.

England

catering, souvenir shop, museum. Private functions, weddings and parties catered for. Trackside path to picnic and viewing area
Length of line: 1-mile — extension underway
Public opening: Steam-hauled trains Sundays and Bank Holidays all year round, plus Saturdays in July. Also open every day (except Mondays) in August. Site open 11.00-17.00
Footplate courses: Available on steam, diesel shunters or DMUs
Facilities for disabled: Access to site, platforms, museum, buffet, shop and for train rides, no wheelchair access to toilets at present
Special events: Firework display in September; Father Christmas on the four weeks before Christmas; Mothers and Fathers Days; Easter Bunny Days. Plus may be more, please ring for details
 Ticket price includes unlimited rides and visit to signalbox. Loco shed/workshop visits when accompanied by society member

Leeds Industrial Museum

West Yorkshire
Museum

Location: The Leeds Industrial Museum, Armley Mills, Canal Road, Leeds LS12 2QF
OS reference: SE 275342
Operating society/organisation: Leeds City Council, Department of Leisure Services, The Town Hall, The Headrow, Leeds LS1 3AO
Curator: D. C. Rooke
Telephone: (0113) 263 7861
Car park: Cark park adjacent to the Museum
Access by public transport: Nos 14 or 5A from City Square, Leeds (outside the railway station)
Public opening: April-September: Tuesdays-Saturdays 10.00-16.00, Sundays 14.00-16.00. October-March: Tuesdays-Saturdays 10.00-16.00, Sundays 14.00-16.00. Closed Mondays (except Bank Holidays)
On site facilities: Museum shop, refreshments (vending machines), picnic area
Special notes: Facilities for the disabled (toilets, etc), lifts. Museum can be viewed by visitors in wheelchairs (most areas are accessible)
Details of locomotive and rolling stock: Locomotive collection includes steam, diesel, mines locomotives and a narrow gauge railway and engines

Notes
*On loan to Moseley Industrial Railway Museum
†On loan to Red RoseSteam Society/Astley Green Colliery Museum

Industrial locomotives

Name	No	Builder	Type	Built
1ft 6in gauge				
Jack	—	Hunslet 684)	0-4-0WT	1898
Coffin	—	G/Bat (1326)	0-4-0BE	1933
2ft gauge				
Barber	—	T/Green (441)	0-6-2ST	1908
Cheetal	—	Fowler (15991)	0-6-0WT	1923
Simplex	—*	M/Rail (1369	4wPM	1918
Hudson Fordson	—	Hudson (36863)	4wDM	1928
Layer	—	Fowler (21294)	4wDM	1936
Hudson Hunslet	—	Hunslet (2959)	4wDM	1944
Resin	—	Hunslet (2008)	0-4-0DM	1939
Nacob	—	Hunslet (5340)	0-4-0DM	1957
Sharlston	—†	H/Clarke (1164)	0-4-0DM	1959
Demtox	—†	Hunslet (6048)	0-4-0DM	1961
2ft 1in gauge				
Fricl	—	Hunslet (4019)	0-4-0DM	1948
Pitpo	—	Hunslet	0-4-0	1955
Calverton	—	H/Clarke (1368)	0-4-0DM	1965
2ft 6in gauge				
Ordnance	—	G/Bat (1877)	0-4-0BE	1943
Junin	—	H/Clarke (D557)	2-6-2DM	1930
Fimyn	—†	Hunslet (3411)	0-4-0DM	1947
2ft 8in gauge				
Ficol	—	Hunslet (3200)	0-4-0DM	1945
2ft 11in gauge				
Lurch	—	H/Clarke (D571)	4wDM	1932
3ft gauge				
Lord Granby	—	H/Clarke (633)	0-4-0ST	1902
Cement	—	Fowler (20685)	2-4-0DM	1935
Lofti	—	Hunslet (4057)	0-6-0DM	1953
3ft 6in gauge				
Progress	—	H/Clarke (D634)	0-6-0DM	1946
Festival of Britain	—	H/Clarke (D733)	0-6-0DM	1951
Standard gauge				
Hodbarrow	—	Hunslet (299)	0-4-0ST	1882
Aldwyth	—	M/Wardle (865)	0-6-0ST	1882
Capper	—	Fowler (22060)	0-4-0DM	1938
Fort William	—	Fowler (22893)	0-4-0DM	1940
Trecwn	—	Hunslet (2390)	0-4-0DM	1941
Elizabeth	—	H/Clarke (1888)	0-4-0ST	1958
Southam No 2	—	H/Clarke (D625)	0-4-0DM	1942
Luton	—	G/Bat (1210)	0-4-0BE	1930
Smithy Wood	—	G/Bat (2543)	0-4-0WE	1955

Leighton Buzzard Railway

Member: AIRPS, TT

Bedfordshire
Timetable Service

Built in 1919 this is one of England's foremost narrow gauge centres. In places, this line bears the air of a Continental roadside tramway, running as it does behind the backs of houses before it passes into the open countryside; there is no denying the quaintness of its engines or the friendliness of the little trains and their staff

General Manager: J. Horsley
Headquarters: Leighton Buzzard Railway, Page's Park station, Billington Road, Leighton Buzzard LU7 8TN
OS reference: Page's Park SP 928242
Telephone: (01525) 373888, 24hr answerphone with service and event details
Main station: Pages Park (A4146, Leighton Buzzard)
Other public stations: Halts at Vandyke Road and Stonehenge Works
Car park: Pages Park
Access by public transport: Leighton Buzzard BR station then by bus to town centre
Refreshment facilities: Pages Park. Picnic area by station. Cafe for hot & cold snacks, refreshments and ice creams
Souvenir shop: Pages Park
Depots: Pages Park and Stonehenge Works
Length of line: 3 miles, 2ft gauge
Journey time: Single 25min, return 65min
Passenger trains: Pages Park-Stonehenge Works
   Group discounts and packages such as Birthday Breaks, Schools specials, Twilight Trains available
Period of public operation: Sundays 16 March-12 October; Good Friday; Easter Saturday; Bank Holiday Mondays 31 March, 5/26 May, 25 August; Wednesdays 28 May-27 August; Thursdays 7-28 August; Saturdays 3, 17, 24 May, 5 July, 1-30 August, 6 September
Special events: Industrial Train Displays — 27 April, 18 May, 15 June, 6 July, 17 August, 7 September, 5 October; Quarry Excavator Demonstrations — 31

Locomotives

Name	No	Builder	Type	Built
—	740	O&K	0-6-0T	1907
—*	—	Baldwin (778)	4-6-0T	1917
Berlin	—	Freudenstein (73)	0-4-0WT	1901
Alice	—	Hunslet (780)	0-4-0ST	1902
Peter Pan	—	K/Stuart (4256)	0-4-0ST	1922
Chaloner	1	de Winton	0-4-0VBT	1877
Pixie	2	K/Stuart (4260)	0-4-0ST	1922
Rishra	3	Baguley (2007)	0-4-0T	1921
Doll	4	Barclay (1641)	0-6-0T	1919
Elf	5	O&K (12740)	0-6-0WT	1936
Falcon	7	O&K (8986)	4wDM	1939
Gollum	8	Ruston (217999)	4wDM	1943
Madge	9	O&K (7600)	4wDM	1934
Haydn Taylor	10	Simplex (7956)	4wDM	1945
P. C. Allen	11	O&K (5834)	0-4-0WT	1912
Carbon	12	Simplex (6012)	4wPM	1930
Arkle	13	M/Rail (7108)	4wDM	1937
—	14	Hunslet (3646)	4wDM	1946
Tom Bombadil	15	Hibberd (2514)	4wDM	1941
Thorin Oakenshield	16	Lister (11221)	4wDM	1939
Damredub	17	Simplex (7036)	4wDM	1936
Feanor	18	M/Rail (11003)	4wDM	1956
—	19	M/Rail (11298)	4wDM	1965
—	20	M/Rail (60s317)	4wDM	1966
Festoon	21	Simplex (4570)	4wPM	1929
Fingolfin	22	under construction	—	—
—	23	Ruston (164346)	4wDM	1932
Ad-a-Cab	25	Simplex (7214)	4wDM	1938
Yimkin	26	Ruston (203026)	4wDM	1941
Poppy	27	Ruston (408430)	4wDM	1957
RAF Stanbridge	28	Ruston (200516)	4wDM	1940
Creepy	29	Hunslet (6008)	4wDM	1963
—	30	M/Rail (8695)	4wDM	1941
—	31	Lister (4228)	4wDM	1931
—	32	Ruston (172892)	4wDM	1934
—	33	Hibberd (3582)	4wDM	1954
Red Rum	34	M/Rail (7105)	4wPM	1936
—	35	Hunslet (6619)	0-4-0DM	1966
Caravan	36	Simplex (7129)	4wDM	1938
—	37	Ruston (172901)	4wPM	1934
—	38	Lister (37170)	4wDM	1951
T. W. Lewis	39	Ruston (375316)	4wDM	1954
—	40	Ruston (283507)	4wDM	1949
—	41	Hunslet (2536)	4wDM	1941
—	42	Ruston (223692)	4wPM	1944
—	43	Simplex (10409)	4wDM	1954
Kestrel	44	Simplex (7933)	4wDM	1941
—	46	Ruston (209430)	4wPM	1942
—	47	Hudson (38384)	4wDM	1930
—	48	Hunslet (RFST2)	4wDM	1952
—	—	M/Rail (1377)	4wPM	1918
—	—	M/Rail (11297)	4wDM	1965

* on loan from Amberley Museum

Dismantled for spares: M/Rail 4805, 5613, 5612, 5603; Ruston 218016 converted to brake vans: M/Rail 5608, 5875

52

England

March, 26 May, 5 July, 3, 25
August; Demonstration freight train
runs— 6 April, 1 June,
21 September; Easter steam
weekend — 28 -31 March; Teddy
Bears' Outing — 20 April;
Heritage weekend — 5/6 July;
Model Mania — 3 August; Autumn
Steam Up — 6/7 September
(includes photographic cavalcade
and evening Steam Glow on
Saturday); Mad Hatter's Tea
Party— 28 September; Xmas
Trains Weekends 6-21 December

Locomotive notes: 1, 2, 3, 4, 5, 11, *Alice* and *Peter Pan* are potentially
operational during 1997.

Stock
10 coaches and a number of miscellaneous vehicles

Facilities for disabled: Access to
shop, buffet, platform and toilets.
Wheelchairs can be conveyed on
trains
Special notes: Visiting steam
locomotives expected during 1997
Membership details: Membership

secretary c/o above address
Membership journal: *Chaloner*
— quarterly
Marketing name: England's
Friendly Little Line

Liverpool Museum

Merseyside
Museum

A fine selection of vehicles in a
traditional 'stuffed and mounted'
display. *Lion* is on display
throughout the year and is no
longer steamed.
Location: William Brown Street,
Liverpool
Curator: Post vacant. Enquiries to
Regional History Dept tel: 0151
478 4060
Operating society/organisation:
National Museums and Galleries
on Merseyside, William Brown
Street, Liverpool L3 8EN
Telephone: 0151-207 0001
Car parks: Public car parks
nearby
Access by public transport:
Adjacent Lime Street stations (BR

Locomotives

Name	No	Origin	Class	Type	Built
Lion	57	L&MR	—	0-4-2	1838

Industrial locomotives

Name	No	Builder	Type	Built
—	1	Avonside (1465)	0-6-0ST	1904

Stock
LOR electric coach of 1893
L&MR replica coach built Derby 1929

and Merseyrail). Numerous bus
routes
On site facilities: Cafe, shop
Public opening: Monday to
Saturday 10.00-17.00. Sundays
12.00-17.00
Special notes: Transport gallery

within large general museum.
Facilities for disabled visitors
Journal: *The Guide,* published
twice yearly covering entire
activities of National Museums &
Galleries on Merseyside

London Transport Museum

Member: AIRPS, TT

London
Museum

Spectacular displays of buses,
trams and trains reveal a
fascinating story of travel, people
and the history of London itself.
Special exhibitions, family
activities, actors, videos and
working models all bring the story
to life
Location: Covent Garden, London
WC2E 7BB
OS reference: TQ 303809
Operating society/organisation:
London Regional Transport
Telephone: 0171 379 6344. (24hr
0171 836 8557)
Access by public transport:
Underground to Covent Garden,

Locomotives

Name	No	Origin	Class	Type	Built
—	23	Met Rly	A	4-4-0T	1866
John Hampden	5	Met Rly		Bo-Bo	1922

Industrial locomotives

Origin	Builder	Type	Built
Wotton Tramway	A/Porter (807)	0-4-0TG	1872

Electric stock
4248 District Rly Q23 stock driving motor coach 1923
11182 LPTB 1938 stock driving motor coach
400 Met Rly bogie stock coach 1899
30 City & South London Rly 'Padded Cell' coach 1890
Great Northern Piccadilly & Brompton Railway 'Gate stock' car 1906
(sectioned)

Leicester Square or Charing Cross. Buses to Strand/Aldwych
On site facilities: Museum shop, lecture theatre, photo and research libraries (by appointment), resource centre and café
Public opening: Daily 10.00-18.00 (except Fridays 11.00-18.00) (last admissions 17.15). Closed 24/25/26 December. Reduced admission prices for children, students, senior citizens, registered disabled, UB40 holders and pre-booked parties. Family season ticket available
Facilities for disabled: Disabled toilets available, wheelchair access to all displays. Reduced admission

for registered disabled visitors and person accompanying them. Please advise in advance if a party of disabled visitors would like to visit
Special notes: Visitors can put themselves in the driving seat of a bus, a tube simulator, there are also 'hands-on' demonstrations of signals and points. In addition to the vehicles and rolling stock there are models, signs, posters, photographs, audio-visual displays

and a 1906 Otis lift car. The museum runs a full programme of events and activities in addition to temporary exhibitions on a variety of topics. In addition to the vehicles on display there is a growing reserve collection
Membership details: Details from the Friends of the London Transport Museum

Mangapps Farm Railway Museum
Essex
Steam Centre

Members: AIRPS

Mangapps recreates the atmosphere of a rural light railway. Featuring a large museum collection, strong in items of East Anglian interest, railway signalling and goods rolling stock. Other features include original station buildings from Mid-Suffolk Light, Great Eastern and Midland & Great Northern Railways.
Superintendent of the Line: John Jolly
Commercial Manager: June Jolly
Location: Mangapps Farm Railway Museum, Southminster Road, Burnham on Crouch, Essex CM0 8QQ. (Entrance on B1021, 1-mile north of Burnham)
Telephone: 01621 784898
Access by public transport:
Burnham station approx 1-mile
On site facilities: Station, car park, souvenir shop, toilets, amenity and picnic areas
Refreshment facilities: teas and light refreshments
Length of line: Three quarter-mile

Locomotives and multiple-units

Name	No	Origin	Class	Type	Built
—	D2089	BR	03	0-6-0DM	1960
—	03399	BR	03	0-6-0DM	1961
—	D2325	BR	04	0-6-0DM	1961
—	11104	BR	04	0-6-0DM	1953
—	54287	BR	121	DTS	1960
—	22624	LT	R38	DMS	1938

Industrial locomotives

Name	No	Builder	Type	Built
Minnie	—	F/Walker(358)	0-6-0ST	1878
Brookfield	—	Bagnall(2613)	0-6-0PT	1940
Demelza	—	Bagnall(3061)	0-6-0ST	1954
Elland	No 1	H/Clarke(D1153)	0-4-0DM	1959
—	—	S/Henshaw(7502)	4wDM	1966
—	226	Drewry(2180)/ V/Foundry(5261)	0-4-0DM	1945

Public opening: Weekends & Bank Holidays all year (except 25/26 December, and daily during school holidays. Closed January/February. Steam trains operate 1st Sunday of March to December, every Sunday during

August & December
Opening times: 13.00-17.30 diesel days; 11.30-17.30 steam days
Special events: Friends of Thomas the Tank — date to be confirmed; Gala Day — 7 July; Santa Specials — during December

Mid-Hants Railway
Hampshire
Timetable Service

Member: AIRPS

Originally built as the Winchester to Alton link, the Mid-Hants Railway became known as the Watercress Line through reguarly carrying this local produce to London markets. Now restored the

line runs from its BR connection at Alton through rolling countryside to its terminus at Alresford. Large and powerful locomotives work impressively over the steeply inclined route, known to

railwaymen as 'The Alps'. No 31625 entered traffic for the first time in September 1996. Nos 30499, 35018 and 41312 are expected to be the next locomotives to enter service

Chief Executive: Margaret Parker
Headquarters: Mid-Hants
Railway PLC, Alresford Station,
Alresford, Hants SO24 9JG
Telephone: Alresford (01962)
733810
Fax: 01962 735448
Talking timetable: 01962 734866
Internet address:
http://www.hartlana.co.uk/itoeye
Main station: Alresford
Other public stations: Ropley,
Medstead & Four Marks, Alton
OS reference: Alresford SU
588325, Ropley SU 629324
Car park: Alresford-HCC, pay &
display (free Sundays & Bank
Holidays). Alton pay & display
Access by public transport:
South West Train services — just
over 1hr from London. Through
ticketing arrangements available
from Waterloo and all BR stations.
Alternatively, travel to Winchester
station and take the bus to
Alresford from nearby City Road.
Bus services — are operated by
Stagecoach (01962) 852352, or dial
100 and ask for freefone County
Bus Line
Refreshment facilities: Buffet
service on most trains; 'West
Country' buffet at Alresford;
'T-Junction' picnic/barbeque area
at Ropley; tea/coffee available at
Alton when information office
open

Class S15 No 30506 has recently
re-entered traffic after overhaul.
Tony Genever

Locomotives

Name	No	Origin	Class	Type	Built
—††	30499	LSWR	S15	4-6-0	1920
—	30506	LSWR	S15	4-6-0	1920
—	31625	SR	U	2-6-0	1929
—	31806	SR	U	2-6-0	1926
—*	31874	SR	N	2-6-0	1925
Bodmin	34016	SR	WC	4-6-2	1945
Tangmere†	34067	SR	BB	4-6-2	1947
249 Squadron	34073	SR	BB	4-6-2	1948
Swanage	34105	SR	WC	4-6-2	1950
Shaw Savill†	35009	SR	MN	4-6-2	1942
British India Line	35018	SR	MN	4-6-2	1945
—	41312	LMS	2MT	2-6-2T	1952
—	73096	BR	5MT	4-6-0	1956
—	76017	BR	4MT	2-6-0	1954
Franklin D. Roosevelt	701	USATC	S160	2-8-0	1944
—	D3358	BR	08	0-6-0DE	1957
—	D5353	BR	27	Bo-Bo	1961
—	45132	BR	45	1Co-Co1	1961

*Currently running as No 5 *James*, will be running as 31874 May to end
July 1997
†Currently under restoration at Swindon Railway Workshop
††Currently under restoration at Riley Engineering, East Lancs

Industrial locomotives

Name	No	Builder	Type	Built
—	4	Fowler (22889)	0-4-0DM	1939
Thomas	1	Hunslet (3781)	0-6-0T	1954
Barbara	—	Hunslet (2890)	0-6-0T	1943

Stock
3 steam cranes; 1 Plasser & Theurer AL250 lining machine; 26 ex-BR Mk
1 coaches; 15 ex-BR Mk 2 coaches; 4 ex-SR coaches; 1 ex-LSWR coach; 2
ex-LMS coaches; Numerous goods vehicles

Owners
30499 and 30506 the Urie Locomotive Society
34105 the 34105 Light Pacific Group
76017 the Standard 4 Locomotive Group

Catering facilities: The 'Countryman' pre-booked Sunday lunch trains. The 'Watercress Belle' operates on certain Saturday evenings April-October. Early booking is essential, please telephone to confirm seat availability for both trains. Real Ale trains — certain special events and Saturday evenings featuring beers from local breweries
Souvenir shops: Alresford, Alton and Ropley — which also specialises in secondhand books
On-site facilities: Picnic area and viewing facilities at Ropley, including children's playground
Depot: Ropley
Length of line: 10 miles
Passenger trains: Phone Talking Timetable (01962 734866) to confirm details. Sundays February; Weekends and Bank Holidays March to end October; mid-week June/July; daily July to first week September. Santa Specials (bookings commence end of August)
Journey time: Round trip 1hr 40min max
Special events: Real Ale Evening Train — 22 March; Friends of Thomas the Tank Engine — 28 March-6 April, 9-17 August inclusive; 20th Anniversary of MHR — 3-5 May; Alton Model Railway Exhibition — 4/5 May; Real Ale Evening Train — 24 May; Morris Day — 8 June; Father's Day and Watercress William's Birthday — 15 June; End of Steam on the Southern — 5/6, 12/13 July; Real Ale Evening Train — 19 July; Bus Rally — 20 July; Jaguar Enthusiast's Day — 7 September; Country Market/Craft Fair — 14 September; Open Day (the chance to see behind the scenes) — 28 September; Real Ale Evening Train — 4 October; Teddy Bears' Day — 5 October; S&D Weekend — 25/26 October; Santa Specials — 30 November, 6/7, 13/14, 20/21, 22/23/24 December
Facilities for disabled: Toilets at Ropley and 100yd from Alresford station. Passengers in fixed wheelchairs can be carried in the brake compartment of all trains. Ramps are provided to ease entry to trains
Membership details: Membership Secretary, c/o above address

Mid-Norfolk Railway

Member: AIRPS

Norfolk
Diesel Centre

A scheme to preserve part of the former Great Eastern line from Wymondham to Wells Next the Sea. The section from Wymondham to Dereham has been purchased and initial services will operate from Dereham to Yaxham. Re-opening to Wymondham is anticipated during 1997.
Headquarters: Yaxham Railway Station, Yaxham, Dereham, Norfolk NR19 1RD
Main station: Dereham
Telephone: 01362 690653 (answerphone)
Car park: At Dereham
Museum: A 'Goods Handling Throughout the Ages' is being developed in Dereham goods shed
Souvenir shop: Dereham
Access by public transport: Bus from Norwich and Kings Lynn
Period of public operation: Occassional trains from Dereham to Yaxham and will extend to Wymondham. Occassional freight demonstration trains
Membership details: Stuart Moye, 21 The Brambles, Ware, Herts SG12 0XU
Membership journal: *The Blastpipe* (three times a year)

Class 20 No 20206 provides the power at the temporary Dereham (Rushs Green) halt during 1996.
Alan C. Butcher

Locomotives & multiple-units

Name	No	Origin	Class	Type	Built
—	20069	BR	20	Bo-Bo	1961
—	20206	BR	20	Bo-Bo	1967
—	51073	GRCW	119	DMBC	1958
—	51572	BR	108	DMC	1959
—	54224	BR	108	DTC	1959
—	55009	GRCW	122	DMBS	1958
—	56301	GRCW	100	DTC	1957
—	51503	M/Cam	101	DMC	1959

Industrial locomotives

Name	No	Builder	Type	Built
—	—	R/Hornsby (497753)	0-4-0DE	1963

Rolling stock
5 BR Mk 2 coaches. Selection of freight wagons

Mid-Suffolk Light Railway

Members: AIRPS

**Suffolk
Museum**

Location: Wetheringsett, Nr
Stowmarket, Suffolk
OS reference: TM 129659 (Sheet
155)
Operating society/organisation:
Mid Suffolk Light Railway
Company
Car park: On site
Access by public transport: BR
Stowmarket (8 miles); by bus from
Ipswich on summer Sundays and
by bus on weekdays, passing
within three-quarters of a mile on
A140 from Ipswich, Diss or
Norwich. Tel: 01473 265676
On site facilities: Souvenir shop,
refreshments, railway walk, rolling
stock under restoration, railwayana
and photographic exhibition.
Toilets and picnic area
Period of public opening:

Industrial locomotives

Name	No	Builder	Type	Built
—	1604	H/Clarke (1604)	0-6-0ST	1928

Rolling stock

Ex-GER closed vans, ex-BR open wagon (now converted to coal wagon), 3
ex-GER 5-compartment coaches, ex-GER 2-compartment brake coach, ex-
GER full brake, ex-LNER brake van, ex GER open wagon, ex-LMS horse
box

Sundays and Bank Holidays plus
Wednesdays during school
holidays, Easter to end September
Special events: 'Art Weekend —
4/5 May; LNER Day — 16 July;
trackbed walk to Laxfield — 7
September; 1950s Day — 21
September
Special notes: Museum dedicated
to Mid-Suffolk Light Railway.

Original MSLR restored buildings
and artifacts. Reproduction MSLR
ticket on entry. *Railway World*
award winner
Membership details: Membership
Secretary, 4 Felix Road,
Stowupland, Stowmarket, Suffolk
IP14 4DD
Society journal: *Making Tracks:*
quarterly MSLRS Newsletter

Middleton Railway

Members: AIRPS, TT

**West Yorkshire
Steam Centre**

This is a preserved section of one
of the world's oldest railways,
authorised by Act of Parliament in
1758, and also the first to be re-
opened by volunteers
Headquarters: Middleton Railway
Trust Ltd, Moor Road, Leeds
LS10 2JQ
Telephone: 0113 271 0320
(Ansaphone) or 0113 271089 after
6pm
Main station: Moor Road, Hunslet
OS reference: SE 302309
Car parks: Tunstall Road/Moor
Road (free)
Access by public transport: Any
bus from Corn Exchange to
Tunstall Road, walk down the
troad, across Waterway and the
MR is on the right, walking time
5min
Souvenir shop: Moor Road
Museum: Depot now open 10.00
to 18.00 during season (10.00 to
16.00 during winter). There is no
charge for admission to site
Length of line: 1.25 miles
Passenger trains: Sunday trains all
steam operated. Saturday services
may be diesel hauled. Special trains

Locomotives

Name	No	Origin	Class	Type	Built
—	1310	NER	Y7	0-4-0T	1891
—	54	LNER	Y1	0-4-0VB	1933
—	385	DSB	HsII	0-4-0WT	1893
—	7401	LMS	—	0-6-0DM	1932

Industrial locomotives

Name	No	Builder	Type	Built
John Blenkinsop	—	Peckett (2003)	0-4-0ST	1941
Henry de Lacy II	—	H/Clarke (1309)	0-4-0ST	1917
—	67	H/Clarke (1369)	0-6-0T	1919
Mirvale	—	H/Clarke (1882)	0-4-0ST	1955
Brookes No 1	—	Hunslet (2387)	0-6-0ST	1941
Windle	—	Borrows (53)	0-4-0WT	1909
Matthew Murray	—	Bagnall (2702)	0-4-0ST	1943
Arthur	—	M/Wardle (1601)	0-6-0ST	1901
—*	—	Brush (91)	0-4-0DE	1958
—	No 6	H/Leslie (3860)	0-4-0ST	1935
Carroll	—	H/Clarke (D631)	0-4-0DM	1946
—	—	Hunslet (1786)	4wD	1935
Mary	—	H/Clarke (D577)	0-4-0DM	1932
—	—	Fowler (3900002)	0-4-0DM	1945
—	—	Fowler (4200038)	0-4-0DH	1966
—	—	Sentinel (10252)	0-4-0DH	1966
—	—	Thomas Hill (138C)	0-4-0DH	1963
Rowntrees No 3†	—	R/Hornsby (441934)	4wDM	1960

*On loan from BSC Orb Works, Newport
†On loan from North Yorkshire Moors Railway

Cont

operate on request, contact
J. Wickinson, Tel: (0532)719785
Period of public operation: Every
Saturday, Sunday and Bank
Holiday Monday from 29 March to
26 October. Saturday service —
13.30, 14.13, 15.00, 15,45, 16.30.
Sunday service — every 30min,
13.00-16.30. Trains depart from
Moor Road at 11.00, 11.45, 12.30,
13.00 then every 30min until 16.30.
Winter steam service — Sundays
13.00 to 16.30
Special events: Please contact for
details

Stock
2 CCTs converted for passenger use Nos 1867 and 2048; CCT as stores van
No 2073; Norwegian brake coach; Various goods vehicles; 5-ton Booth rail
crane; 1 3-ton Smith steam crane; 1 3-ton Isles steam crane; 7.5 ton steam
crane

Owners
1310, 385 the Steam Power Trust

Facilities for disabled: Access
very good
Special notes: It was the first
standard gauge railway to be
opened by volunteers, in June

1960. The railway terminates in a
large car park and a nature trail has
been provided by the local council

Midland Railway Centre
Member: AIRPS, TT

The Centre is a rapidly developing
Preservation Scheme with a
difference. The massive 57 acre
Museum site and 35 acre Country
Park enables the Centre to become
'More Than Just a Railway' as its
publicity says. The seven road
Matthew Kirtley Museum allows
much of the historic collection to
be on display and allows most of
the locomotives to be stored and
displayed under cover. A Miniature
Railway (3.5 and 5in gauge) and a
Narrow Gauge Line (2ft gauge)
carry passengers and the Narrow
Gauge Line is being extended into
the Country Park. A new
development is the Brittain Pit
Farm park, with its wide variety of
livestock. And of course there is a
3.5-mile standard gauge line
complete with Midland signals,
three restored signalboxes,
Butterley station, the scenic
delights of Butterley Reservoir and
Golden Valley!

1997 will see a host of new
developments, including the
opening of the Princess Royal
Locomotive Trust depot, the
opening of the narrow gauge line to
Golden Valley, the completion of
the Victorian 'Tin Tabernacle'
Church and the development of
Swanwick Junction station as a true
Midland Railway junction station
complete with a short branch line.
In addition exciting new projects
include a headquarters building for
the Historical Model Railway
Society and a purpose built diesel
depot.

Locomotives and multiple-units

Name	No	Origin	Class	Type	Built
Princess Elizabeth	6201	LMS	8P	4-6-2	1936
Princess Margaret Rose	46203	LMS	8P	4-6-2	1936
Duchess of Sutherland	6233	LMS	8P	4-6-2	1938
—	44027	LMS	4F	0-6-0	1924
—	44932	LMS	5MT	4-6-0	1945
—	45491	LMS	5MT	4-6-0	1943
—	47564	LMS	3F	0-6-0T	1928
—	47327	LMS	3F	0-6-0T	1926
—	47357	LMS	3F	0-6-0T	1926
—	47445	LMS	3F	0-6-0T	1927
—	158A	MR	—	2-4-0	1866
—	53809	S&DJR	7F	2-8-0	1925
—	73129	BR	5MT	4-6-0	1956
—	80080	BR	4MT	2-6-4T	1954
—	80098	BR	4MT	2-6-4T	1955
—	92214	BR	9F	2-10-0	1959
—	92219	BR	9F	2-10-0	1959
—	D2138	BR	03	0-6-0DM	1960
—	08590	BR	08	0-6-0DE	1959
—	12077	BR	11	0-6-0DE	1950
—	20001	BR	20	Bo-Bo	1957
—	20102*	BR	20	Bo-Bo	1961
—	20108*	BR	20	Bo-Bo	1961
—	20133*	BR	20	Bo-Bo	1966
—	20205	BR	20	Bo-Bo	1967
Traction	20227	BR	20	Bo-Bo	1967
—	D7671	BR	25	Bo-Bo	1967
—	31108	BR	31	A1A-A1A	1959
—	31162	BR	31	A1A-A1A	1960
—	37190	BR	37	Co-Co	1964
Aureol	40012	BR	40	1Co-Co1	1959
Great Gable	D4	BR	44	1Co-Co1	1959
Royal Tank Regiment	45041	BR	45/1	1Co-Co1	1962
—	45133	BR	45/1	1Co-Co1	1961
—	46045	BR	46	1Co-Co1	1963
—	47401	BR	47	Co-Co	1963
—	47417	BR	47	Co-Co	1963
Sir Edward Elgar	50007	BR	50	Co-Co	1967
Tulyar	55015	BR	55	Co-Co	1961
Western Lady	D1048	BR	52	C-C	1962

58

On the locomotive front it is hoped that 1997 will see the return to traffic of Nos 47357, 44932, 80098 and possibly others

Location: Midland Railway Centre, Butterley station, near Ripley, Derbyshire DE5 3QZ

OS reference: SK 403520

General Manager: John Hett

Operating society/organisation: Midland Railway Trust Ltd

Telephone: Ripley (01773) 747674/570140

Fax: (01773) 570271

Car park: Butterley station on B6179 1-mile north of Ripley

On site facilities: Museum, award winning country park, Brittain Pit Farm park, souvenir shops, miniature railway, narrow gauge railway, garden railway, model railways

Refreshment facilities: Butterley Station Buffet, Johnson Buffet (Swanwick), on-train bars and extensive 'Wine and Dine' trains. 'The Midlander' (details from above address)

Length of line: Standard gauge 3.5 miles, narrow gauge 0.8-mile

Public opening: Every Sunday and Bank Holiday Weekend. Every Saturday March-October and December. Every Wednesday April-October. Daily 26 March-10 April; 24 May-1 June; 1-31 July ; 1-8 August; 1-8 September, 25 October; 2 November and 20-31 December (except Christmas Day)

Journey time: Approximately 1hr

Special events: Friends of Thomas the Tank Engine — 1/2 March, 4 May-1 June, 2-10 August; Diesel & steam 1960s galas — 26/27 April, 17/18 May, 19/20 July; 16/17 August; 13/14 September; Diesel Spectaculars — 22/23 March, 21/22 June, 11/12 October; Narrow gauge event and garden railway convention 16/17 August; Model Railway Exhibition — 10/11 May, 21/22 September; Edwardian Gala — 3-5 May; Victorian Gala — 23-25 August

Facilities for disabled: Toilets, special coach, access to shop and cafeteria, special weekend

Membership details: S. Hett, at above address

Membership journal: *The Wyvern* — quarterly

Cont

Electra	27000	BR	EM2	Co+Co	1953
—	50019	BR	114	DMBS	1956
—	55966	BR	127	DPU	1959
—	55976	BR	127	DPU	1956
—	56006	BR	114	DTC	1956
—	59609	BR	127	TC	1959
—	29663	M/Cam	—	TC	1931
—	29666	M/Cam	—	TC	1931
—	29670	M/Cam	—	TC	1931
—	56171	W/ham	109	DMBS	1957
—	50416	W/ham	109	DMBS	1957

*Stored for British Nuclear Fuels Ltd

Locomotive notes: In service 44932, 80080, 47327, 20001, 20227, 08590, 31162, Class 114 DMU, D4, 47401, D2138, 40012, 12077, 45133, 55015 and D7671. Under restoration 6201, 44027, 53809, 73129, 92214, 45491, 80098, Wickham unit, 127 unit. Awaiting repairs or stored 31108, 47417, 47445, 92219. Boiler and frames only 47564. Static display 158A, 6233, 47357, 27000

Industrial locomotives

Name	No	Builder	Type	Built
Gladys	—	Markham (109)	0-4-0ST	1894
Stanton	24	Barclay (1875)	0-4-0CT	1925
Lytham St Annes	—	Peckett (2111)	0-4-0ST	1949
Brown Bailey	4	N/Wilson (454)	0-4-0ST	1894
Castle Donnington	1	RSH (7817)	0-4-0ST	1954
—	27	RSH (7086)	0-6-0ST	1943
Neapsend	—	Sentinel (9370)	4wVBT	1947
Andy	2	Fowler (16038)	0-4-0DM	1923
—	RS9	M/Rail (2024)	0-4-0DM	1921
—	RS12	M/Rail (460)	0-4-0DM	1912
Boots	2	Barclay (2008)	0-4-0F	1935
Castle Donnington	2	Barclay (416)	0-4-0DM	1957
Boots	—	R/Hornsby (384139)	0-4-0DE	1955
*Handyman**	—	H/Clarke (573)	0-4-0ST	1900
*Rothwell Colliery**	—	H/Clarke (D718)	0-6-0DM	1950
—	—	H/Clarke (D1152)	0-6-0DM	1959
Albert Fields	—	H/Clarke (D1114)	0-6-0DM	1958
—†	—	Deutz (10249)	4wDM	1932
Campbell Brick Works†	—	M/Rail (60S364)	4wDM	1968
—†	—	Lister (3742)	4wDM	1931
—†	—	M/Rail (5906)	4wDM	1932
—†	—	M/Rail (11246)	4wDM	1963
—†	2	O/Koppel (7529)	0-4-0WT	1914
—†	—	O/Koppel (5215)	4wDM	1936
Wheal Save†	19	BEV	4wBE	1985
—†	—	Ruston	4wDM	—
—†	—	Ruston (222068)	4wDM	1943
Hucknall Colliery†	3	Ruston (480678)	4wDM	1961
—†	—	Hunslet (7178)	4wDH	1971
Calverton Colliery†	22	H/Clarke (1117)	0-6-0DM	1958
Welbeck Colliery††	—	H/Clarke	0-6-0DM	—
Linby Colliery††	—	H/Clarke (DM647)	0-6-0DM	1954
—†	—	Lister (53726)	4wDM	1963
—†	—	SMH (40SD529)	4wDM	1983
—†	NG24	Baguley/ Drewry (3703)	4wBE	1974
—§	—	Chrzanow (3226)	0-6-0T	1954
—§	—	Chrzanow (1983)	0-6-0T	1949
*Princess Elizabeth***	6201	H/Clarke (D611)	4-6-2DM	1938
*Princess Margaret Rose***	6203	H/Clarke (D612)	4-6-2DM	1938

*3ft gauge
†2ft gauge

Marketing names: 'More than just a railway'; Golden Valley Light Railway (narrow gauge); Butterley Park Miniature Railway (miniature line)

††2ft 4in gauge
§2ft 6in gauge
**21in gauge

Locomotive notes: In service: Boots, *Lytham St Annes*, NG24 , SMH (40SD529), Calverton Col No 22, Lister, Deutz 10249, *Albert Fields*, M/Rail 60S364. Under restoration: *Andy* RS12, *Princess Margaret Rose*. Awaiting repairs or stored on display: Stanton, RS9, Hunslet 7178, M/Rails 5906/11246. Static display *Gladys*, 4, Boots No 2, *Handyman*, Sentinel 9370, both Chrzanows.

Stock
Numerous carriages, wagons and cranes. Museum display includes MR Royal saloon, MR 4-wheeled coac, MR brake third, LD & ECR all third, BR horsebox, LMS travelling Post Office, L&YR family saloon, MR motor carvan, MR bogie brake third, restored freight vehicles, and much more

Owners
6201 the 6201 Princess Elizabeth Society Ltd
158A, 44027 on loan from the National Railway Museum
53809 the 13809 Preservation Group
47357, 47327, 47445, 47564, 73129 Derby City Council
6233, 46203, 80080, 80098 the Princess Royal Locomotive Trust
55015 the Deltic Preservation Society
D4 the Peak Locomotive Preservation Co Ltd
D7671 Derby Industrial Museum

Monkwearmouth Station Museum
Tyne & Wear
Museum

The Museum is one of Britain's finest neo-classical stations built in 1848 to commemorate the election of George Stephenson as MP for Sunderland. Restored features include the booking office, unchanged since it was installed in 1866, waiting shelter on the west platform and siding area
Location: North Bridge Street, Sunderland
Telephone: 0191 5677075
OS reference: NZ 3957
On site facilities: Car paking on museum forecourt, shop

Rolling stock
NER brake van 1915, LNER CCT van 1939

Access by public transport: 10min walk from Sunderland Central station. Served by several bus routes from Sunderland city centre, Newcastle and South Shields
Public opening: Daily 1 January-31 December (except New Years Day, Good Friday, Christmas Day, Boxing Day). Monday-Friday

10.00-17.00. Saturday 10.00—16.30. Sunday 14.00-17.00. Free Admission. Hours are under review for 1997, telephone 0191 565 0723 for confirmation
Access for disabled: Ramped access, suitable for wheelchair users

Moseley Railway Museum
Cheshire
Museum

The collection concentrates on diesel and petrol power with some battery units and one steam outline locomotive. There are also hand, rope and chain operated vehicles on site. Emphasis is placed on operational locomotives and stock which, by prior appointment, can be observed and photographed performing the tasks for which they

were originally designed. There are a number of unique running exhibits including the Kent Construction petrol locomotive and a single cylinder diesel Simplex. Petrol-powered locomotives dating back to 1918 form a key part of the working locomotive fleet. Passenger train rides and demonstration goods trains are

always available on official open days
Location: Grounds of Ridge Danyers College, Northdowns Road, Cheadle, Cheshire SK8 5HA
OS reference: SJ 864871
Operating society: The Moseley Industrial Narrow Gauge Tramway Museum Society (MTM), c/o 63 Honford Road, Brownley Green,

60

Wythenshawe, Greater Manchester
M22 9PE
Telephone: 01663 766992
Car park: Extensive, free, adjacent
to the museum buildings
Station: One boarding area
adjacent to the museum. Other
request stops
Length of line and gauge:
Approximately one third-mile, 2ft
gauge
Access by public transport:
Nearest BR station Cheadle Hulme
(10min walk). Bus from
Manchester 157, bus from
Stockport 368/369, ask for Cheadle
Adult Education Centre/Ridge
Danyers College
On site facilities: Free access and
parking, a small selection of hot
and cold drinks and other
refreshments, access to all site.
Visitor centre,with photographic
and other displays
Period of public operation:
Throughout the year. Second
Sunday of every month plus any
other time by appointment. 11.00-
17.00 (dusk in winter)
Train services: Return journey
(round trip) approximately 20min
Facilities for the disabled: The
museum operates the same policy
as Stockport Education Authority.
Every effort is made to
accommodate disabled persons
Special events: Please contact for
details or see Internet details

Industrial locomotives

Name	No	Builder	Type	Built
—	1	W/Rgers (C6717)	4wBE	1963
Cable Mill	2	W/Rgers (C6716)	4wBE	1963
—	3	M/Rail (8878)	4wDM	1944
—	5	R/Hornsby (223667)	4wDM	1943
—	6	M/Rail (9104)	4wPM	1942
—	7	M/Rail (8663)	4wDM	1941
—	8	Kent	4wPM	c1926
—	9	M/Rail (4565)	4wPM	1928
—	10	M/Rail (7552)	4wDM	1948
Ald Hague	11	Hiberd (3465)	4wPM	1954
—	13	M/Rail (11142)	4wDM	1960
Knothole Worker	14	M/Rail (22045)	4wDM	1959
—	18	H/Hunslet (6299)	4wDM	1964
—	21	M/Rail (8669)	4wDM	1941
—	23	Lister (52031)	4wDM	1960
—	29	R/Hornsby (195846)	4wDM	1939
—	31	Lister (3834)	4wPM	1931
—	32	L/Blackstone (52885)	4wDM	1962
PMW 2214	35	Wickham (4131)	2w-2PMR	1947
Commercial	36	R/Hornsby (280865)	4wDM	1949
—	37	R/Hornsby (260719)	4wDM	1948
Kenneth	38	R/Hornsby (223749)	4wDM	1944
LR 2832	39	M/Rail (1111)	4wPM	1918
Chaumont	44	Hudson (LX1002)	4wDH	1968
Mavis	46	R/Hornsby (7002/0967/6)	4wDM	1968
—	47	M/Rail (1369)	4wDM	1918

Stock
Nearly 100 items of rolling stock including Groudle Glen and Corris-type
replica coaches under construction

Special notes: Museum buildings
and displays are now open
Internet details: e-mail:
mitm@djr12ecg.demon.co.uk
Web site:

http://www.djr12ecg.demom.co.uk/
mitm.html
Membership details: 11 Ashwood
Road, Disley, Stockport, Cheshire
SK12 2EL

Museum of Army Transport
Member: TT

North Humberside
Museum

Operating a substantial network of
railways in wartime, the Army is
still responsible for railways
feeding MoD depots in this
country. Not only does the
Museum hold extensive archives
and display some fascinating maps,
drawings and photographs, it
contains some very interesting
stock from the former military
railways
Location: Museum of Army
Transport, Flemingate, Beverley,
North Humberside HU17 0NG
OS reference: TA 041392
Operated by: The Museum of
Army Transport Ltd (Charitable
Status Company)
Telephone: Hull (01482) 860445

Locomotives

Name	No	Builder	Type	Built
Gazelle	—	Dodman	0-4-2WT	1893
Woolmer	—	Avonside (1572)	0-6-0ST	1910
Waggoner	92	Hunslet (3792)	0-6-0ST	1953
Rorke's Drift	—	Drewry (2047)	0-4-0DM	1934
Lyddia	AD41†	R/Hornsby (191646)	4WDM	1933
—	110	R/Hornsby (411319)	4wDM	1958
—	1035	Wickham Rail Car	4w	1958
—	3282*	Wickham Target Trolley	4w	1943
—	WD2182†	M/Rail (461)	4wDM	1917
—	—†	M/Rail (3849)	4wDM	1927
—	LOD 758009†¹	M/Rail	4wDM	1941-3
—	LOD 758220†²	M/Rail	4wDM	1941-3
—	LOD 758228†	M/Rail (8667)	4wDM	1941
—	LOD 758028†	M/Rail (8855)	4wDM	1943
—	RTT 767182†	Wickham Target Trolley	4w	WW2

*2ft 6in gauge   †2ft gauge
¹Fitted with air-brake for use with passenger stock
²Stored on site, may be moving

Cont

Car park: Yes, 1.25 acres
Access by public transport: Rail: 10min walk from Beverley station. Bus: served by East Yorks Motor Service
On site facilities: Museum — The Royal Corps of Transport Collection of road, rail, sea, air and movement control artefacts. Licensed cafeteria. Shop in building. Lavatories, including special for handicapped. Large car and bus park
Facilities for disabled: The Museum is on one floor. This allows viewing of all vehicles. Access is available by ramp into the Armoured Train. Access is not possible into the Beverley aircraft, the railway locos and the signalbox

Rolling stock
Collection of various rolling stock items including Lord Kitchener's coach (c1885), a World War 1 Armoured Train gun truck and a World War 2 ramp wagon

Owners
Gazelle the National Railway Museum

A 2ft gauge system based on the ADLR of World War 1, some 200yd long, and worked by World War 2 Simplex rail tractors operated by volunteers, on Saturday and Sunday afternoons and at other times as advertised locally during the summer. Intending travellers should check the line is operating.

frame
Public opening: 10.00-17.00 every day except 24-26 December. Group discount rate for parties of 20 or more
Special notes: Please bear in mind that while what is reported here

deals with railways, other parts of this extensive museum cover movement by road, sea and air
Honorary Railway (and Port) Consultant: Major J. A. Robins (Retd)

The Museum of Science and Industry in Manchester

Manchester
Museum

Based in the buildings of the world's oldest passenger railway station, the Museum has colourful hands-on galleries that amuse, amaze and entertain. There are train rides on Sundays (please ring for details) and visitors can find out about our industrial past, walk through a Victorian sewer complete with sounds and smells and hunt an alien!
Location: Liverpool Road, Castlefield, Manchester (off Deansgate near Granada)
OS reference: SJ 831987
Operating society/organisation: The Museum of Science and Industry in Manchester, Liverpool Road, Castlefield, Manchester M3 4FP
Telephone: 0161 832 2244
Car parks: On site, plus parking in the area (Museum car park £1.50)
Access by public transport: Manchester Victoria, Piccadilly, Oxford Road and Deansgate BR stations. GM bus 33. G-Mex Metrolink station
On site facilities: Oldest passenger railway station, weekend train rides, listed buildings containing exhibitions about science, industry, aviation, space, water supply and sewage disposal, gas and electricity. Xperiment! the hands-on science centre and the 'Out of

Locomotives and multipe-units

Name	No	Origin	Class	Type	Built
Pender	3††	IoMR	—	2-4-0T	1873
Novelty	Replica of 1829 locomotive using some original parts				1986
—	3157†	PR	—	4-4-0	1911
—	2352§	SAR	GL	4-8-2+2-8-4	1929
Ariadne	1505 (27001)	BR	EM2 (77)	Co-Co	1954
Hector	26048	BR	EM1 (76)	Bo-Bo cab only	1952
Planet*	—	Replica	—	2-2-0	1992

Industrial locomotives

Name	No	Builder	Type	Built
Lord Ashfield	—	Barclay (1964)	0-4-0ST	1929
—	258	E/Electric (1378)	4wBE	1944
—	—	Fowler	0-4-0D	1952

*Replica of 1830-built locomotive
††Ex-Isle of Man Railways, 3ft gauge, sectioned (B/Peacock 1255)
†Ex-Pakistan Railways, 5ft 6in gauge (V/Foundry 3064)
§Ex-South African Railways, 3ft 6in gauge (B/Peacock 6693)

Rolling stock
BR Mk 2 SO E5241, 1966
Replica M&BR 1st class carriage c1840 using original fragments
2 replica L&MR 2nd class carriages c1835
c1908 L&YR ambulance carriage re-built 1923 as Medical Examination Car, LMS No 10825
B955209 20-ton goods brake van, BR (Ashford), 1962
B782903 4-wheeled covered goods van, BR (Wolverton), 1961
B783709 4-wheeled covered goods van, BR (Wolverton), 1962
3-plank loose coupled goods wagon, MSLR (Dukinfield)?, c1890

Owners
Novelty on loan from the National Railway Museum, York
MSLR Wagon on loan from G. Maskin
Industrial locomotives (except Fowler) on loan from PowerGen

Cont

62

Brockford, the reconstructed station at Mid-Suffolk Railway's site. *John Brodribb*

The North Norfolk Railway's Sheringham station as Nos D5386 and 8572 await the next duty.

this world' space gallery. World's largest collection of working steam mill engines in the Power Hall. Xpressions coffee shop, Kites Cafe and Mosaics gift shop

Public opening: Daily except 24-26 December, including Saturdays and Sundays, 10.00-17.00. Entrance in Lower Byrom Street. Admission charged

Special notes: Good wheelchair access, toilets for the disabled, lecture and conference facilities

National Railway Museum
Members: AIRPS, TT, MLSOG

North Yorkshire
Museum

Location: National Railway Museum, Leeman Road, York YO2 4XJ
OS reference: SE 594519
Operating society/organisation: Part of the National Museum of Science and Industry
Telephone: York (01904) 621261
Car park: Limited parking for cars and pre-booked coaches at the Museum. York City's Leeman Road car park for cars and coaches visiting the NRM adjoins the main entrance
Access by public transport: The Museum is within a few minutes' walking distance of the railway and bus stations in York. The York City and District Bus Service operates to the door
On site facilities: Museum shop, restaurant and toilets. Reference Library (free by appointment)
Public opening: Daily 10.00-18.00. Closed 24-26 December
Facilities for disabled: Most areas of the museum are accessible by the disabled
Special notes: The Museum has been open since 1975 and has welcomed over 19 million visitors.

The museum offers the visitor two extensive exhibition halls, the Great Hall .and the South Hall which house the world's premier collection of railway related material.

The Great Hall displays are on the theme of railway technology. There is a magnificent display of railway locomotive development round the turntable. Signalling, permanent way, the modern railway and the Channel Tunnel are also represented. The displays reflect the future, the present and the past and include a full-sized model of the nose cone of a state of the art Transmanche Super Train which head trains between England and the Continent. Displays on the operation of the railways, tape/slide presentations and the current temporary exhibition can be found on the Balcony Galleries. A new exhibition 'Moving Things: The Mail' opened in October 1996

The South Hall illustrates the concept of travel by train — for passengers and freight. Short but representative trains are drawn up at platforms and several footplates and carriages are open to the visitors. The vehicles displayed range from the superb Royal carriages to humble freight wagons.

Magician's Road, the children's activity centre, provides visitors with hands-on experience of various aspects of railway operation.

The Museum's extensive Reference Library (including the Photographic and Drawings collections) continues to be free to all booked enquirers every weekday from 10.30-17.00.

The Tables which follow indicate the whereabouts (display, on loan, in store) of the National Railway Collection. It must be emphasised that the appearance of any particular item on public display cannot be guaranteed. If it is vital to discover the exact whereabouts of a specific item enquirers should contact the Museum in York before the trip.

The National Railway Museum is open for evening hire for private viewings and celebrations; menus and details are available on request

Details of membership of the Museum's support group, including free entry and a quarterly newsletter are available from: The Secretary, Friends of the National Railway Museum, c/o the above address.

Locomotives — Steam

Name	No	Origin	Builder	Class	Type	Built
Agenoria	—	Shutt End Colliery	Foster/Raistrick	—	0-4-0	1829
Columbine	1868	LNWR	Crewe	—	2-2-2	1845
Coppernob	3	FR	Bury, Curtis & Kennedy	—	0-4-0	1846
Pet	—	LNWR	Crewe	—	0-4-0STT	1865
Aerolite	66	NER	Gateshead	X1(LNER)	2-2-4T	1869
—	1	GNR	Doncaster		4-2-2	1870
Bauxite	2	Hebburn Works	B/Hawthorn	—	0-4-0ST	1874
—	1275	NER	Dübs & Co	—	0-6-0	1874
—	910	NER	Gateshead	E6	2-4-0	1875
Boxhill	82	LB&SCR	Brighton	A1	0-6-0T	1880
Gladstone	214	LB&SCR	—	—	0-4-2	1882
Wren	—	LYR	B/Peacock	—	0-4-0ST	1887
—	1008	LYR	Horwich	—	2-4-2T	1889

Name	No	Origin	Builder	Class	Type	Built
Hardwicke	790	LNWR	Crewe	—	2-4-0	1892
—	563	LSWR	Nine Elms	T3	4-4-0	1893
—	1621	NER	Gateshead	M	4-4-0	1893
—	245	LSWR	Nine Elms	M7	0-4-4T	1897
—	673	MR	Derby	—	4-2-2	1899
—	737	SECR	Ashford	D	4-4-0	1901
—	251	GNR	Doncaster	C1	4-4-2	1902
—	1000	MR	Derby	4	4-4-0	1902
City of Truro	3440	GWR	Swindon	'City'	4-4-0	1903
—	87	GER	Stratford	J69	0-6-0T	1904
—	1217	GER	Stratford	J17	0-6-0	1905
—	2818	GWR	Swindon	2800	2-8-0	1905
Lode Star	4003	GWR	Swindon	'Star'	4-6-0	1907
Butler Henderson	506	GCR	Gorton	'Director'	4-4-0	1920
—	485	LNWR	Crewe	Super D	0-8-0	1921
Cheltenham	925	SR	Eastleigh	V	4-4-0	1934
—	5000	LMS	Crewe	5MT	4-6-0	1935
—	KF7	Chinese Govt Rlys	Vulcan	KF	4-8-4	1935
Green Arrow	4771	LNER	Doncaster	V2	2-6-2	1936
Duchess of Hamilton	46229	LMS	Crewe	'Coronation'	4-6-2	1938
Mallard	4468	LNER	Doncaster	A4	4-6-2	1938
Eustace Forth	15	—	RSH (7063)	—	0-4-0ST	1942
Winston Churchill	34051	SR	Brighton	BB	4-6-2	1946
Ellerman Lines	35029	BR(SR)	Sectioned		4-6-2	1949
—	—	Imperial Paper Mills	Barclay	—	0-4-0P	1956
Frank Galbraith	—	Tees-Side Bridge & Engineering Co	Sentinel	—	4wTG	1957
Evening Star	92220	BR	Swindon	9F	2-10-0	1960
Rocket (replica)	—	—	Loco Enterprises	—	0-2-2	1979
Iron Duke (broad gauge replica)	—	GWR	RESCO	—	4-2-2	1985

Locomotives — Electric

Name	No	Origin	Builder	Class	Type	Built
—	75S	W&CR	Siemens (6)	—	Bo electric	1898
—	1	NER	BTH	—	Bo-Bo electric	1904
—	1	NSR	Bolton	—	4wE	1917
—	809	GPO	—	—	2w-2E	1931
—	8143	SR	—	4-SUB	EMU	1925
—	26020	BR	Gorton/Metrovick	76	Bo-Bo Electric	1951
—	E3036	BR	N/British	84	Bo-Bo	1960

Locomotives — Diesel

Name	No	Origin	Builder	Class	Type	Built
—	—	—	Simplex (4217)	—	4wPM	1925
Hexhamshire	15	CEGB	A/Whitworth (D21)	—	0-4-0DE	1933
—	08064	BR	Darlington	08	0-6-0 DE	1953
BEA Carrington Station	3	CEGB	RSH (7746)	—	0-6-0 DM	1954
—	D8000	BR	E/Electric	20	Bo-Bo	1957
Deltic	—	E/Electric	E/Electric	—	Co-Co	1957
—	D200	BR	E/Electric	40	1Co-Co1	1958
—	03090	BR	—	03	0-6-0DM	1960
—	D2860	BR	YEC	02	0-4-0 DH	1960
Western Fusilier	D1023	BR	Swindon	52	Co-Co	1963
Glorious	50033	BR	E/Electric	50	Co-Co	1968
—*	41001	BR	Crewe	41	Bo-Bo	1972

*Stored at MoD Kineton

Rolling Stock Powered Units— Gas Turbine
1972   BR Advanced Passenger Train

Rolling Stock Powered Units — Electric
1915   LNWR Motor Open Third Brake No28249
1925   SR Motor Third Brake No S8143S
1937   SR Motor Third Open Brake No S11179S
1940   SR (W&C) Motor Driving Car No 61

Rolling Stock Powered Units — Diesel
1959   BR DMU Class 108 Nos 51562 & 51922
1977   Leyland Motors LEV-1 experimental railbus

Rolling Stock — Departmental
1850   GNR 4-wheel hand crane
1890   GNR Locomotive Tender No 1002
1891   NER Snow Plough No DE900566
1899   GWR Hand Crane No 537
1904   MR Officers' Saloon No 2234
1906   NER Dynamometer Car No 902502
1907   NER Steam Breakdown Crane No CME 13
1907   Match Truck No DE942114
1911   GWR Track Testing Coach
1926   LNER Match Truck No DE320952
1931/2   LNER Petrol-driven platelayers' trolley No 960209
1936   GWR Ballast Wagon No 80659
1938   LMS Mobile test unit No 1, No 45053
1949   BR Matisa tamping machine No 74007
1949*   GWR/BR Inspection Saloon No ADW80970
1955   GEC 12.5ton Coles Crane
1957   BR Track recording trolley No DX 50002 Neptune
1969   BR Plasser Tamping & Liner No 73010

Rolling Stock — Passenger
1834   B&WR 1st & 2nd composite
1834   B&WR 2nd class
1834   B&WR 3rd class
1842   L&BR Queen Adelaides' Saloon
1845   S&DR 1st/3rd Composite No 59
1850   NER Brake End (body only)
1851   ECR 1st class No 1
1860   Cornwall Rly broad gauge coach (body only)
1861   NBR Port Carlisle branch 'dandy car'
1869   LNWR Queen Victoria's Saloon
1872   NLR Directors' Saloon No 1032
1885   MR 6-wheel composite brake No 901
1885   WCJS 8-wheel TPO No 186
1887   GNR Brake Van No 848
1887   GWR 6-wheel tricomposite No 820
1897   Lynton & Barnstaple Rly brake composite No 6992
1898   ECJS 3rd class No 12
1899   Privately owned Duke of Sutherland's Saloon 57A
1900   LNWR (ex-WCJS) Dining Car LMSNo 76
1902   LNWR King Edward's Saloon No 800
1902   LNWR Queen Alexandra's Saloon No 801
1903   LSWR Tricomposite brake No 3598
1905*   LNWR Corridor 1st Brake 5154 (Royal Train)
1908   ECJS Royal Saloon No 395
1913   Pullman Car Co 1st class parlour car *Topaz*

1914   MR Dining car No 3463
1920   LNWR Royal Saloon No 45000
1925   LMS 3rd class vestibule No 7828
1928   LMS 3rd Sleeping Car No 14241
1930   L&MR 1st *Huskinson* (replica)
1930   L&MR 1st *Traveller* (replica)
1930   L&MR 2nd (replica)
1930   L&MR 2nd (replica)
1934   GWR Buffet Car No 9631
1936   CIWL Night Ferry sleeping car No 3792
1937   LNER Buffet Car No 9135
1938   GJR TPO (replica)
1941   LMS Royal Saloon 799
1945*   GWR Royal Saloon No 9006
1955   BR Lavatory composite No E43046
1956   BR 2nd class open No E4286
1960*   BR Griddle car No Sc1100
1960   Pullman Car Co 1st class Parlour car No 326 *Emerald*
1962*   BR Prototype Mk II 1st class corridor No 13252
1962   BR Mk II 2nd brake corridor No 35468
1962*   BR Mk II 2nd brake corridor No 21274
1969   BR Mk IIb 2nd open No 5455
1985   GWR 2nd (broad gauge replica)
1985   GWR 3rd (broad gauge replica)

Rolling Stock — Freight & Non Passenger Carrying
1815   Little Eaton (Derby Canal) Gangroad Wagon
1815   Peak Forest Canal Tramway Wagon No 174
1816   Grantham Canal Tramway Truck
1826   Cramlington Colliery Chaldron Wagon
1828   Two replica chaldron wagons
1840   Stratford & Moreton Tramway wagon
1850   South Hetton Colliery chaldron wagon No 1155
1870   Seaham Harbour Colliery Chaldron Wagon
1889   Shell-Mex oil tank wagon No 512
1894   LSWR Brake van No 99
1895   LSWR Open carriage truck No 5830
1901   Shell/BP Tank Wagon No 3171
1902   NER 20-ton wooden hopper wagon No 4551
1907   NER 16ton bogie stores van No 041273
1908   LNWR Open Carriage Truck No 11275
1912   LB&SCR Open wagon No 27884
1912   LSWR Gunpowder van No KDS61209
1912   NER Sand wagon No DE14974
1914   GWR Shunters' truck No W94988
1917   Shell tank wagon No 3171
1917   MR 8ton open wagon
1917   GCR Box Van
1917   LNWR Box Van
1917   NER Box Van
1920   GNR double bolster wagon
1920   GNR single bolster wagon
1924   LMSR Van
1926   GWR Fitted open wagon No 108246
1927   LNER 40 ton flat wagon No DE633433
1928   ICI Nitric acid tank wagon No 14
1931   GWR Fruit Van No 112884
1931   Stanton Iron Works 12ton wagon
1933   LMSR 20ton Goods Brake Van No 295987
1935   SR Bogie goods brake van No 56297
1935   GWR Motor car van No 126438

1936	LMSR 3 Plank Open Wagon No 472867
1936	LMS Tube wagon No 499254
1937	GWR Siphon bogie milk van No 2775
1937	LMSR Milk Tank Wagon No 44057
1938	GWR 20ton Goods Brake Van No DW56518
1938	LMS Single bolster wagon No 722702
1940	WD Warflat No 161042
1944	LMS Lowmac No M700728
1944	GWR 13ton open wagon No DW143698
1946	SNCF 16ton mineral wagon No ADB192437
1946	LNER 20ton hopper wagon No E270919
1947*	GWR Inspection Saloon No 45049
1949	BR Bogie bolster D No B941000
1950	BR 24-ton iron ore hopper wagon No B436275
1950	BR 20ton Weltrol No B900805
1951	ICI Liquid chlorine tank wagon No 47484
1951	BR(SR) Show cattle wagon No S3733S
1951	BR 8ton cattle wagon No B893343
1952	BR 30ton bogie bolster wagon No B943139
1954	BR 27ton Iron Ore Tippler No B383560
1954	National Benzole oil tank wagon No 2022
1955	BR china clay tip wagon No B743141
1957	BR Horse box No S96369
1959	BR Conflat No B737725
1960	BR Banana Van No B882593
1960	BR 25ton Weltrol WP No ADB 900916
1961	BR Presflo cement wagon No B873368
1961	BR 30ton bogie bolster No B923123
1962	BR Speedfreight container No BA 4324B
1966	Milk Marketing Board 6-wheel tank No 42801
1970	Phillips Petroleum 100-ton GLW tank wagon No PP85209
1970	BR 2,000gal Road/Rail Milk Tank No ADM707111
1979	S&DR Chaldron wagon (replica)

*Stored at MoD Kineton

Table 3
Items on Loan from the NRM
Locomotives

Original type/No/Name	Location	Builder	Built
Wylam Colliery	Science Mus	—	1813
Hetton Colliery 0-4-0	Beamish	G. Stephenson	1822
SDR 0-4-0 *Locomotion*	Darlington	R. Stephenson & Co	1825
L&MR 0-2-2 *Rocket*	Science Mus	R. Stephenson & Co	1829
L&MR 0-4-0 *Sans Pareil*	Science Mus	T. Hackworth	1829
L&MR 0-2-2 *Novelty*	Museum of Science & Technology (Manchester)	Braithwaite & Ericsson	1829
SDR 0-6-0 No 24 *Derwent*	Darlington Nth Rd Mus	A. Kitching	1845
LNWR 2-2-2 No 3020 *Cornwall*	Crewe	Crewe	1847
Wantage Tramway 0-4-0WT No 5 *Shannon*	Didcot Rly Ctr	G. England	1857
LNWR 0-4-0ST 1439	East Lancs	Crewe	1865
MR 2-4-0 No 158A	Midland Rly Ctr	Derby	1866
South Devon Rly 0-4-0WT *Tiny*	South Devon Rly	Sara	1868
LSWR 2-4-0WT No 0298	South Devon Rly	B/Peacock	1874
NER 2-4-0 No 910	Darlington Nth Rd Mus	Gateshead	1875
NER 2-4-0 No 1463	Darlington Nth Rd Mus	Gateshead	1885
C&SL Bo electric No 1	London Trans Mus	B/Peacock	1890
S&MR 0-4-2WT *Gazelle*	Mus of Army Transport, Beverley	Dodman	1893
GER 2-4-0 No 490	Bressingham	Stratford	1894
GWR 0-6-0 No 2516	Swindon GWR Mus	Swindon	1897
TVR 0-6-2T No 28	Dean Forest	TVR	1897
GNR No 990 *Henry Oakley*	Steamtown	Doncaster	1898
LSWR 4-4-0 No 120	Bluebell Rly	Nine Elms	1899
GNR 0-6-0ST 1247	East Somerset	S/Stewart	1899
LT&SR 4-4-2T No 80 *Thundersley*	Bressingham	R. Stephenson	1909
GCR 2-8-0 No 102	Great Central	Gorton	1911
WD No 1377 (2ft Gauge)	LBR	Simplex	1918
NER 0-8-0 No 901	North York Moors Rly	Darlington	1919
NSR No 2	Cheddleton	Stoke	1922
GWR 4-6-0 No 4073 *Caerphilly Castle*	Didcot	Swindon	1923
LMS 0-6-0 No 4027	Midland Rly Ctr	Derby	1924
GWR 2-2-2 *North Star* (replica)	Swindon GWR Mus	R. Stephenson	1925
SR 4-6-0 No 777 *Sir Lamiel*	GCR	N/British	1925
SR 4-6-0 No 850 *Lord Nelson*	Steamtown	Eastleigh	1926
LMS 2-6-0 No 2700	East Lancs	Derby	1934
GWR No 6000 *King George V*	Swindon GWR Mus	Swindon	1927
LMS 2-6-4T No 2500	Bressingham	Derby	1934
SR 0-6-0 No C1	Bluebell Rly	Eastleigh	1942

Original type/No/Name	Location	Builder	Built
GWR 0-6-0PT No 9400	Swindon GWR Mus	Swindon	1947
BR 4-6-2 No 70013 *Oliver Cromwell*	Bressingham	Crewe	1951
BR Bo-Bo0 No E5001	Hastings	Eastleigh	1958
BR A1A-A1A No 5500	East Lancs	Brush Traction	1957
BR Co-Co 55002	East Lancs	E/Electric	1960

Powered Units

NER	electric parcels van No 3267, G. Stephenson
SR	2BIL unit, No 2090, Hastings (private site)
LPTB	driving motor car No 3327, Kineton (stored)
GWR	diesel railcar No 4, Swindon GWR Mus
LMS	electric motor brake 2nd No 28361, Southport
LMS	electric driving trailer composite No 29896, Southport
BR	APT-P pre-production Advanced Passenger Train, Crewe Heritage Ctr
BR	Magnetic LEV prototype, Science Museum (Wroughton store)

Departmental Stock

1908	LNWR match truck, No 284235, Steamtown
1908	LNWR steam crane, No 2987, Steamtown
1932	LMS Ballast plough brake van No 197266, Embsay
1937	SR Match Truck No ADB975672, North York Moors
1949	BR(LMS) Dynamometer car No 3, No 45049, East Lancs

Passenger Stock

1846	SDR 1st & 2nd composite No 31, Darlington
1850	SDR 3rd No 179, Timothy Hackworth Mus,
1850	NER 4-wheel coach body, Darlington
1905	LNWR Corridor 1st Brake No 5155 (Royal Train), East Lancs
1908	ECJS Passenger Brake van LNERNo 109, East Lancs
1908	ECJS Passenger Brake van LNER No 396, Bressingham
1910	GCR Open 3rd class No 666, Great Central
1925	GWR 3rd class dining car No 9653, Severn
1925	GWR 3rd class dining car No 9654, Severn
1928	Nord (France) 2nd class corridor No 7122, Nene Valley
1930	GWR composite dining car No 9605, Science Mus (Wroughton)

1936	LNER 3rd Open, No 13254, Great Central
1937	LMS corridor 3rd class brake No 5987, Steamtown
1937	SR buffet car No S125295, Nene Valley Rly
1941	LMS Royal saloon No 798, Glasgow Museum
1945	GWR Royal Saloon No 9007, West Somerset
1950	BR (LMS) 3rd brake, No 27093, Midland Rly
1960	Pullman Car Co 1st class Kitchen car No 311 *Eagle*, Steamtown

Freight & non-passenger carrying stock

1917	GWR Hydra-D No 42193, Didcot
1920	LSWR Lowmac, No DE563024, North York Moors
1922	LB&SCR cattle truck No 7116, Isle of Wight
1933	LMSR gunpowder van, No 288824, North York Moors
1936	LNER 20ton goods brake van No 187774, North York Moors
1939	SR postal sorting van No 4920, Nene Valley
1941	LNER 20 ton brake van, No 246710, North York Moors
1945	GWR 25 ton machine truck, Embsay
1947	GWR Motorcar van No 65814, Bristol Ind
1948	BR(SR) 12-ton shock absorbing wagon No 14036, North York Moors
1949	BR 40-ton Gane-A No DB996724, Churnet
1949	BR(LMS) Postal sorting van No M30272M, Birmingham Rly Mus
1950	BR 12-wheel well wagon, No KDB901601, East Lancs
1955	BR 16ton mineral wagon No B227009, Middleton
1955	BR 16ton mineral wagon No B234830, North York Moors
1959	BR Fish van No B87905, Hull
1970	S&D Chaldron wagon (replica), Shildon

National Tramway Museum

Derbyshire
Tram Service

Member: AIRPS, TT

An experience of living transport history with vintage horse-drawn, steam and electric trams running through a recreated townscape of authentic buildings, stone setts, iron railings and historic street furniture. The heart of the Museum is its collection of over 70 vintage trams and you can enjoy the thrill of travelling on the scenic mile-long track

Location: Crich, near Matlock, Derbyshire DE4 5DP
OS reference: SK 345549
Manager: Vacant
Operating society/organisation: Tramway Museum Society
Telephone: 01773 852565
Car park: Site, coach parking also available

Access by public transport:
Nearest stations: Cromford (BR) or Alfreton (BR) then by bus; or Whatstandwell (BR) and steep uphill walk
On site facilities: Souvenir shop, bookshop and picnic areas. 1-mile electric tramway. Tramway period street, depots, displays, exhibitions and video theatre. Large exhibition

Crich is home to the NTM's vast collection of trams, Leicester No 76 is at the centre of this scene. *NTM*

hall now open, with new interpretive display depicting history of the tram
Refreshment facilities: Hot and cold snacks and meals
Public opening: March — Sundays; April, May, September, October — daily except *some* Fridays; June, July, August — daily. Open: 10.00 to 17.30 (18.30 Saturdays/Sundays/Bank Holidays)
Family tickets: Available
Facilities for disabled: Access available for most of site, but most trams excluded, Braille guide book available. New for 1997 – tram converted to lift wheelchairs and carry wheelchair bound passengers
Special Notes: Crich houses the largest collection of preserved trams in Europe and has a 1-mile

Locomotives

Name	No	Builder	Type	Built
—	—	B/Peacock (2464)	0-4-0VB tram loco	1885
—	—	E/Electric (717)	4wE	1927
Rupert*	—	R/Hornsby (223741)	4wDM	1944
GMJ*	—	R/Hornsby (326058)	4wDM	1952
—*	—	R/Hornsby (373363)	4wDM	1954

*Not on display

Also some 70 trams (including examples from Czechoslovakia, Germany, the Netherlands, Portugal, USA and South Africa), about a third of which have been restored to working order

working tramway on which restored electric trams are regularly operated. Special events are arranged at weekends and bank holidays throughout the season. Part of tram line occupies route of narrow gauge mineral railway built

by George Stephenson
Membership details: From above address
Membership journal: *The Journal* — quarterly

National Waterways Museum
Member: AIRPS

Gloucestershire Museum

Location: Gloucester Docks signposted
OS Reference: SO826183
Operating Society/Organisation: National Waterways Museum Charitable Trust Ltd, Llanthony Warehouse, Gloucester Docks, Gloucester GL1 2EH.

Curator: Tony Conder
Volunteer co-ordinator: David McDougal (Keeper of Collections)
Car parks: Outside museum, free coach parking
Access by Public Transport: BR Gloucester station, 1-mile
On site facilities: Tea room,

souvenir and book shop (canal related). School room/children's holiday activities. Working demonstrations vary. Tug rides (summer weekends). Trip boat and other museums in docks
Facilities for disabled: Full facilities, lifts, ramps, toilets. All

Cont

indoor displays, quaysides and cafe accessible. Floating exhibits not accessible

Public opening: Daily, except Christmas Day. 10.00-17.00. Admission charged

Special events: Horses weekend; preservation, modellers' & craft events; leisure learning courses (send for leaflet). Steam crane demonstrations some weekends during summer

Membership details: 'Friends' support organisation. Membership Secretary c/o Museum address, Volunteers active in

restoration/fundraising. Winter Meetings programme.
Membership journal: *Llanthony Log* — quarterly

Industrial locomotives

Name	No	Builder	Type	Built
—	1	A/Barclay(2126)	0-4-0F	1942

Ex-Gloucester Corporation,Castle Meads Power Station, Gloucester Docks. Under restoration for static display

Rolling stock

William Balmforth of Rodley crane, c1880. Small collection of GW, Midland, LMS and BR vans. Sharpness Docks open wagons and Gloucester-built flat wagon

---

Nene Valley Railway

Member: AIRPS, TT

Cambridgeshire
Timetable Service

This unique railway's collection includes locomotives and coaches from 10 countries and two continents. It is a regular location for TV and film makers — from films like *Goldeneye* with Pierce Brosnan as 007 to TV — *Hannay, Christobel* — to commercials for cars, beer and soft drinks. The railway and the pleasant Cambridgeshire countryside have doubled for as diverse locations as Russia and Spain

General Manager: Mr M. A. Warrington

Headquarters: Nene Valley Railway, Wansford station, Stibbington, Peterborough, Cambs PE8 6LR

Telephone: Stamford (01780) 782854; Talking Timetable (01780) 782921

Main station: Wansford

Other public stations: Orton Mere, Ferry Meadows, Peterborough NVR (10min walk from city centre)

OS reference: TL 903979

Car park: Wansford, Orton Mere, Ferry Meadows, Peterborough NVR

Access by public transport: Buses from Peterborough to Orton Mere and Ferry Meadows

Refreshment facilities: Wansford, Orton Mere. Bar coach on most trains

Souvenir shops: Wansford, Orton Mere, Ferry Meadows

Museum: Wansford

Depot: Wansford

Locomotives

Name	No	Origin	Class	Type	Built
Mayflower	1306	LNER	B1	4-6-0	1948
92 Squadron	34081	SR	BB	4-6-2	1948
City of Peterborough	73050	BR	5MT	4-6-0	1954
—	D2122	BR	03	0-6-0DM	1959
—	D3871	BR	08	0-6-0DE	1960
—	D9516	BR	14	0-6-0DH	1964
—	D9523	BR	14	0-6-0DH	1964
—	14029 (D9529)	BR	14	0-6-0DH	1965
Atlantic Conveyor	D306	BR	40	1Co-Co1	1960
—	64.305-6	DB	64	2-6-2T	1936
—	7173	DB	52	2-10-0	1943
—	656	DSB	F	0-6-0T	1949
—	3.628	Nord	3500	4-6-0	1911
—	101	SJ	B	4-6-0	1944
—	1178	SJ	S	2-6-2T	1914

Industrial locomotives

Name	No	Builder	Type	Built
—	—	Avonside (1945)	0-6-0ST	1926
Toby	—	Cockerill (1626)	0-4-0VBT	1890
Muriel	—	E/Electric (1123)	0-4-0DH	1966
Rhos	—	H/Clarke (1308)	0-6-0ST	1918
Derek Crouch	—	H/Clarke (1539)	0-6-0ST	1924
Thomas	—	H/Clarke (1800)	0-6-0T	1947
Jacks Green	—	Hunslet (1953)	0-6-0ST	1939
—	68081	Hunslet (2855)	0-6-0ST	1943
—	—	R/Hornsby (294268)	4wDM	1951
Doncaster	—	YEC (2654)	0-4-0DE	1957
—	11	Rebuilt Hill	4wD	1963
Stanton No 50	—	YEC (2670)	0-6-0DE	1958
—	DL83	R/Royce (10271)	0-6-0DH	1967

Stock

14 BR Mk 1 coaches; Wagons Lits sleeping car, Italian-built; Wagons Lits dining car, Belgian-built; 6 coaches from Denmark; 1 coach from France; 4 coaches from Belgium; 3 steam rail cranes; SR Travelling Post Office; 20 12ton Vanfits plus items of freight stock

Length of line: 7.5 miles
Passenger trains: Yarwell Mill-Wansford-Orton Mere-Peterborough NVR
Period of public operation: Open all year at Wansford (loco yard). Services operate every Sunday March-end October; Saturdays April-end October; Wednesdays May-end August; every day (except Mondays mid-July-end August
Special events: May to September including Thomas events and Santa Specials in December (phone for

Owners
34081 the Battle of Britain Locomotive Preservation Society
73050 Peterborough City Council

details)
Facilities for disabled: Ramp access to all stations and shops. Full toilets in Wansford station, souvenir shop. Disabled persons and helpers are eligible for concessionary fares. Passengers can be assisted on and off trains
Membership details: Bill

Foreman, c/o above address
Membership journal: *Nene Steam* — 3 times/year; *Nene Staff* (workers' newsletter) — 6 times/year
Marketing names: Britain's International Steam Railway

North Norfolk Railway

Member: AIRPS, TT

Norfolk
Timetable Service

Part of the former Midland & Great Northern Joint Railway, other elements of the LNER have crept in in the guise of the 'B12' and a Gresley buffet car. The GER 'J15' is being restored. Guest locomotives can be viewed at various times throughout the year. The line runs through beautiful coast, wood and heathland scenery with a nature trail running along its side between Weybourne and Kelling Heath
Genaral Manager: Trevor Meakin
Headquarters: North Norfolk Railway, Sheringham station, Sheringham, Norfolk, NR26 8RA
Telephone: Sheringham (01263) 822045. Talking timetable: (01263) 825449
Fax: 01263 823794
Main station: Sheringham
Other public stations: Weybourne, Kelling Heath Park, Holt
OS reference: Sheringham TG 156430, Weybourne TG 118419
Car parks: Sheringham, Weybourne, Holt
Access by public transport: By train to Sheringham station (200yd)
Refreshment facilities: Sheringham, Weybourne
Souvenir shops: Sheringham, Weybourne, Holt
Museum: Sheringham
Depot: Weybourne
Length of line: 5.25 miles
Passenger trains: Steeply graded, Sheringham-Weybourne-Holt
Period of public operation: Please contact for details
Special events: Friends of Thomas

Locomotives and multiple-units

Name	No	Origin	Class	Type	Built
—	564	GER	J15	0-6-0	1912
—	8572	LNER	B12	4-6-0	1928
—	08767	BR	08	0-6-0DE	1961
—	12131	BR	11	0-6-0DE	1952
—	D5207	BR	25	Bo-Bo	1962
Holt Pioneer	D5386	BR	27	Bo-Bo	1962
—	37032	BR	37	Co-Co	1962
—	79960	W&M	—	Railbus	1958
—	79963	W&M	—	Railbus	1958
—	Car 87*	M/Cam	5BEL	TPS	1932
—	Car 91*	M/Cam	5BEL	DMPBS	1932
—	51346	P/Steel	117	DMBS	1959
—	51388	P/Steel	117	DMS	1959
—	59516	P/Steel	117	TCL	1960

*Ex-'Brighton Belle' Pullman cars, converted to locomotive-hauled

Industrial locomotives

Name	No	Builder	Type	Built
Ring Haw	—	Hunslet (1982)	0-6-0ST	1940
—	3809	Hunslet (3809)	0-6-0ST	1954
—	68009	Hunslet (3825)	0-6-0ST	1953
Birchenwood	4	Bagnall (2680)	0-6-0ST	1944
—	10	E/Electric (C8431)	0-4-0DH	1963
Wissington	—	H/Clarke (1700)	0-6-0ST	1938
—	—	Bagnall (2370)	0-6-0F	1929

Stock
7 ex-LNER coaches; Small number of wagons

Owners
564 and 61572 the Midland & Great Northern Railway Society

the Tank — 3-6 April and 26/27 October; Victorian Weekend — 5/6 May; Diesel Weekend — 14/15 June; Gala Weekend — 5-7 September; 1940s Weekend — 20/21 September. Santa Specials in December.
Facilities for disabled: Specially adapted Pullman Car available,

advanced booking essential
Membership details: Midland & Great Northern Joint Railway Society, Clive Morris, c/o above address
Membership journal: *Joint Line* — quarterly
Marketing names: The Poppy Line

North Woolwich Old Station Museum

No expense has been spared in the very imaginative restoration of this attractive Victorian terminus building overlooking the Thames. Railway artefacts, documents, drawings, etc are well displayed in glass cases or on the walls, the stock being stabled in the platform area. Convenient for the new City airport and connections for the Docklands Railway

Location: North Woolwich Old Station Museum, Pier Road, North Woolwich, London E16 2JJ
OS reference: TQ 433798
Organisation: Newham Museum Service
Telephone: 0171-474 7244
Car park: Only in adjoining

Locomotives

Name	No	Origin	Class	Type	Built
—	229	GER	209	0-4-0ST	1876

Industrial locomotives

Name	No	Builder	Type	Built
—	—	Hibberd (3294)	4wDM	1948
—	—	Peckett (2000)	0-6-0ST	1942

Stock
1 ex-LNER coach; 2 compartment sections of LTSR coach; NLR Luggage Van; 1 ex-Royal Arsenal Ammunition Van (18in gauge)

streets
Public transport: BR North London Link. Buses: 101, 69 and 473
Facilities: Museum shop
Public opening: Open April to September, Saturdays 10.00-17.00, Sundays 10.00-17.00. Mondays to Wednesdays (school summer holiday only) 13.00-15.00. Winter – closed
Admission: Free

North Yorkshire Moors Railway

Member: AIRPS, TT

This 18-mile line runs through the picturesque North York Moors National Park and is host to an extensive collection of main line locomotives

Financial & Commercial Director: Ken Kitching
Headquarters: Pickering station, Pickering, North Yorkshire YO18 7AJ
Telephone: Pickering (01751) 472508 for passenger enquiries, charter and diner bookings
Main station: Pickering
Other public stations: Grosmont, Goathland, Newtondale Halt, Levisham
OS reference: Pickering NZ 797842, Levisham NZ 818909, Goathland NZ 836013, Grosmont NZ 828053
Car parks: Grosmont, Goathland, Levisham, Pickering
Access by public transport: BR service to Grosmont from Whitby and Middlesbrough. Bus services Malton-Pickering, York or Scarborough-Pickering and Whitby-Goathland and Pickering
Refreshment facilities: Available on most trains and at Grosmont, Goathland and Pickering

Locomotives and multiple-units

Name	No	Origin	Class	Type	Built
George Stephenson†	44767	LMS	5MT	4-6-0	1947
Eric Treacy	45428	LMS	5MT	4-6-0	1937
—	65894	NER	P3	0-6-0	1923
—	2238	NER	T2	0-8-0	1918
—	901	NER	T3	0-8-0	1919
Blue Peter	60532	LNER	A23	4-6-2	1948
—†	62005	LNER	K1	2-6-0	1949
—	69023	LNER	J72	0-6-0T	1951
—	3814	GWR	2884	2-8-0	1940
—	6619	GWR	5600	0-6-2T	1928
—	30841	SR	S15	4-6-0	1936
Repton	30926	SR	V	4-4-0	1934
Hartland	34101	SR	WC	4-6-2	1950
—	75014	BR	4MT	4-6-0	1951
—	80135	BR	4MT	2-6-4T	1956
Dame Vera Lynn	3672	MoS	WD	2-10-0	1943
—	90775	MoS	WD	2-10-0	1943
—	2253	USATC	S160	2-8-0	1942
—	D2207	BR	04	0-6-0DM	1953
—	08556	BR	08	0-6-0DE	1959
—	D5032	BR	24	Bo-Bo	1959
—	24061	BR	24	Bo-Bo	1960
—	D7541	BR	25	Bo-Bo	1965
—	D7628	BR	25	Bo-Bo	1965
Alycidon†	55009	BR	55	Co-Co	1961

†Not on site

Industrial locomotives

Name	No	Builder	Type	Built
—	29	Kitson (4263)	0-6-2T	1904

Souvenir shops: Pickering, Goathland, Grosmont
Museum: Situated at locomotive depot, Grosmont
Depot: Grosmont
Length of line: 18 miles
Passenger trains: Steam-hauled services Grosmont-Pickering. Pullman evening dining service and 'Moorlander' Sunday lunch service run regularly. GWR and NER saloons are also available for special occasions (eg wedding parties, conferences etc)
Special events: Throughout the season, ring for details
Period of public operation: Daily 22 March-2 November (excluding Sundays in March), Santa Specials and other Xmas services in December/January
Facilities for disabled: The NYMR welcomes visitors who may be suffering from a disability and special attention will gladly be provided if advanced notice is given
Special notes: Operates through North York Moors National Park.

Name	No	Builder	Type	Built
—	5	R/Stephenson (3377)	0-6-2T	1909
Stanton	No 44	Yorkshire (2622)	0-4-0DE	1956
No 21	—	Fowler (4210094)	0-4-0DH	1954
Antwerp	—	Hunslet (3180)	0-6-0ST	1944
—	12139	E/Electric (1553)	0-6-0DE	1948
—	16	Drewry	0-4-0DM	1941
—	2	R/Hornsby (421419)	4wDM	1958
—	3*	R/Hornsby (441934)	4wDM	1960
—	1	Vanguard (129V)	0-4-0DM	1963
—	2	Vanguard (131V)	0-4-0DM	1963

*On loan to Middleton Railway

Stock
36 x BR Mk 1, 4 x Pullman, 2 x BR XP64, 1 x BR Mk 2, 3 x GUV, 7 x Gresley, 6 x Thompson, 1 x GW Saloon, 1 x SR Bulleid, 3 x LMS, 1 x GCR Barnum, 1 x GNR Brake, 3 x NER, 2 x H&BR, 2 x diesel cranes, 2 x 45ton steam cranes, over 40 wagons.

Owners
90775 and 30841 the Essex Locomotive Society
62005, 2238, 65894, 69023 the North Eastern Locomotive Preservation Group
60532 on loan to the North Eastern Locomotive Preservation Group
63460 on loan from the National Railway Museum
75014 the 75014 Locomotive Operators Group
Antwerp the National Coal Board
55009 the Deltic Preservation Society
21, 44 the British Steel Corporation
29 the Lambton 29 Syndicate
5, 926, 2253, 3814, 6619, 34101 and 80135 are private

Northampton & Lamport Railway
Northamptonshire Steam Centre
Members: AIRPS

Headquarters: Pitsford & Brampton Station, Pitsford Road, Chapel Brampton, Northampton NN6 8BA
Location: About 5 miles north of Northampton, Pitsford road off A50 or A508
General Manager: Mr R. Faulkner
Operating company: Northampton Steam Railway Ltd
Operating society: Northampton & Lamport Railway Preservation Society
Telephone: 01604 820327 (mainly Sundays, recorded announcements other times)
Car parks: On site
Access by public transport: None
On site facilities: NLR sales shop, toilets, buffet coach
Length of line: Three quarters of a mile at present. Work on southern extension to start early 1997
Public opening: Every Sunday from Easter to end October

Locomotives and multiple-units

Name	No	Origin	Class	Type	Built
—	3862	GWR	2884	2-8-0	1942
Castel Dinas Bran	25035	BR	25	Bo-Bo	1963
—	26010	BR	26	Bo-Bo	1959
—	D5401	BR	27	Bo-Bo	1962
The Royal Artilleryman	45118	BR	45	1Co-Co1	1962
—	54495	BR	108	DTCL	1960
—	51367	BR	119	DMBS	1959
—	13004	SR	4DD	DMBS	1949

Industrial locomotives

Name	No	Builder	Type	Built
Colwyn	45	Kitson (5470)	0-6-0ST	1933
—	2104	Peckett (2104)	0-4-0ST	1948
Vanguard	5374	Chrzanow (5374)	0-6-0T	1959
—	17646	Chrzanow (5387)	0-6-0T	1959
Bunty	146C	Fowler (4210018)/ rebuilt T/Hill	0-4-0DM	1950 1964
—	1	R/Hornsby (275886)	4wDM	1949
Sir Alfred Wood	53	R/Hornsby (319214)	0-6-0DM	1965
Sir Gyles Isham	764	R/Hornsby (319286)	0-4-0DM	1953

Cont

Special events: Easter — 29-31 March; Diesel Gala — 10/11 May; Teddy Bears Weekend — 23-25 August; Autumn Steam Gala — 13/14 September; Autumn Diesel Gala — 4/5 October; Autumn Members' Day — 12 October; Santa Specials — every weekend in December from 6th

Membership details: Mr I. Rivett, Pitsford & Brampton Station, Pitsford Road, Chapel Brampton, Northampton NN6 8BA

Membership journal: *Premier Line* — 4 times a year

Stock

Coaches: 1 BR Mk 1 FK; 2 BR Mk 1 TSO; Mk 1 BSO; 1 BR Mk 1 BSK; 1 BR Mk 1 SK; 1 BR Mk 1 CK; 1 BR Mk 1 RBR; 1 Mk 2 BSO (trolley buffet); 1 Mk 2 SO; 1 SR CCT van; 2 BR Mk 1 Suburban CL; 1 BR Mk 1 NAV; 2 BR NAV; 2 SR PMV; 1 GWR full brake; 1 LMS CCT
Wagons — A number of various wagon types

Owners

Colwyn the *Colwyn* Preservation Society
17646 the Northampton Locomotive Co
54495 & 51367 the Northampton & Lamport Railway DMU Group

Nos 1, 2104 and 5374 await their next turns of duties at Pitsford & Brampton station. *J. B. Pepper*

Northamptonshire Ironstone Railway Trust

Northamptonshire Steam Centre

Location: Hunsbury Hill Industrial Museum, Hunsbury Hill Country Park, Hunsbury Hill Road, Camp Hill, Northampton

OS reference: SP 735584

Operating organisation: Northamptonshire Ironstone Railway Trust Ltd, Mr M. Smith, 6 Burmans Way, Cogenhoe, Northampton. Tel: 01604 890229

Telephone: Northampton (01604) 811130

Access by public transport: Terminus of Northampton Transport bus routes, 24, 26 to Camp Hill from Northampton Greyfriars bus station. Operated by United Counties Bus Co on Sundays

On site facilities: Light refreshments, shop, toilets in car

Industrial locomotives

Name	No	Builder	Type	Built
Blue Circle*	—	A/Porter	2-2-0WT	1926
Vigilant	—	Hunslet (287)	0-4-0ST	1882
Brill	14	M/Wardle (1795)	0-4-0ST	1912
Sir Vincent	8800	A/Porter (8800)	0-4-0GT	1917
Belvedere	—	Sentinel (9365)	0-4-0TG	1946
Musketeer	—	Sentinel (9369)	0-4-0TG	1946
Hylton	—	Planet (3967)	0-4-0DH	1961
Spitfire	39	R/Hornsby (242868)	4wDM	1946
—	16	Hunslet (2087)	0-4-0DM	1940
—	—	M/Rail (9711)	0-4-0DM	1946†
—	—	Lister (14006)	0-4-0PM	1950†

†2ft gauge
*On loan from Bluebell Railway

park. Brake van rides given on standard gauge railway. Children's playground and picnic areas within the park boundary
Length of line: 2.25 miles

Public opening: Easter Sunday to end of September and Bank Holidays
Times of opening: Museum: 11.00-17.00. Railway: First train

14.00, last train 17.10
Facilities for the disabled: Site relatively flat. Members willing to assist.
Special notes: Museum to the Ironstone Industry of Northamptonshire, the museum houses photographs, documents and other items connected with the Ironstone Industry of Northamptonshire. The railway has been relaid on part of the trackbed of the former 3ft 8.5in gauge line of now defunct Hunsbury Ironstone Co
Membership details: Mr M. Harvey, 52 Bourton Road, Buckingham MK18 1BE

Nottingham Heritage Centre
Member: AIRPS

Nottinghamshire
Steam Centre

Location: On the A60 just south of Ruddington, 3 miles south of Nottingham city centre, off A52, 7 miles north of Loughborough. Signposted
Operating Society/organisation: Great Central (Nottingham) Ltd, Nottingham Heritage Centre, Mere Way, Ruddington, Nottingham NG11 6NX
Telephone number: 0115 940 5705
Access by public transport: Buses from City Centre and Broad Marsh (tel: 0115 9240000)
On site facilities: Car park, shop and cafe, picnic area and country park walks. 700m long passenger carrying miniature railway
Facilities for disabled: Accessible
Public Opening: Steam Shuttle service Sundays & Bank Holidays from Easter-mid October. 10.45-17.30
Membership details: Great

Locomotives and multiple-units

Name	No	Origin	Class	Type	Built
—	20094	BR	20	Bo-Bo	1961
—	20135	BR	20	Bo-Bo	1966
—	08885	BR	08	0-6-0DE	1962
—	68088	LNER	Y7	0-4-0T	1927

Industrial locomotives

Name	No	Builder	Type	Built
—	54	H/Clarke (1682)	0-6-0ST	1937
Powergen No 2	—	RSH (7818)	0-4-0ST	1954
—	—	R/Hornsby (512572)	4wDM	1965
—	—	Yorkshire (2895)	0-6-0DE	1964
—	56	RSH (7667)	0-6-0ST	1950
Staythorpe	—	R/Hornsby	0-4-0DE	—

Rolling stock: 1 BR Mk 1 FO, 1 BR Mk 2 BSO, 1 BR Mk 2 BFK, 1 BR (ex-WR) cinema coach, 1 LNER 45ton steam breakdown crane, 1 SR GUV, various goods wagons

Central Northern Development Association c/o above address
Society journal: Quarterly

Paignton & Dartmouth Steam Railway
Member: AIRPS

Devon
Timetable Service

A line that succeeds in imparting the feeling of running from A to B, linking, as it does, the Dartmouth ferry at Kingswear to Paignton and BR. A trip in the observation car is well worth the supplement for the views of the sea, the climb through the tunnel, and the descent through the wooded hillside to Brunel's terminus at Kingswear on the banks of the River Dart
Director & General Manager: J. B. S. Cogar
Headquarters: Paignton Queen's Park station, Paignton, Devon

Locomotives and multiple-units

Name	No	Origin	Class	Type	Built
—	4555	GWR	4500	2-6-2T	1924
—	4588	GWR	4575	2-6-2T	1927
Goliath	5239	GWR	5205	2-8-0T	1924
—	6435	GWR	6400	0-6-0PT	1937
Lydham Manor	7827	GWR	7800	4-6-0	1951
Ardent	D2192	BR	03	0-6-0DM	1962
Volunteer	D3014	BR	08	0-6-0DE	1954
Mercury	D7535	BR	25	Bo-Bo	1965
Superb	50002	BR	50	Co-Co	1967
—	59003*	BR	116	TS	1957
—	59004*	BR	116	TS	1957
—	59488*	P/Steel	117	TCL	1959
—	59494*	P/Steel	117	TCL	1959
—	59503*	P/Steel	117	TCL	1959

Cont

Telephone: Paignton (01803) 555872
Main station: Paignton Queen's Park
Other public stations: Goodrington, Churston, Kingswear (for Dartmouth)
OS reference: SX 889606
Car parks: Paignton municipal car park, Goodrington, Dartmouth (ferry to Kingswear)
Access by public transport: Adjacent to both BR station and Devon General bus station
Refreshment facilities: Paignton and Kingswear
Depot: Churston
Length of line: 7 miles
Passenger trains: Paignton-Kingswear, views of Torbay and

Name	No	Origin	Class	Type	Built
—	59507*	P/Steel	117	TCL	1959
—	59513*	P/Steel	117	TCL	1959
—	59517*	P/Steel	117	TCL	1959

*Converted to locomotive-hauled vehicles

Stock
15 ex-BR Mk 1 coaches; 1 Pullman observation coach; 2 auto-coaches; 1 ex-GWR coaches

Owners
50002 the Devon Diesel Society

Dart estuary, 495yd tunnel
Period of public operation: Easter to October
Facilities for disabled: Limited
Special events: Santa Specials — please see timetable and press for details

Membership details: Paignton & Dartmouth Railway Society, Mrs P. Mackey, Renewals Officer, 68 Osney Crescent, Paignton TQ4 5EZ
Membership journal: *Torbay Express* — quarterly

Peak Rail plc
Member: AIRPS

Derbyshire
Timetable Service

Location: *Registered Office:* Matlock Station, Matlock, Derbyshire DE4 3NA; *Trains operate from:* Darley Dale station, Darley Dale,
OS reference: Matlock SK 060738
Operating society/organisation: Peak Rail PLC, Matlock station, Matlock, Derbyshire
Car parks: Matlock station, DFS Furniture Store at Darley Dale, Rowsley South station
Access by public transport: Monday to Saturday between Derby and Matlock
Length of line: 4 miles between Rowsley South and Matlock Riverside
On site facilities: Shops and buffets at Darley Dale. Shop at Matlock. Restaurant car seats 70
Public opening: Not finalised but will be every Sunday. Saturdays probably April-October. Midweek during summer. Timetable varies
Facilities for disabled: Advance notice not necessary but contact telephone is (01629) 580381
Period of public operation: Please contact for details
Special events: Friends of Thomas the Tank Engine — 3-5 May. Please contact for other events
Special notes: Peak Rail plc, has outline permission to relay the 20-mile line from Buxton to Matlock from all relevant local authorities.

Locomotives and multiple-units

Name	No	Origin	Class	Type	Built
—	48624	LMS	8F	2-8-0	1943
Penyghent	D8	BR	44	1Co-Co1	1959
3rd Carabinier	D99	BR	45	1Co-Co1	1961
—	D3429	BR	08	0-6-0DE	1958
—	D5705*	BR	28	Bo-Bo	1958
—	D7615	BR	25	Bo-Bo	1963
—	20048	BR	20	Bo-Bo	1959
—	51566	BR	108	DMC	1959
—	51933	BR	108	DMBS	1960
—	53933	BR	108	DMBS	1959
—	54484	BR	108	DTC	1960
—	54504	BR	108	DTC	1960
—	59387	BR	108	TS	1958
—	977806	BR	108	DMBS	1958

Industrial locomotives

Name	No	Builder	Type	Built
Vulcan	—	V/Foundry (3272)	0-4-0ST	1918
The Duke	2746	Bagnall (2746)	0-6-0ST	1944
Warrington*	150	RSH (7136)	0-6-0ST	1944

*At Darley Dale

Rolling Stock — coaches: 2 BR Mk 1 RMB; 1 BR Mk 1 SLF, 3 BR Mk 1 TSO, 2 BR Mk 1 SO, 1 BR Mk 1 BSOT, 3 BR Mk 1 SK, 1 BR Mk 1 BSK, 2 BR Mk 1 BG, 1 BR Mk 1 GUV, 1 BR Mk 2 SO, 1 BR Mk 2 BSO, 1 BR Mk 2 BFK, 1 BR Mk 3 HST coach, 1 LMS TK, 2 LMS BCK, 1BTK

Rolling stock — wagons: 1 MR brake van, 2 LMS brake vans, 1 LMS Shark brake van, 1 BR brake van, 1 Mess & Tool van, 1 Smith & Rodley 15ton diesel crane, 1 Sturgeon rail wagon, 1 Lowmac wagon, 2 Dogfish ballast hoppers, 1 mineral hopper wagon, 2 LMS 16ton fish vans, 1 SR PMV, 3 BR 12ton box van, 1 12ton van, 1 Shell tank wagon, 2 Esso tank wagons, 3 LNER wagons, 2 LMS wagons, 1 21ton mineral wagon, 2 ex-LMS match wagons, 1 Plasser & Theurer tamper, 1 Plasser & Theurer track slewer, 1 ex-LMR drain train water bowser, 2 Austrian ferry wagons

At the time of writing the first 2 miles from Matlock to Darley Dale is open operating steam and diesel trains every weekend

Plym Valley Railway

Member: AIRPS

Devon
Steam Centre

A scheme dedicated to the restoration of services over the former GWR Marsh Mills-Plym Bridge line, a distance of 1.5 miles
Location: 5 miles from centre of Plymouth, Devon, north of A38. From Marsh Mills roundabout, take B3416 to Plympton, follow signs
OS reference: SX 517564
Operating society/organisation: Plym Valley Railway Co Ltd, Marsh Mills Station, Coypool Road, Marsh Mills, Plymouth, Devon PL7 4NL
Access by public transport: Buses from Plymouth, Nos 20, 20A, 21, 22A, 51 stop close to site
On site facilities: Shop and refreshments at Marsh Mills, Coypool (Sundays only)
Public opening: Sundays from 10.00, and other selected days
Length of line: Half-mile, plus sidings
Special events: Please see press

Locomotives and multiple-units

Name	No	Origin	Class	Type	Built
—	75079	BR	4MT	4-6-0	1956
—	13002	BR	08	0-6-0DE	1953
—	51365	BR	117	MBS	1960
—	51407	BR	117	DMS	1960

Industrial locomotives

Name	No	Builder	Type	Built
—	3	H/Leslie (3597)	0-4-0ST	1926
—	—	T/Hill (125V)	4wDH	1963
—	—	Hibberd (3281)	4wDM	1948

Rolling stock: Self propelled Smith & Rodley diesel crane of 1956

for details
Special notes: Visitors are advised that, at the moment, the railway and two locomotives are still under restoration. 3 working locomotives and DMU. Prospective visitors are advised to take the advice of their guides. Steam and diesel demonstration trains on some

Sundays (tel: Alan Smith 01503 250539)
Membership details: Pat Elbrolo, 75 Rigdale Close, Eggbuckland, Plymouth, Devon PL6 5PR
Membership journal: *Plym Valley News* — 3/year
Marketing name: The Woodland Line

The Railway Age, Crewe

Cheshire
Steam Centre

Location: Crewe Heritage Centre, Vernon Way, Crewe
OS reference: SJ 709552
Operating society/organisation: Crewe Heritage Trust Ltd
Telephone: (01270) 212130
Car park: On site, Town Centre, Forge Street, Oak Street,
Access by public transport: BR Crewe
Refreshment facilities: Brief Encounter buffet
On-site facilities: Gift shop, picnic area, children's corner, weekend train rides, standard gauge and miniature railway, exhibition hall, main line viewing area, 3 working signalboxes with hands-on visitor operation
Public opening: Daily 10.00-16.00, family tickets available

Locomotives and multiple-units

Name	No	Origin	Class	Type	Built
—	03073	BR	03	o-6-0DM	1959
—	08375	BR	08	0-6-0DE	1957
—	D8233	BR	15	Bo-Bo	1963
—	37029	BR	37	Co-Co	1961
—*	D120	BR	45	1Co-Co1	1961
Ixion	D172	BR	46	1Co-Co1	1962
—	D1842	BR	47	Co-Co	1965
—	47449	BR	47	Co-Co	1964
—	E3003	BR	81	Bo-Bo	1960
—	82008	BR	82	Bo-Bo	1961
—	85101	BR	85	Bo-Bo	1961
—	18000	BR	—	A1A-A1A	1949
—	53986	BR	108	DMBs	1959
—	55032	P/Steel	121	DMBS	1960

*On loan to West Somerset Railway during most of 1997

Cont

England

77

Special events: International Model Railway Exhibition — 11/12 May; Friends of Thomas the Tank Engine — June. LNWR 150 events — July; Signalling Gala — October. Please contact for details of other events
Facilities for disabled: Toilets
Membership details: Heritage Centre Supporters Association, c/o above address
Notes: Steam locomotives passed

Industrial locomotives

Name	No	Builder	Type	Built
Robert	—	H/Clarke (1752)	0-6-0T	1943
—	—	K/Stuart (4388)	0-4-0ST	1926

Rolling stock
APT vehicle Nos 48103, 48106, 48602, 48603, 48606, 49002; 1 BR Mk 1 BSK; 2 BR brake vans

for use over BR tracks are stabled between duties on the North Wales Coast and Settle & Carlisle line

Ravenglass & Eskdale Railway — Cumbria
Member: AIRPS
Timetable Service

Originally built to serve iron ore mines in Eskdale, this delightful line makes an ideal 'tourist' line running as it does through wooded valleys and along rugged hillsides
General Manager: Steve Wood
Headquarters: Ravenglass & Eskdale Railway, Ravenglass, Cumbria
Telephone: (01229) 717171
Main station: Ravenglass
Other public stations: Muncaster Mill, Irton Road, The Green, Beckfoot, Eskdale (Dalegarth)
OS reference: SD 086964
Car parks: All stations
Access by public transport: BR services to Ravenglass
Refreshment facilities: Ravenglass, Dalegarth. Bar meals at 'Ratty Arms'
Picnic areas: At both termini
Souvenir shops: Ravenglass, Dalegarth
Museum: Ravenglass
Length of line: 7 miles, 15in gauge
Passenger trains: Steam or diesel-hauled narrow gauge trains Ravenglass-Dalegarth
Period of public operation: Daily from late March-late October. Limited winter service November-

Locomotives

Name	No	Builder	Type	Built
River Irt	—	Heywood	0-8-2	1894
River Esk	—	Davey Paxman (21104)	2-8-2	1923
River Mite	—	Clarkson (4669)	2-8-2	1966
Northern Rock	—	R&ER	2-6-2	1976
Bonnie Dundee	—	K/Stuart (720)*	0-4-2	1901
Shelagh of Eskdale	—	R&ER/Severn-Lamb	4-6-4DH	1969
Quarryman	—	Muir-Hill (2)	0-4-0P/Paraffin	1928
Perkins	—	Muir Hill (NG39A)	0-4-4DM	1929
Silver Jubilee	—	R&ER	DMU	1977
Lady Wakefield	—	R&ER	B-B	1980
Synolda	—	Bassett-Lowke	4-4-2	1912
—	—	Greenbat (2782)	0-4-0BE	1957
Cyril	—	Lister	0-4-0DM	1987

*Rebuilt to 15in gauge 1981

March
Family ticket: All day travel at reduced price
Special events: *Northern Rock* 21st Birthday Celebrations — May Day bank holiday
Facilities for disabled: Special coaches for wheel-chair passengers. Advance notice preferred. Wheelchair access to toilets and museum at Ravenglass; toilets, shop and cafe at Eskdale (Dalegarth)
Special notes: At Ravenglass the R&ER has two camping coaches and the company also operates the

'Ratty Arms' public house formed by conversion of the former BR station buildings. During the high summer, mid-July through August, five steam locomotives are normally in use Monday-Thursday
See also — Muncaster water mill
Membership details: Mr N. Dickinson, 3 Clifton Terrace, Ravenglass, Cumbria CA18 1SE
Membership journal: *The R&ER Magazine* — quarterly
Marketing names: 'Ratty' or 'T laal Ratty'

Romney, Hythe & Dymchurch Railway — Kent
Member: AIRPS
Timetable Service

This line was built in 1926/27 as a one-third size miniature main line, and is by far the longest and most fully-equipped 15in gauge railway in the world. It carries not only

daytrippers and holidaymakers but also children to and from the local school at New Romney.
Headquarters: Romney, Hythe & Dymchurch Railway, New Romney

station, Kent TN28 8PL
Telephone: 01797 362353/363256
OS reference: TR 074249
Main station: New Romney
Other public stations:

Dymchurch, Jefferstone Lane, New Romney, Romney Sands, Dungeness

Car parks: Hythe, Dymchurch, New Romney, Dungeness

Access by public transport: Folkestone Central station (Connex South Eastern) and then bus to Hythe (4 miles) or Rye station (Connex South Eastern) and then bus to New Romney (8 miles)

Refreshment facilities: Cafeterias at New Romney and Dungeness, picnic area at New Romney. Also an observation coach on certain trains

Souvenir shops: Hythe and New Romney (plus Dymchurch and Dungeness in main season)

Toy and Model Museum: New Romney with displays of old, and not so old, toys; plus two large operating model railways

Depot: New Romney

Length of line: 13.5 miles, 15in gauge

Passenger trains: Train frequency depends on the time of year: maximum frequency is 45 minutes

Period of public operation: Trains run daily from Good Friday until last Sunday in September. Also runs at weekends in March and October. Out of season the school train departs New Romney at 15.00 with limited public accommodation (Monday to Friday, term times only)

Special events: Steam & Diesel Gala — 11 May; Friends of

Locomotives

Name	No	Builder	Type	Built
Green Goddess	1	Davey Paxman	4-6-2	1925
Northern Chief	2	Davey Paxman	4-6-2	1925
Southern Maid	3	Davey Paxman	4-6-2	1926
The Bug	4	Krauss (8378)	0-4-0TT	1926
Hercules	5	Davey Paxman	4-8-2	1926
Samson	6	Davey Paxman	4-8-2	1926
Typhoon	7	Davey Paxman	4-6-2	1926
Hurricane	8	Davey Paxman	4-6-2	1926
Winston Churchill	9	YEC (2294)	4-6-2	1931
Doctor Syn	10	YEC (2295)	4-6-2	1931
Black Prince	11	Krupp (1664)	4-6-2	1937
John Southland	12	TMA Birmingham	Bo-Bo	1983
—	14	TMA Birmingham	Bo-Bo	1989
—	PW1	M/Rail (7059)	4wDM	1938
—	PW2	RH&DR	4wPM	1965
Redgauntlet	PW3	RH&DR	4wPM	1975

Stock

42 saloon bogie coaches; 12 open bogie coaches; 3 semi-open coaches; 5 luggage/brake saloons; 1 Parlour car; 1 mess coach; 40 assorted wagons

Thomas Day — 15 June, 6/7 September. Santa specials in December (pre-booking essential)

Special notes: Senior citizen concession Fridays, Saturdays, Sunday, (return journey for single fare). The 'Romney Toy and Model Museum' at New Romney. Special trains can be run at most times by prior arrangement. Parties can be catered for at New Romney and Dungeness cafés

Facilities for disabled: Ramps at level crossings at all stations for easy access. Special wheelchair coach available on any train by prior arrangement. Stair lift between cafe and 'Toy & Model Museum'. Disabled toilets at Hythe, Dynchurch and New Romney

Internet addresses: RHDR web site is on: HTTP:\\WWW.i-way.co.uk\~tburgess\rhdr.html\rhd RHDE e-mail is: 106104.245@compuserve.com

Membership details: RH&DR Association, 26 Norman Close, Battle, East Sussex TN33 0BD

Membership journal: The Marshlander — quarterly

Ruislip Lido Railway

Middlesex
Steam Centre

Member: AIRPS

The 12in gauge line is operated by enthusiast volunteers as an attraction within Ruislip Lido, a country park which is maintained by the London Borough of Hillingdon

Location: Ruislip Lido, Reservoir Road, Ruislip, Middlesex

Operating society/organisation: Ruislip Lido Railway Society Ltd, Membership Secretary, Mrs S. E. Simmons, 9 Wiltshire Lane, Eastcote, Pinner, Middx HA5 2LH

Telephone: 0181-866 9654

Car park: Available at Lido

Access by public transport: Ruislip Underground station

Locomotives

Name	No	Builder	Type	Built
Robert	3	Severn-Lamb	B-2 DH	1973
Lady of the Lakes	5	Ravenglass & Eskdale Rly	B-B DM	1985
Graham Alexander	7	Severn-Lamb	B-B DM	1990

Locomotive notes: All locomotives are available for service and a steam locomotive is under construction

Stock

6 open coaches; 9 closed coaches; miscellaneous service stock

(Metropolitan and Piccadilly lines) then by bus H13 (Monday-Saturday), 331-nearby (Daily). Lido is off the A4180 road

Refreshment facilities: New family pub/restaurant (Brewers Fayre) on site. Picnic areas also available

Length of line: 1-mile single journey, 2 miles return with a planned extension of about 1-mile which will terminate beside main entrance to car park — opening mid-1997
Public opening: The line is open Sundays throughout the year, Tuesdays, Wednesdays, Thursdays and Saturdays in April, May, June, September and October. Every day in July and August, also daily during all Hillingdon school holidays.
  24-hour recorded train information service 01895 622595
Journey time: Single 12min, return 22min

Facilities for disabled: Wheelchair passengers can be accepted for travel
Membership details: c/o above address
Membership journal: Woody Bay News — quarterly

Rutland Railway Museum

Member: AIRPS

Leicestershire Steam Centre

This museum is dedicated to portraying the railway in industry, particularly iron ore mining, and has a wide range of industrial locomotives and rolling stock. Indeed, its collection of quarry freight rolling stock is probably the most comprehensive in the country and regular demonstrations are a feature of the 'steam days'.
Location: Cottesmore Iron Ore Mines Siding, Ashwell Road, Cottesmore, near Oakham, Leicestershire — museum situated mid-way between villages of Cottesmore and Ashwell, approximately 4 miles north of Oakham (locally signposted)
OS reference: SK 886137
Operating society/organisation: Rutland Railway Museum, Cottesmore Iron Ore Mines Siding, Ashwell Road, Cottesmore, Nr Oakham, Leicestershire LE15 7BX
Telephone: Oakham (01572) 813203
Car park: Free car park on site
Access by public transport: Nearest BR station, Oakham. Blands bus service, Leicester-Oakham-Cottesmore. Bartons buses, Nottingham-Melton Mowbray-Oakham-Ashwell, Corby/Peterborough-Oakham-Ashwell (services 117 and 125).
On site facilities: Free train rides, demonstration freight trains, refreshments, toilets, museum, shop, picnic sites, demonstration line with lineside walk and viewing areas, static displays of over 30 steam and diesel locomotives; over 50 wagons, vans and coaches (believed to be the largest collection of preserved quarry freight stock in the UK)
Length of line: Three quarter-mile

Locomotives and multiple-units

Name	No	Origin	Class	Type	Built
NCB No 7	(D9518)	BR	14	0-6-0DH	1964
BSC45	(D9520)	BR	14	0-6-0DH	1964
—	D9555	BR	14	0-6-0DH	1965
—	54274	BR	108	DTC	1959

Industrial locomotives

Name	No	Builder	Type	Built
Firefly	—	Barclay (776)	0-4-0ST	1896
Uppingham	—	Peckett (1257)	0-4-0ST	1912
BSC No 2	—	Barclay (1931)	0-4-0ST	1927
Dora	—	Avonside (1973)	0-4-0ST	1927
Elizabeth	—	Peckett (1759)	0-4-0ST	1928
Singapore	Yard No 440	H/Leslie (3865)	0-4-0ST	1936
Swordfish	—	Barclay (2138)	0-6-0ST	1941
Drake	—	Barclay (2086)	0-4-0ST	1940
Sir Thomas Royden	—	Barclay (2088)	0-4-0ST	1940
Carlton No 3	—	Barclay (352)	0-4-0DM	1941
Salmon	8410/39	Barclay (2139)	0-6-0ST	1942
Coal Products No 6	—	Hunslet (2868)	0-6-0ST	1943
		(Rebuilt Hunslet 3883 1963)		
—	8	Peckett (2110)	0-4-0ST	1950
—	3	N/British (27656)	0-4-0DH	1957
—	—	R/Hornsby (306092)	4wDM	1950
—	—	R/Hornsby (305302)	4wDM	1951
Hays	—	R/Hornsby	0-4-0DE	1969
Phoenix	—	Hibberd (3887)	4wDM	1958
Janus	No 28	YEC (2791)	0-6-0DE	1962
—	1382	YEC (2872)	0-6-0DE	1962
—	65	Hunslet (3889)	0-6-0ST	1964
—	20-90-01	Barclay (499)	0-4-0DH	1965
—	20-90-02	R/Hornsby (504565)	0-4-0DH	1965
Betty	8411/04	R/Royce (10201)	0-4-0DH	1965
—	D21	R/Royce (10270)	0-6-0DH	1967
—	BSC 1	E/Electric (D1049)	0-6-0DH	1965
—	—	E/Electric (D1231)	0-6-0DH	1967
—	No 1	Hunslet (6688)	0-4-0DH	1968
—	CEGB 24	T/Hill (188c)	4wDH	1967
		(Rebuild of Sentinel 9597/1955)		
—	24	Hunslet (2411)	0-6-0ST	1941
—	7	Sentinel (9376)	4wVBT	1947
—	21	H/Clarke (D707)	0-6-0DM	1950
—	1	Barclay (415)	0-4-0DH	1957
—	10	T/Hill	4wDH	1971
—	ROF No 1	T/Hill (132c)	0-4-0DH	1963
		(Rebuild of Fowler 22982/1942)		

Passenger trains: Regular shuttle service operates on open days (approximately every 15min)
Public Opening: Open weekends or by arrangement, some weekdays (please telephone prior to visit). Open 11.00-17.00. (Leaflets available, SSAE please)
Special events: Please contact for details
Facilities for disabled: Site relatively flat. Members willing to assist.
Special notes: The museum houses an extensive collection of industrial locomotives and rolling stock typifying past activity in local ironstone quarries, nationwide mines and factories. A demonstration line approximately three quarter-mile long has been relaid on the former MR Cottesmore mineral branch (originally built to tap local ironstone quarries), on which restored locomotives and stock are run. Among the latter is the body of the only surviving Wisbech & Upwell Tramway coach and the last diesel locomotive built for BR service at Swindon Works
Membership details: Membership Secretary, c/o above address

Locomotive notes: In service *Dora*, 7, BSC45, D9555, 1832, *Betty, Janus*, 1, *Pheonix*, CEGB No 24, No 1 and BSC 1.

Stock
2 coaches; 4 brake vans; 12 covered goods vans; 57 wagons (includes rakes of wagons as used in local ironstone and industrial railways); 2 rail cranes

---

Science Museum

London
Museum

Built on land acquired with the profits from the Great Exhibition of 1851, the Science Museum was one of the first to include industrial archaeology. Here you will find the originals featured in the history books, such as Robert Stephenson's *Rocket*.
Location: South Kensington
OS reference: TQ 268793
Operating society/organisation: Science Museum, Exhibition Road, South Kensington, London SW7
Telephone: 0171-938 8000
Access by public transport: South Kensington Underground station
Catering facilities: Cafe on 3rd floor, tea, coffee, sandwiches etc. Picnic area on 1st floor
On site facilities: Book shop, toilets on most floors
Public opening: Daily 10.00-18.00. Closed 24-26 December
Special events: All organised by the National Railway Museum, York, which is part of the Science Museum. Telephone (01904) 621261 for details
Facilities for disabled: Toilets on most floors, ramp and lifts to all floors. Parties should contact before arrival if extra assistance is required
Special notes: Static exhibits only in Land Transport Gallery, which is currently undergoing a re-display in connection with the construction of an extension to the museum

Locomotives

Name	No	Origin	Type	Built
Rocket	—	L&MR	0-2-2	1829
Sans Pareil	—	L&MR	0-4-0	1829
	13	C&SLR	4wE	1890
Puffing Billy	—	Wylam Colliery	0-4-0	1813

Locomotive notes: All restored to static display condition

Seaton & District Electric Tramway

Devon
Timetable Service

Member: AIRPS

Devon's unique narrow gauge electric tramway, operating on the trackbed of the former Seaton branch line between Seaton, Colyford and Colyton. Panoramic views of the beautiful Axe Valley and estuary. An unforgettable experience for the family
Location: Harbour Road Car Park, Seaton; Swan Hill Road, Colyford; Station Road, Kingsdon, Colyton
OS reference: SY 252904
Operating society/organisation: Seaton & District Electric Tramway Co, Riverside Depot, Harbour Road, Seaton, Devon EX12 2NQ
Telephone: Seaton (01297) 20375/21702
Fax: Seaton (01297) 625626
Access by public transport: Local bus service from Axminster railway station (South West Trains), Sidmouth and Lyme Regis serve Seaton, Colyford and Colyton. Bus enquiries (01392) 382800
On site facilities: Gift shops, Tea rooms, children's playground, picnic area
Length of line: 3 miles, 2ft 9in gauge

Industrial locomotives

Name	No	Builder	Type	Built
Claude	—	R/Hornsby (435398)	4wDM	1959

Cont

Period of public operation: Daily 24 March to 31 October; Santa Specials in December; private hire available all year round
Times: Trams every 20 minutes, 09.40-17.20 (until 20.40 July and August)

Fares: Single, return and rover tickets available. Discounts for local residents, families and parties of 20 or more. Prices on application
Facilities for disabled: Tramcar No 17 carries up to 12 wheelchairs

(by prior arrangement). Disabled toilets
Special notes: Services operated by open top double-deck bogie cars with enclosed single-deck saloon cars during inclement weather

Severn Valley Railway
Member: AIRPS, TT

Worcestershire
Timetable Service

The railway hosts more main line engines than any other preserved line in the country, enjoying the back-up of a large volunteer and professional workforce and extensive engineering workshops and equipment. Railway travel like it used to be
General Manager: Alun Rees
Operating Superintendent: John F. Hill
Headquarters: Severn Valley Railway Co Ltd, Railway Station, Bewdley, Worcs DY12 1BG
Telephone: Bewdley (01299) 403816; 24hr timetable — Bewdley (01299) 401001
Main stations: Bridgnorth, Bewdley, Kidderminster Town
Other public stations: Arley, Highley, Hampton Loade, Northwood Halt, Country Park Halt
OS reference: Bridgnorth SO 715926, Bewdley SO 793753
Car parks: At all main stations
Access by public transport: Midland Red bus service X92 to Kidderminster and Bewdley and 890 to Bridgnorth. BR Sprinter service to Kidderminster (BR) with immediate connections to SVR station. Through tickets available from all manned BR stations
Refreshment facilities: At most stations, but not on all operating days and on most trains. Fully licensed bars at Bridgnorth and Kidderminster Town
Souvenir shops: Bridgnorth, Kidderminster Town
Depots: Bridgnorth (locomotives), Bewdley and Kidderminster (stock)
Model railways: At Bewdley, Kidderminster and Hampton Loade
Length of line: 16.5 miles
Passenger trains: Steam-hauled trains running frequently from Kidderminster Town to Bewdley and Bridgnorth. Diesel-hauled

Locomotives and multiple-units

Name	No	Origin	Class	Type	Built
The Great Marquess	3442	LNER	K4	2-6-0	1938
Gordon	AD600	LMR	WD	2-10-0	1943
—	43106	LMS	4MT	2-6-0	1951
—	46443	LMS	2MT	2-6-0	1950
—	46521	LMS	2MT	2-6-0	1953
RAF Biggin Hill	45110	LMS	5MT	4-6-0	1935
—	47383	LMS	3F	0-6-0T	1926
—	48773	LMS	8F	2-8-0	1940
—	2968	LMS	5P4F	2-6-0	1933
—	813	GWR	—	0-6-0ST	1901
—	2857	GWR	2800	2-8-0	1918
—	5164	GWR	5101	2-6-2T	1930
—	4150	GWR	5101	2-6-2T	1947
—	5764	GWR	5700	0-6-0PT	1929
—	7714	GWR	5700	0-6-0PT	1930
—	4566	GWR	4500	2-6-2T	1924
Bradley Manor	7802	GWR	'Manor'	4-6-0	1939
Erlestoke Manor	7812	GWR	'Manor'	4-6-0	1939
Hinton Manor	7819	GWR	'Manor'	4-6-0	1939
Hagley Hall	4930	GWR	'Hall'	4-6-0	1929
—	1501	GWR	1500	0-6-0PT	1949
—	7325	GWR	4300	2-6-0	1932
—	80079	BR	4MT	2-6-4T	1954
—	78019	BR	2MT	2-6-0	1954
—	75069	BR	4MT	4-6-0	1955
Western Ranger	D1013	BR	52	C-C	1962
Western Courier	D1062	BR	52	C-C	1963
—	D3022	BR	08	0-6-0DE	1952
—	D3586	BR	08	0-6-0DE	1953
—	12099	BR	11	0-6-0DE	1952
—	D7633	BR	25	Bo-Bo	1965
—	D5410	BR	27	Bo-Bo	1962
Hood	50031	BR	50	Co-Co	1968
Ark Royal	50035	BR	50	Co-Co	1968
Exeter	50044	BR	50	Co-Co	1968
—	51935	BR	108	DMBS	1960
—	51941	BR	108	DMBS	1960
—	52064	BR	108	DMC	1960
—	59250	BR	108	TBS	1958

Industrial locomotives

Name	No	Builder	Type	Built
Warwickshire	—	M/Wardle (2047)	0-6-0ST	1926
The Lady Armaghdale	—	Hunslet (686)	0-6-0T	1898
—	—	Ruston (319290)	0-4-0DM	1953
Alan	—	R/Hornsby (414304)	0-4-0DM	1957
William	—	R/Hornsby (408297)	0-4-0DM	1957

England

service on limited occasions as advertised

Period of public operation: Weekends year round, Santa Steam specials in late November and December. Daily service mid-May to early October and all public Bank Holidays and school holidays. Open for limited viewing at other times

Special events: Steam Enthusiasts' weekends in April and September; Santa Specials end November and December; Mince Pie Specials in December/early January 1996. Friends of Thomas the Tank Engine weekends in June and September

Facilities for disabled: Facilities available, special vehicle available to carry wheelchairs by prior arrangement. Disabled peoples' toilets at Kidderminster and Bridgnorth

Special notes: A number of special enthusiasts' weekends and special events are held when extra trains are operated. In addition supplementary trains with diesel haulage are run as advertised. 'Severn Valley Limited' and 'Severn Valley Venturer' Restaurant Car service operates on Sundays and as required on other occasions. Advanced booking recommended. Charter trains with or without dining facilities can be arranged

Stock
27 ex-GWR coaches; 13 ex-LMS coaches; 24 ex-BR Mk 1 coaches; 8 ex-LNER coaches; Numerous examples of ex-GWR, LMS and other freight vehicles and two 30-ton steam cranes

Owners
813 the GWR 813 Fund
1501 the 15xx Fund
2857 the 2857 Fund
2968 theStanier Mogul Fund
3442 the family of the late Earl of Lindsay
4150 the 4150 Locomotive Fund
4566 the 4566 Fund
5164 the 51xx Fund
5764, 7714 the Pannier Tank Fund
46521, 78019 and D1013 are private
7325 the Great Western (SVR) Association
7802 and 7812 the Erlestoke Manor Fund
7819 the Hinton Manor Fund
43106 the Ivatt 4 Fund
46443 the SVR 46443 Fund
47383 the Manchester Rail Travel Society
48773 the Stanier 8F Locomotive Society
50031, 50035 and 50044 the 50 Fund
75069 the 75069 Fund
80079 the Passenger Tank Fund
AD600 the Royal Corps of Transport Museum Trustees
D1062 the Western Locomotive Association
D3022 the Class 08 Society
D5410 Sandwell Metropolitan Council
D7633 the SVR/PW Fund

Membership details: Mrs Pauline Stribblehill c/o above address
Membership journal: *Severn*

Valley Railway News — quarterly
Share details: Mr Alun Rees, c/o above address

Sittingbourne & Kemsley Light Railway   Kent
Member: AIRPS, TT   Steam Centre

The Sittingbourne & Kemsley Light Railway is part of the 2ft 6in gauge railway built to convey paper and other materials between mills at Sittingbourne and Kemsley and the Dock at Ridham on the banks of the Swale. The first section of the line opened in 1906 and two of the engines then in use remain on the line today.

The railway is now leased from U.K. Paper Group and is operated as a tourist attraction. Passenger trains are normally steam-hauled and are formed of a varied selection of open and covered coaches. For the first half mile of the journey the train twists and turns through Milton Regis on a

concrete viaduct which was one of the first reinforced concrete structures to be built

Operating Manager: Malcolm Burton
Headquarters: Sittingbourne & Kemsley Light Railway Ltd, Kemsley Down, Kent
Telephone: Sittingbourne (01795) 424899 (talking timetable) or (01634) 852672 (other enquiries)
Main station: Sittingbourne
Car park: Sittingbourne
Party bookings and enquiries: M. Burton, 85 Balmoral Road, Gillingham, Kent ME7 4QG
Access by public transport: Sittingbourne BR station, A2 and M2 roads

OS reference: Sittingbourne 905643, Kemsley Down 920662
Refreshment facilities: Kemsley Down
Souvenir shop: Kemsley Down
Small Exhibits Museum: Kemsley Down
Depot: Kemsley Down (access by rail only)
Length of line: 2 miles, 2ft 6in gauge
Passenger trains: Ex-industrial line Sittingbourne-Kemsley Down
Journey time: 15min each way
Period of public operation: Good Friday, Easter Monday and bank holidays; Saturdays 29 March and during August; Sundays 30 March-mid October; Wednesdays in *Cont*

August. Santa specials, contact for details

Special events: Hot Cross Bun Day — 29 March; Chocolate Eggs Day — 30 March; Easter Bunny Day — 31 March; Friends of Thomas the Tank Engine — 7/8 June; Special Open Day — 12 October

Special notes: There is no public access to Kemsley Down other than by the railway on operating dates. When the line is closed all stock is stored in security compounds, on the mill premises. Family ticket available, special rates for parties and senior citizens. Picnic area at Kemsley Down

Membership details: Mr & Mrs K. Widdowson, 60 Doveney Close, St Paul's Cray, Orpington, Kent BR5 3WT

Marketing name: Sittingbourne Steam Railway

Industrial locomotives

Name	No	Builder	Type	Built
Alpha	—	Bagnal (2472)	0-6-2T	1932
Triumph	—	Bagnall (2511)	0-6-2T	1934
Superb	—	Bagnall (2624)	0-6-2T	1940
Unique	—	Bagnall (2216)	2-4-0F	1924
Premier	—	K/Stuart (886)	0-4-2ST	1905
Leader	—	K/Stuart (926)	0-4-2ST	1905
Melior	—	K/Stuart (4219)	0-4-2ST	1924
Edward Lloyd	—	R/Hornsby (435403)	4wDM	1961
Victor	—	Hunslet (4182)	4wDM	1953

Industrial standard gauge locomotives

Name	No	Builder	Type	Built
—	4	H/Leslie (3718)	0-4-0ST	1928
Bear	—	Peckett (614)	0-4-0ST	1896
—	1	Barclay (1876)	0-4-0F	1925

Locomotive notes: In service: *Superb, Melior*. Under repair: *Leader, Triumph, Premier*. On static display *Alpha, Unique* and standard gauge exhibits

Stock

10 bogie coaches (4 ex-Chattenden & Upnor Railway); 2 open coaches; various wagons

---

Snibston Discovery Park
Members: TT

Leicestershire
Museum

Location: Snibston Discovery Park, Ashby Road, Coalville, Leicestershire LE67 3LN
Telephone: (01530) 510851
Fax: (01530) 813301
Operating group: Leicestershire County Council, Museums Arts & Records Service
Museum contact: Mr I. D. Stones, Snibston Discovery Park, Ashby Road, Coalville, Leicestershire LE67 3LN
Public opening: Daily 10.00-18.00 (during British Summer Time); 10.00-17.00 at other times. Closed Christmas Day & Boxing Day
Car & coach parking: On site, free

Access by public transport: Midland Fox from Loughborough and Nottingham (route 99); from Leicester (route 117); from Ashby de la Zouch (route 118), Mon-Sat; route 217/8 Sun & bank holiday Mondays. Further information, tel: (01533) 511411.
Stevensons Bus Services from Hinckley (route 179); limited service from Tamworth via Ashby (route 97). Connections at Ashby

Industrial locomotives

Name	No	Builder	Type	Built
Mars II†	—	RSH (7493)	0-4-0ST	1948
—	2	Barclay (1815)	0-4-0F	1924
—†*	—	Brush (314)	0-4-0ST	1906
—††	2416	E/Electric	0-4-0	1978
—††	—	Huwood	0-6-0DM	1980
—	—	Hunslet (3851)	0-6-0ST	1962
—†	—	Hunslet	0-6-0DM	1966
—††	—	Hunslet (8973)	4WDM	1964

†Locomotives are stored
*Originally Powlesland & Mason No 6 taken over by GWR in 1924 and numbered 921
††2ft 6in gauge
Plus 2ft 6in gauge English Electric battery-operated electric man-riding locomotives — ex-NCB

with Burton on Trent. Further information, tel: (01283) 44662
On site facilities: Shop, toilets, car park, cafe. Conference facilities, tourist information centre (Tel: [01530] 813608). Family tickets, picnic areas, science play area, Sheepy Magna wheelwrights workshop. Special event days, nature reserve, golf driving range, colliery building tours
Railways on site: Approx 300yd

of standard gauge track, aiming towards future operation of a demonstration trains. Track to be extended when possible. No public riding on line.
Narrow gauge railway about 350yd in length. Colliery manriding underground train to operate at a future, subject to availability of equipment

Somerset & Dorset Railway Trust

Member: AIRPS

Situated at Waashford on the West Somerset Railway the Trust Museum houses Somerset & Dorset memorabilia and artifacts to stir memories of cross-country travel in the era of steam. The sidings and restoration shed give the visitor a chance to see locomotives, wagons and carriages in close up

Headquarters: Washford station, Minehead Road, Washford, Somerset TA21 0PP

Telephone: 01984 640869 (opening hours); 01278 683574 (otherwise)

Car park: small car park by main road

Access by public transport: West Somerset Railway trains on operating days, March to end October. Nearest main line station: Taunton. Southern National Omnibus Co service 28 (Taunton-Minehead) passes the station

Locomotive

Name	No	Origin	Class	Type	Built
—*	53808	S&DJR	7F	2-8-0	1925

*Undergoing heavy overhaul at Minehead

Industrial locomotives

Name	No	Builder	Type	Built
Isabel*	—	H/Leslie (3437)	0-6-0ST	1919
Kilmersdon	—	Peckett (1788)	0-4-0ST	1929

*Undergoing restoration at Washford

Stock

3 Somerset & Dorset 6-wheeled coaches undergoing restoration. Large wagon collection. Display of narrow gauge equipment from Sedgemoor peat railways

On site facilities: Souvenir counter at the station. No refreshments on station but adjacent Inn offers food and children are welcome

Public opening: 10.30-16.30 on WSR operating days. Other times by arrangement, Tel: 01278 683574

Special events: 23/24 August, special weekend with reunion of ex-Somerset & Dorset Railway staff on 24th

Membership details: S&DJR Trust, 21 Greenhaven, Yateley, Hampshire GU17 7NA

Membership journal: *Pines Express* (6 issues/year)

Peckett *Kilmersdon,* visiting Hymek No D7018, and S&DJR No 88 (BR No 53808) at Washford. *S&DRT*

A typical West Country branch line meandering up the Dart Valley to Buckfastleigh which is home to the railway's workshops, a butterfly and otter farm and several other attractions. After many years of isolation the line is now accessible from Totnes (BR) via a new footbridge (4min walk)

General Manager: R. Elliott

Headquarters: South Devon Railway, Buckfastleigh station, Buckfastleigh, Devon TQ11 0D2

Telephone: Buckfastleigh (01364) 642338

Main station: Buckfastleigh

Other public stations: Staverton, Totnes Littlehempston

OS reference:
Buckfastleigh SX 747663,
Staverton SX 785638

Car park: Buckfastleigh (free), Staverton (free). Totnes — use BR pay & display or council car parks

Access by public transport: Bus, X38/9 Exeter-Plymouth; 188 Newton Abbot-Buckfastleigh. BR trains to Totnes

Refreshment facilities: Buckfastleigh

Souvenir shop: Buckfastleigh

Museum: Buckfastleigh

Depot: Buckfastleigh

Length of line: 7 miles

Passenger trains: Buckfastleigh-Totnes (Littlehempston) alongside the River Dart

Period of public operation: Telephone above for details

Facilities for disabled: Good

Membership details: South Devon Railway Association, c/o above address

Membership journal: *Bulliver* — quarterly

Marketing name: The Primrose Line

Locomotives and multiple-units

Name	No	Origin	Class	Type	Built
—	0298	LSWR	0298	2-4-0WT	1874
—	1420	GWR	1400	0-4-2T	1933
—	1369	GWR	1366	0-6-0PT	1934
—	3803*	GWR	2884	2-8-0	1939
Dumbleton Hall	4920†	GWR	Hall	4-6-0	1929
—	5526	GWR	4500	2-6-2T	1929
—	5786	GWR	5700	0-6-0PT	1930
—	80064	BR	4MT	2-6-4T	1953
—	D3666	BR	09	0-6-0DE	1959
—	D8110	BR	20	Bo-Bo	1960
—	51592	BR	127	DMBS	1959
—	51604	BR	127	DMBS	1959
—	59659	BR	115	TS	1960
—	59719	BR	115	TCL	1960
—	59740	BR	115	TS	1960
Broad gauge – 7ft 0.25in					
Tiny	—	SDR	—	0-4-0VBT	1868

*Undergoing restoration at the Birmingham Railway Museum, Tyseley
†Will be away on loan during 1997

Industrial locomotives

Name	No	Builder	Type	Built
Ashley	1	Peckett (2031)	0-4-0ST	1942
Lady Angela	1690	Peckett (1690)	0-4-0ST	1926
—	1738	Peckett (1738)	0-4-0ST	1928
Sapper	WD132	Hunslet (3163)	0-6-0ST	1943
Glendower	—	Hunslet (3810)	0-6-0ST	1954
Carnarvon	47	Kitson (5474)	0-6-0ST	1935
—	—	Fowler (421014)	0-4-0DM	1958
Errol Lonsdale	68011	Hunslet (3796)	0-6-0ST	1953
Meteor	31	RSH (7609)	0-6-0T	1950

Stock
13 ex-BR Mk 1 coaches; 7 ex-GWR coaches; 3 ex-GWR auto trailers; 25 wagons

Owners
0298 and *Tiny* on loan from the National Railway Museum
3803, 4920, *Errol Lonsdale* and *Sapper* the South Devon Railway Trust
Glendower is privately owned
1369 and 1420 the South Devon Railway Association
5526 the 5526 Ltd
D8110 the Class 20 Group
5786 the Worcester Locomotive Society

South Tynedale Railway

Member: AIRPS, TT

Cumbria
Timetable Service

A narrow gauge line passing through the attractive scenery of the South Tyne valley, in the North Pennine area of outstanding natural beauty

Location: Approximately ¼-mile north of Alston town centre, on A686 Hexham road

OS reference: NY 717467

Operating society: South Tynedale Railway Preservation Society, The Railway Station,

Alston, Cumbria CA9 3JB
Telephone: Alston (01434) 382828 (timetable information), 381696 (other enquiries)
Car park: Alston station
Access by public transport: Wright Bros buses, Haltwhistle-Alston and Newcastle-Alston-Keswick. Also summer buses from Durham and Stanhope. Bus links from Langwathby in connection with Settle-Carlisle line trains on certain dates (Details of all buses: [01228] 812812)
On site facilities: Book and souvenir shop, tourist information centre, picnic area, toilets (including disabled persons), parking
Catering facilities: Tea room at Alston, serving selection of snacks and home baking (not operated by Society)
Length of line: 1.5 miles (2.25 to Kirkhaugh), 2ft gauge
Public opening: 1996 passenger train service: Weekends & Bank Holidays — Easter-October; daily — Easter week, Spring Bank Holiday week, July and August, October school holiday week. Thursdays in June and September   Steam haulage scheduled at weekends from Spring Bank Holiday until September, also Easter and May Day Weekends, most days in August and special event days
Journey time: c40min (round trip)
Special events: Programme includes Friends of Thomas the Tank Engine weekends, Teddy Bear Day, Steam Gala, Santa and Mince Pie Specials. Please enquire

Locomotives

Name	No	Builder	Type	Built
Phoenix	1	Hibberd (2325)	4wDM	1941
Sao Domingos	3	O/K (11784)	0-6-0WT	1928
Naworth	4	H/Clarke (DM819)	0-6-0DM	1952
Thomas Edmondson	6	Henschel (16047)	0-4-0T	1918
—	9	Hunslet (4109)	0-4-0DM	1952
Naklo	10	Chrzanow (3459)	0-6-0WTT	1957
Cumbria	11	Hunslet (6646)	0-4-0DM	1967
Chaka's Kraal No 6	12	Hunslet (2075)	0-4-2T	1940
—	13	Hunslet (5222)	0-4-0T	1958
Helen Kathryn	14	Henschel (28035)	0-4-0T	1948
—	—	Hunslet (4110)	0-4-0DM	1952
—	—	H/Clarke (DM1167)	0-6-0DM	1960
—	15	H/Clarke (DM1366)	0-6-0DM	1965
—	—	EE/Baguley (2519/3500)	4wBE	1958
Permanent Way Trolley	DB965062	Wickham	4WDM	?

Owners
1, 6, 9 & 10 the South Tynedale Railway Preservation Society
4, 11, 4110, DM1107, 2519/3500 & DB965082 the Durham Narrow Gauge Group
12 the North Gloucestershire Narrow Gauge Co
13 the Ayle Colliery Co
3, 14 & 15 are privately owned

Stock
7 bogie coaches; 2 brake van; 1 bogie box van; 1 bogie open wagon; 3 4-wheel open wagons; 2 4-wheel box vans; 4 4-wheel flat wagons; 1 4-wheel fuel tank wagon; 2 bogie well wagons, 4 4-wheel skip wagons; 6 bogie flat wagons; 4 bogie hopper wagons; 1 4-wheel hopper wagon; 1 4-wheel weed-killer wagon

for event dates
Special notes: The line has been constructed on the trackbed of the former BR Haltwhistle-Alston branch. Extension of the line from Gilderdale towards Slaggyford, a further 3 miles, is in progress. It is expected to open another three-quarter-mile, from Gilderdale to

Kirkhaugh, during 1997
Membership details: Membership Secretary c/o above address
Membership journal: *Tynedalesman* — quarterly
Marketing name: England's Highest Narrow Gauge Railway

South Yorkshire Railway

Member: AIRPS

South Yorks Museum

Location: Barrow Road Railway Sidings, Barrow Road, Meadowhall, Wincobank, Sheffield S9 1HN
OS Reference: SK391914
General Manager: John Wade
Operating Society: South Yorkshire Railway
Telephone: (0114) 2424405
Car Park: Car parking facilities available, more facilities being developed nearby
Access by public transport: From
Cont

Locomotives

Name	No	Origin	Class	Type	Built
—	D2953	BR	01	0-4-0DM	1956
—	D2854	BR	02	0-4-0DH	1960
—	D2866	BR	02	0-4-0DH	1961
—	D2867	BR	02	0-4-0DH	1961
—	03020	BR	03	0-6-0DM	1958
—	03037	BR	03	0-6-0DM	1959
—	03066	BR	03	0-6-0DM	1959
—	03094	BR	03	0-6-0DM	1960
—	D2099	BR	03	0-6-0DM	1960
—	D2118	BR	03	0-6-0DM	1959
—	D2134	BR	03	0-6-0DM	1960

Sheffield: By bus, No 93 Firth Park, alight at the top of Barrow Road, and follow the signposts. From Rotherham, Doncaster and Sheffield No X77 bus alighting on Barrow Road.

By rail: Meadowhall, 100yd

By Supertram: From City Centre to Meadowhall Interchange

Other on site facilities: Small shop

Length of line: 3.5 miles in total, although only three quarter-mile is currently occupied

Period of public operation: Not operating a service as yet

Journey time: See above

Membership Secretary: K. Guest

Membership details: c/o above address

Membership journal: *41Z —* quarterly

Name	No	Origin	Class	Type	Built
—	D2139	BR	03	0-6-0DM	1960
—	03180	BR	03	0-6-0DM	1962
—	03197	BR	03	0-6-0DM	1961
—	D2199	BR	03	0-6-0DM	1961
—	D2229	BR	04	0-6-0DM	1955
—	D2246	BR	04	0-6-0DM	1956
—	D2284	BR	04	0-6-0DM	1960
—	D2302	BR	04	0-6-0DM	1960
—	D2310	BR	04	0-6-0DM	1960
—	D2324	BR	04	0-6-0DM	1961
Dorothy	D2337	BR	04	0-6-0DM	1961
—	D2420	BR	06	0-4-0DM	1958
—	07012	BR	07	0-6-0DE	1962
—	07013	BR	07	0-6-0DE	1962
—	D3000	BR	08	0-6-0DE	1952
Gwyneth	D3019	BR	08	0-6-0DE	1953
—	D3023	BR	08	0-6-0DE	1953
—	08133	BR	08	0-6-0DE	1955
—	08216	BR	08	0-6-0DE	1956
—	08308	BR	08	0-6-0DE	1957
—	08436	BR	08	0-6-0DE	1958
—	08507	BR	08	0-6-0DE	1960
—	08936	BR	08	0-6-0DE	1962
—	D3476	BR	10	0-6-0DE	1957
Christine	D4092	BR	10	0-6-0DE	1962
—	12074	BR	11	0-6-0DE	1950
—	D9500	BR	14	0-6-0DM	1964
—	D9502	BR	14	0-6-0DM	1964
—	20096	BR	20	Bo-Bo	1961
—	D8056	BR	20	Bo-Bo	1961
—	26038	BR	26	Bo-Bo	1959
—	33203	BR	33	Bo-Bo	1962
Andania	40013	BR	40	1Co-Co1	1959
—	53556	BR	104	DMCL	1958

Industrial locomotives

Name	No	Builder	Type	Built
WD75133	2	Hunslet (3183)	0-6-0ST	1944
—	7	H/Clarke (1689)	0-4-0ST	1937
Cathyrn	—	H/Clarke (1884)	0-4-0ST	1955
George	—	Sentinel (9596)	4wVBT	1955
Ken	67	Sentinel (10180)	0-6-0DH	1964
Bigga	—	Fowler (4200019)	0-4-0DH	1947
Rotherham	2	YEC (2480)	0-4-0DE	1950
—	—	Hibbard (3817)	0-4-0DM	1956
—	44	Hunslet (6684)	0-6-0DH	1968
—	47	T/Hill (249V)	0-6-0DH	1974
—	8	T/Hill (288V)	0-6-0DH	1980
Speedy	—	Barclay (361)	0-4-0DM	1942
Hotwheels	—	Barclay (422)	0-6-0DM	1958
Toffo	2	R/Hornsby (432479)	4wDM	1959
—	20	YEC (2688)	0-4-0DE	1959
—	220	Barclay (359)	0-4-0DM	1941

Rolling stock

2 diesel-electric cranes; 4 BR Mk 1 coaches; 6 BR Mk 1 General Utility Vehicles; 1 BR Mk 1 bogie van; 2 Covered Carriage TruckS; 2 LNER brake vans; Several other wagons

Southall Railway Centre

London
Steam Centre

Situated close by BR Southall station the Southall Railway Centre is set up on a large part of the former steam shed and diesel depot site. Vacated by BR in 1986 the GWRPG moved in during 1988. Negotiations were completed with BR in 1992. The Centre opened to the public in 1994. Amongst the planned attractions available to the public is the return of the 'Brentford Branch Special' which proved to be popular when the Group operated from its former site at Bridge Road

Access by public transport: Buses 105, 120, 195, 232, E5, N89. Access is only possible via the footbridge at the London end of Southall station, during opening times only

Operating society/organisation: GWR Preservation Group Ltd, Southall Railway Centre, Southall, Middx UB2 4PL

Telephone: 0181-574 1529 R. A. Gorringe

On-site facilities: Souvenir shop, refreshments, toilets

Public opening: Static viewing: weekends and Bank Holidays all year (except Good Friday, 27/28 December; operational days: 30/31 March, 12/13 April, 4/5, 25/26 May, 15, 28/29 June, 27 July, 24/25 August, 13/14 September, 18/19 October, 6/7, 13/14, 20/21 December

Locomotives and multiple-units

Name	No	Origin	Class	Type	Built
—*	2885	GWR	2884	2-8-0	1938
—*	4110	GWR	5101	2-6-2T	1936
—	9682	GWR	5700	0-6-0PT	1949
—	68078	LNER	J94	0-6-0ST	1946
—	53628	BR	108	DMBS	1958
—	54233	BR	108	DTCL	1958

*Under restoration at Swindon Railway Workshops

Industrial locomotives

Name	No	Builder	Type	Built
—	—	AEC Southall	4wDM	1938
William Murdoch	2100	Peckett (2100)	0-4-0ST	1949
Birkenhead	7386	RSH (7386)	0-4-0ST	1948
Francis Baily of Thatcham	AD251	R/Hornsby (390772)	0-4-0DM	1957
—	WD9117	B/Drewry railcar	0-4-0	1975

Stock

1 BR 'Gane' wagon; 1 BR 'Rectank' wagon; 1 BR Generator van; 1 GWR 'Mink' van; 1 GWR brake van; 2 BP oil tank wagons; 1 GWR bogie bolster wagon; 1 LMS parcels van; 1 LMS stores van; 1 Staff coach, former LMS BCK; 1 Wagons Lits coach; 2 Mk 2 TSO coaches; 1 Mk 1 BSK coach

Owners

2100 the Portsmouth City Council Museum & Record Service

Special events: Take place on most steaming dates

Car parking: No on-site parking

Facilities for disabled: Access to the centre is not possible, involving two flights of steps, those wishing to visit are advised to make contact before their visit and alternative arrangements will be made

Membership details: Apply above address

Membership journal: Southall Semaphore

Southport Railway Centre

Lancashire
Steam Centre

Member: AIRPS, TT

Housed in the largest locomotive shed of its type exhibits include ex-Liverpool Riverside signalbox and the restored turntable facilities using the turntable from York (Queen St). A working ex-Midland Railway water column from London St Pancras is a dominant feature of the site. Steamport has been a servicing point for the annual Southport-Manchester steam specials since 1985

Location: Five minutes from BR

Locomotives and multiple-units

Name	No	Origin	Class	Type	Built
Cecil Raikes	5	Mersey Railway	—	0-6-4T	1886
—	19†	L&Y	Pug	0-4-0ST	1910
—	5193	GWR	5101	2-6-2T	1934
—	D2148	BR	03	0-6-0DM	1960
—	D2595	BR	05	0-6-0DM	1959
—	03189	BR	03	0-6-0DM	1960
—	28361	LMS	502	DMBSO	1939
—	28896	LMS	502	DTSO	1930

†On loan from L&Y Saddletanks Fund (K&WVR)

Cont

England

station, via London Street. Behind car park (free on Sundays)
OS reference: SD 341170
Secretary: H. J. M Royden
Operating society/organisation: Southport Railway Centre, (Steamport, Southport Ltd), Derby Road, Southport PR9 0TY
Telephone: Southport (01704) 530693
Car park: Derby Road
Access by public transport: BR station, Merseyrail from Liverpool, Regional Railways from Manchester
On site facilities: Souvenir shop. Cafe open summer Sundays and Bank Holidays at weekends. Steam hauled rides in passenger coaches LMS brake vans June-mid September, plus special events. Buffet car in operation on special events. Santa Steam trains in December, 'Friends of Thomas the Tank' weekends etc. Picnic area
Length of line: 600yd
Public opening: Weekends October-April 13.00-17.00; Weekdays June-mid September 12.00-17.00 (closed Mondays in June); weekends June-September 11.00-17.00
Facilities for disabled: Access to all parts of museum. Limited access to toilets. No advanced notice required for disabled visitors —

groups always welcome. Enquiries always welcomed
Membership journal: *27C*
Newsletter — quarterly

Industrial locomotives

Name	No	Builder	Type	Built
—	5	Peckett (2153)	0-6-0ST	1954
North Western Gas Board		Peckett (1999)	0-4-0ST	1941
Fitzwilliam	—	Hunslet (1954)	0-6-0ST	1939
—	—	Hunslet (3155)	0-6-0ST	1943
Glasshoughtone	4	Hunslet (3855)	0-6-0ST	1954
Shropshire	193	Hunslet (3793)	0-6-0ST	1953
—	47	Barclay (1865)	0-4-0ST	1926
—	—	Barclay (1950)	0-4-0F	1928
Persil	—	Fowler (4160001)	0-4-0DM	1952
*Efficient**	—	Barclay (1598)	0-4-0ST	1918
Agecroft No 2	—	RSH (7485)	0-4-0ST	1948
St Monans	—	Sentinel (9373)	4wVBT	1947
Hornet	—	Peckett (1935)	0-4-0ST	1937
Whitehead	—	Peckett (1163)	0-4-0ST	1908
—	—	Batley (2000)	0-4-0BE	1958
Sefton	—	T/Hill (123V)	4wDM	1963
Stanlow No 4	4	T/Hill (160V)	0-4-0DM	1966
—	—	N/British (27653)	0-4-0DH	1956
—	D2870	YEC (2677)	0-4-0DM	1960

*On loan to North Staffordshire Railway, Cheddleton

Stock
Small selection of rolling stock including buffet car Sc1839, TSO 4886 and BSK 35128, 1 Smith-Rodley diesel crane

Owner
Cecil Raikes the Liverpool Museum
Class 502 the National Railway Museum

Steamtown, Carnforth

Lancashire
Museum

Member: TT

Formerly BR Carnforth motive power depot. Carnforth is a centre for 'Steam on BR' steam-hauled railtours over BR main lines.
Location: Steamtown Railway Centre, Warton Road, Carnforth, Lancashire LA5 9HX
OS reference: SD 496708
Operating society/organisation: Steamtown Railway Museum Ltd
Telephone: Carnforth (01524) 732100
car park: Free car park on site
Access by public transport: BR services to Carnforth station. Bus services to Carnforth by Ribble and Lancaster City Transport
Catering facilities: Picnic area
On site facilities: Signalbox, 15in gauge railway locomotives in steam on Bank Holidays, Sundays from Easter-October, and daily

Locomotives

Name	No	Origin	Class	Type	Built
Lord Nelson	850	SR	LN	4-6-0	1926
—	48151	LMS	8F	2-8-0	1942
Henry Oakley	990	GNR	C2	4-4-2	1898
Olton Hall	5972	GWR	Hall	4-6-0	1937
—	D2381	BR	03	0-6-0DM	1960
—	03196	BR	03	0-6-0DM	1959
—	08220	BR	08	0-6-0DE	1956

Industrial locomotives

Name	No	Builder	Type	Built
John Howe	5	Barclay (1147)	0-4-0ST	1908
Coronation	3	Barclay (2134)	0-4-0ST	1942
Cooke & Nuttal	1	Barclay (2230)	0-4-0ST	1947
British Gypsum	4	Barclay (2343)	0-4-0ST	1953
Lindsay	—	Wigan Coal & Iron Co	0-6-0ST	1887
Gasbag	—	Sentinel (8024)	4wVBTG	1923
Esso	—	General Electric (30483)	Bo-Bo	1949
Lord Trenchard	—	Barclay (401)	0-4-0DM	1956
Tom Rolt	7049	Hunslet (2697)	0-6-0DM	1944

England

during July-August
Length of line: Standard gauge three quarter-mile, 15in gauge 1-mile
Public opening: Daily Easter-October 09.00-17.00.

Stock
4 pre-Grouping vehicles; 1 GWR saloon; 5 LNER coaches; 2 LMS coaches; 6 BR coaches; Small selection of freight vehicles; 3 steam cranes; 1 diesel crane

Owners
850 and 990 on loan from the National Railway Museum

Stephenson Railway Museum & North Tyneside Steam Rly

Tyne & Wear
Steam Centre

Member: AIRPS

A display in buildings which began life as the Tyne & Wear Metro Test Centre now features locomotives and exhibitions which illustrate railway development from waggonways to the present day
Location: Middle Engine Lane, North Tyneside
OS reference: NZ 396576
Operating society/organisation: Tyne & Wear Museums operates Stephenson Railway Museum and North Tyneside Steam Railway Association operates North Tyneside Steam Railway for North Tyneside Council, address c/o Stephenson Railway Museum, Middle Engine Lane, West Chirton, North Shields NE29 8DX
Car park: On site
Length of line: North Tyneside Steam Railway, 3 miles, Stephenson Railway Museum to Percy Main
Access by public transport: Tyne & Wear Metro to Percy Main when North Tyneside Steam Railway is in operation
Public opening: Weekends and bank holidays only — Easter to September. Write or 'phone 0191-262-2627 for details, including early/late season variations and

Locomotives and multiple-units

Name	No	Origin	Class	Type	Built
—	03078	BR	03	0-6-0DM	1959
—	12098	BR	11	0-6-0DE	1951
—	3267	NER	—	DMLV	1904

Industrial locomotives

Name	No	Builder	Type	Built
Billy	—	Killingworth or RS & Co (1)	0-4-0	1816-26
—	A No 5	Kitson (2509)	0-6-0PT	1883
Ashington No 5	5	Peckett (1970)	0-6-0ST	1939
MEA No 1	1	RSH (7683)	0-6-0T	1951
—	E4	Siemens-Schuchert (457)	Bo-BoWE	1909
Thomas Burt MP 1837-1902	401	Bagnall (2994)	0-6-0ST	1950
—	10	Consett Iron Co	0-6-0DM	1958

Stock
1 LNER Gresley BFK; 3 BR non-gangwayed coaches, 1 LNER Gresley BGP

Owners
12098 is private
NER van the National Railway Museum

special events
Special notes: Stephenson Railway Museum and North Tyneside Steam Railway share facilities in buildings. North Tyneside Steam Railway Association operates and maintains exhibits from the

Museum Collection
Facilities for disabled: Access for wheelchairs to Museum building at Middle Engine Lane. Access to stations also wheelchair ramp onto train

Swanage Railway — 'The Purbeck Line'

Dorset
Timetable Service

Member: AIRPS

Overlooked by the historic ruins of Corfe Castle, this railway is slowly extending towards Wareham and a connection to the Railtrack network
Location: Swanage station
Operations Manager: Paul McDonald

Passenger Services Manager: David Green
Operating society/organisation: Swanage Railway Co Ltd, Station House, Swanage, Dorset BH19 1HB
Telephone: Swanage (01929)

425800. Talking Timetable — 01929 424276
Fax: 01929 426680
Main station: Swanage
Other public stations: Herston Halt, Harman's Cross, Corfe Castle and Norden.

Cont

OS reference: SZ 026789

Car park: Norden park & ride signposted off A351 Wareham-Swanage road on the approach to Corfe Castle. Limited parking available at Swanage station

Access by public transport: Regular bus services operated by Wilts & Dorset from Bournemouth, Poole and Wareham to Swanage

On site facilities: Souvenir shopat Swanage and Corfe Castle. Buffet car on most trains. Picnic areas at Swanage, Harmans Cross and Norden. Exhibition and cinema coach at Swanage. 5in gauge railway at Swanage on some weekends. Travel Agency at Swanage station

Length of line: 6 miles, Swanage-Herston Halt-Harman's Cross-Corfe Castle-Norden

Public opening: Swanage station open every day except Christmas Day. Trains operate during 1997 daily 15-23 February; Sundays only March; daily 28 March-13 April then Wednesdays, Thursdays, weekends until 25 April; daily (except Mondays & Fridays until 22 May; daily 24 May-28 September; weekends in October; daily 30 October- 7 November; Sundays only in November

Special events: Please contact for details

Facilities for disabled: Access to shop and toilets specially adapted coach on most trains

Membership details: Sue Payne c/o Southern Steam Trust at above address

Membership journal: *Swanage Railway News* — quarterly

Locomotives and multiple-units

Name	No	Origin	Class	Type	Built
—	6695	GWR	5600	0-6-2T	1928
—	30053	LSWR	M7	0-4-4T	1905
257 Squadron	34072	SR	BB	4-6-2	1948
—	80078	BR	4MT	2-6-4T	1954
—	80104	BR	4MT	2-6-4T	1955
—	1708	MR	IF	0-6-0T	1880
—	30075	JZ	USA	0-6-0T	1950s
—	D3591	BR	08	0-6-0DE	1958
—	D9521	BR	14	0-6-0DH	1964
—	52048	BR	108	DMCL	1960
—	51919	BR	108	DMBS	1956

Industrial locomotives

Name	No	Builder	Type	Built
Cunarder	47160	Hunslet (1690)	0-6-0T	1931
May	2	Fowler (4210132)	0-4-0DM	1957
Beryl	—	Planet (2054)	4wPM	1937
—	2150	Peckett (2150)	0-6-0T	1954
Rosedale	110070	—	0-4-0DE	—

Locomotive notes: 30053 and 34072 will be away periodically on short-term loan. *Cunarder* is on loan to the Lavender Line. 35022's frames are at Sellinge for shot blasting

Stock

3 ex-LSWR coach bodies; 4 ex-SR vans; 9 ex-SR coaches; 18 ex-BR Mk 1 coaches; 15 various types of wagons; 1 ex-BR Mk 3 Sleeping coach; 1 ex-SR 15ton diesel-electric crane; 1 ex-London Transport Plasser & Theurer ballast tamper; 1 ex-BR Corridor 2nd converted to disabled persons coach. Brake vans from SR, LMS, LSWR, GWR; 3 ex-BR M/Camm Pullmans (2 restored for 'Wessex Belle', 1 under restoration

Owners

6695 the Great Western Railway Preservation Group
Cunarder the 1708 Locomotive Preservation Trust Ltd
1708 the 1708 Locomotive Preservation Trust Ltd
34072 and 80104 the Southern Locomotives Ltd
30053 the Drummond Locomotive Society
30075 and 80078 the Project 62 Group
Pullmans by Flying Scotsman Railways

Marketing name: The Purbeck Line

Swindon & Cricklade Railway

Wiltshire
Steam Centre

Member: ARPS, TT

This is the only preserved section of the former Midland & South Western Junction Railway, the society having had to relay track and associated works. The line is being extended to a new station Hayes Knoll and is expected to open 1997/98 to serve the planned engine shed complex

Location: Tadpole Lane, Blunsdon (approximately mid way between Blunsdon St Andrew and Purton)

Chairman: J. Larkin

Locomotives and multiple-unit

Name	No	Origin	Class	Type	Built
Foremarke Hall	7903	GWR	'Hall'	4-6-0	1949
—*	5637	GWR	56xx	0-6-2T	1924
—	3845	GWR	2884	2-8-0	1942
—	D2152	BR	03	0-6-0DM	1960
—	56317	BR	100	MBS	1958
—	51434	M/Cam	101	MBS	1958
—	52005	BR	107	DMBS	1960
—	52025	BR	107	DMBS	1960
—	59117	M/Cam	101	TC	1958

* expected to return to service during 1997 for the first time since 1964

92   *Cont*

Activity on the Swanage Railway as No 34072 *257 Squadron* leaves the station and the driver of No 41708 contemplates the next move. *Andrew P. M. Wright*

Telford's vertical-boilered narrow gauge tram locomotive waits patiently for both crew and passengers. *Melvyn Hopwood*

Operating society/organisation:
Swindon & Cricklade Railway,
Blunsdon Station, Blunsdon,
Swindon, Wiltshire SN2 4DZ
Telephone: Swindon (01793)
771615 (weekends only)
Station: Blunsdon
OS reference: SU 110897
Length of line: 1-mile
Car park: Tadpole Lane,
Blunsdon
Refreshment facilities: Blunsdon
station amenities building
Toilet: Blunsdon station amenities
building
Souvenir shop: Blunsdon station
amenities building. Various sales
stands on Open Days around
station area. Museum in converted
coach
Depot: Blunsdon
Public opening: Saturdays and
Sundays throughout the year.

Industrial locomotives

Name	No	Builder	Type	Built
—†	22	Barclay (2320)	0-4-0ST	1952
—	—	Fowler (4210137)	0-4-0DM	1958
Woodbine	—	Fowler (21442)	0-4-0DM	1936
Richard Trevithick	—	Barclay (2354)	0-4-0ST	1955
Merlin/Myrddin	1371	Peckett (1967)	0-4-0ST	1939

†on loan from Embsay Steam Railway for 1997

Stock
6 BR Mk 1 coaches; 2 GWR coaches; Selection of goods rolling stock;
Wickham railcar

Owners
7903 the Foremarke Hall Locomotive Group
5637 the 5637 Locomotive Group

Passenger trains: Details from
Public Relations Manager c/o
above address
Special events: Please contact for
details
Facilities for disabled: Access to
shop and refreshments
Membership details: Membership
Secretary c/o above address
Membership journal: Quarterly
Marketing names: Tiddlydyke

Swindon GWR Museum

Member: AIRPS

Wiltshire
Museum

The Great Western Railway
Museum began life as a lodging
house for railway workers, and was
then a Wesleyan Methodist Chapel
for 90 years before being acquired
by Swindon Borough Council and
converted into a museum.
Alongside the museum, in the
heart of the railway village, visitors
can glimpse the living conditions
of the railworkers at the turn of the
century, in the carefully restored
workman's house.
   Plans are well advanced for a new
enlarged Railway Heritage Centre
on the old Swindon Works site to
replace the existing GWR Museum
collection. This may well involve
the closure of the Faringdon Road
building in the autumn of 1997,
and readers are advised to
telephone the museum before
travelling. It is hoped that the new
museum will open in
spring/summer 1998, if funds are
forthcoming
Keeper: T. Bryan
Location: Faringdon Road,
Swindon, Wiltshire

Locomotives

Name	No	Origin	Class	Type	Built
—	2516	GWR	2301	0-6-0	1897
Kings George V	6000	GWR	'King'	4-6-0	1927
—	9400	GWR	9400	0-6-0PT	1947
North Star*	—	GWR	—	2-2-2	1837
—	4	GWR	Diesel railcar	Bo-Bo	1934

*Broad gauge (7ft 0.25in) replica

Owners
All locomotives are part of the National Railway Museum Collection

OS reference: SU 145846
Operating society/organisation:
Borough of Thamesdown, GWR
Museum, Faringdon Road,
Swindon, Wiltshire
Telephone: Swindon (01793)
493189
Car park: Swindon BR station and
street parking
Access by public transport:
Swindon BR (10 minutes)
On site facilities: A selection of
souvenirs is available
Public opening: Weekdays 10.00-
17.00, Sundays 14.00-17.00.
Closed Good Friday, Christmas
Eve, Christmas Day, Boxing Day,
New Year's Day
Special Notes: The Museum also
houses a considerable number of
photographs depicting scenes of the
GWR along with nameplates,
models, posters, tickets, etc. 1992:
Return to Swindon Exhibition
continues this year
Membership details: The Friends
of Swindon Railway Museum, c/o
The GWR Museum
Membership journal: North Star
— quarterly

Tanfield Railway
Member: AIRPS

Tyne & Wear
Timetable Service

The oldest railway in the world, featuring 1725 route, 1725 Causey embankment, 1727 Causey arch, 1766 Gibraltar bridge and 1854 Marley Hill engine shed. Also collection of local engines, Victorian carriages and vintage workshop

Location: Off the A6076 Sunniside to Stanley road

OS reference: NZ 207573

Operating society/organisation: The Tanfield Railway, Marley Hill Engine Shed, Sunniside, Gateshead, Tyne & Wear. Postal address: 33 Stocksfield Avenue, Newcastle-upon-Tyne NE5 2DX

Telephone: Newcastle (0191) 2742002

Main stations: Andrews House, Sunniside, Causey, East Tanfield

Car park: Marley Hill, Causey picnic area

Access by public transport: X30 (weekdays) stops outside main entrance; 706, 708, 722 Sundays to Sunniside only, near to Sunniside station

Catering facilities: Light refreshment available on operating days

On site facilities: Shop and toilets

Length of line: 3 miles

Public opening: Trains run every Sunday and bank holiday weekend January to November. Also Thursdays and Saturdays from 24 July-30 August. Santa trains in December. Marley Hill engine shed open daily for viewing

Special events: Teddy Bear Weekends — 19/20 April, 20/21 September; Children's weekends — 14/15 June, 9/10 August; Two Train Days — 4/5, 25/26 May, 24/25 August; Santa Steamings — 6/7, 13/14. 20/21-24 December; Mince Pie Specials — 26 December

Family tickets: Available

Facilities for disabled: Access to Andrews House station and Marley Hill engine shed. Toilets at Causey car park

Membership details: Miss E. Martin, 33 Stocksfield Avenue, Fenham, Newcastle-upon-Tyne NE5 2DX

Membership journal: *Tanfield*

Cont

Locomotives

Name	No	Origin	Class	Type	Built
—	M2*	TGR	M	4-6-2	1951

*3ft 6in gauge, Tasmanian Government Railways (RSH 7630)

Industrial locomotives

Name	No	Builder	Type	Built
—	9	AEG (1565)	4w-4wE	1913
Gamma	—	Bagnall (2779)	0-6-0ST	1945
Horden	—	Barclay (1015)	0-6-0ST	1904
—	6	Barclay (1193)	0-4-2ST	1910
—	17	Barclay (1338)	0-6-0T	1913
—	32	Barclay (1659)	0-4-0ST	1920
—	3	E. Borrows (37)	0-4-0WT	1898
—	6	Fowler (4240010)	0-6-0DH	1960
Wellington	—	B/Hawthorn (266)	0-4-0ST	1873
Enterprise	—	R&W Hawthorn (2009)	0-4-0ST	1884
Cyclops	112	H/Leslie (2711)	0-4-0ST	1907
—	2	H/Leslie (2859)	0-4-0ST	1911
Stagshaw	—	H/Leslie (3513)	0-6-0ST	1923
—	3	H/Leslie (3575)	0-6-0ST	1923
—	13	H/Leslie (3732)	0-4-0ST	1928
—	3	H/Leslie (3746)	0-6-0F	1929
Irwell	—	H/Clarke (1672)	0-4-0ST	1937
—	38	H/Clarke (1823)	0-6-0T	1949
—	501	Hunslet (6612)	0-6-0DH	1965
—	4	Sentinel (9559)	0-4-0T	1953
—	L2	R/Hornsby (312989)	0-4-0DE	1952
—	35	R/Hornsby (418600)	0-4-0DE	1958
—	158	RSH (6980)	0-4-0DM	1940
Hendon	—	RSH (7007)	0-4-0CT	1940
—	62	RSH (7035)	0-6-0ST	1940
—	3	RSH (7078)	4w-4wE	1940
—	49	RSH (7098)	0-6-0ST	1943
Progress	—	RSH (7298)	0-6-0ST	1946
Cochrane	—	RSH (7409)	0-4-0ST	1948
—	44	RSH (7760)	0-6-0ST	1953
—	38	RSH (7763)	0-6-0ST	1954
—	21	RSH (7796)	0-4-0ST	1954
—	47	RSH (7800)	0-6-0ST	1954
—	1	RSH (7901)	0-4-0DM	1958
—	16	RSH (7944)	0-6-0ST	1957
FGF	—	Barclay (D592)	0-4-0DH	1969
—	2	A/Whitworth (D22)	0-4-0DE	1933

2ft gauge

Name	No	Builder	Type	Built
Escucha	11	B/Hawthorn (748)	0-4-0ST	1883
—	—	Clayton (133141)	4wBE	1984
—	—	Hunslet(7332	4wDM	1973
—	—	L/Blackstone (53162)	4wDM	1962
—	—	L/Blackstone (54781)	4wDM	1962
—	—	R/Harnsby (323587)	4wDM	1952
—	—	R/Hornsby (244487)	4wDM	1946
—	25	RSH (8201)	4wBE	1960
—	—	W/Rogers	4wBE	—

Stock

19 4-wheel carriages; 3 6-wheel carriages; 1 6-wheel van; 14 hopper wagons; 9 contractors bogies; 3 brake vans; 3 steam cranes; 8 covered wagons; 4 open wagons; 4 black wagons; 3 flat wagons

Railway News — 4 times/year
Special notes: Families can alight at Causey station for 2 miles of

walks through the picturesque Causey Woods, picnic facilities and toilet available in car park

Telford Horsehay Steam Trust

Shropshire
Steam Centre

Member: AIRPS

Location: Horsehay, Telford, Shropshire
OS reference: SJ 675073
Operating society/organisation: Telford Horsehay Steam Trust, The Old Loco Shed, Horsehay, Telford, TF4 2LT
On site facilities: Model railway, picnic area, narrow gauge steam tramway, miniature railway (separate charge) ticket gives unlimited travel (except miniature railway)
Public opening: Please contact for details

Locomotives

Name	No	Origin	Class	Type	Built
—	5619	GWR	5600	0-6-2T	1925

Industrial locomotives

Name	No	Builder	Type	Built
Peter	—	Barclay (782)	0-6-0ST	1896
—	MP1	Barclay (1944)	0-4-0F	1944
Tom	—	N/British (27414)	0-4-0DH	1954
Ironbridge No 3	—	Peckett (1990)	0-4-0ST	1940
—	—	Sentinel (9535)	4wVBT	1952
—	D2959	R/Hornsby (382824)	4wDM	1955
Don Atkinson	—	R/Hornsby	0-4-0DH	1968
—	—	R/Hornsby	0-4-0DE	1969
—	—	YEC	0-4-0DE	1967
2ft gauge				
Thomas	—	Kierstead	4wVBT	1979

Stock
1 ex-BR Mk 1 coach; 1 ex-GWR auto-trailer; 1 ex-GWR Toad brake van; 1 ex-GWR 3-ton hand crane; 1 Wickham trolley; Various wagons

Tiverton Museum

Devon
Museum

The Museum, dominated by No 1442, affectionately known as the 'Tivvy Bumper', houses a large collection of railway relics
Location: Tiverton, Devon
OS reference: SS 955124
Operating society/organisation: Tiverton & Mid Devon Museum Trust, St Andrew Street, Tiverton, Devon EX16 6PH
Telephone: Tiverton (01884) 256295

Locomotives

Name	No	Origin	Class	Type	Built
(Tivvy Bumper)	1442	GWR	1400	0-4-2T	1935

Car park: Adjoining access by public transport: Rail to Tiverton Parkway, then by bus, or bus from Exeter
On site facilities: Museum, shop and toilets
Public opening: Daily 10.30-

16.30; except Sundays and from Christmas to end of January
Special notes: Limited facilities for disabled

Transperience — West Yorkshire Transport Discovery Park

West Yorkshire
Museum

The Transperience vehicle collection consists of some 26 items, of which six are rail or tramway vehicles. It is hoped to progressively reopen the Spen Valley Railway commencing at Low Moor.

Transperience looks at the history

Industrial locomotives (all electric)

Name	No	Builder	Type	Built
—	10	Siemens	Bo	1913
—	1	E/Electric	Bo	1935

Stock
Derby 'Lightweight' Battery Electric unit Sc79998/9 (on loan to East Lancashire Railway); 2 Budapest trams 2576/2577; Gratz 210 tram

of public transport in a fun and educational way from 1830 to the present day. It covers the railway revolution and looks at the evolution of the tram, trolleybus, motorbus and supertram.

The five exhibition halls are linked with 700m of tram track. Motorbuses, trams and trolleybuses are run between the halls offering visitors a mix of vehilcle ride experience. Over 90- hands on activities and four hi-tech theatres keep all age groups entertained for a full day.

Location: Transperience Way, Bradford BD12 7HQ, at junction 2 on M606 Bradford or via bus 268 from Bradford Interchange
Operating society/organisation: West Yorkshire Transport Trust Ltd, Transperience Way, Bradford BD12 7HW
Telephone: 01274 690909
Public opening: Daily, except 25/26 December. April-September 10.00-17.30; October-March 10.30-16.00. Groups welcome. Entrance admission prices on application
Membership details: West Yorkshire Transport Museum Society, c/o above address. The Society provides volunteers who support Transperience through the restoration of Trust-owned exhibits and driving the vehicles. Telephone Transperience for details

Vintage Carriage Museum

Member: AIRPS, TT

West Yorkshire
Museum

A fascinating collection of elderly railway carriages and small locomotives, interestingly presented. Sit in a fully restored, prize winning 1876-built Manchester, Sheffield & Lincolnshire Railway carriage or relive the dark days of wartime travel in one of our three Metropolitan Railway carriages. Listen to the 'Travellers' Tales' and view the collection of railway posters and other items. Half hour video presentation. Carriages have appeared in film and television productions

Our carriages are often used at special events and on vintage trains on the Keighley & Worth Valley Railway, and elsewhere
Location: Vintage Carriage Museum, Ingrow Station Yard, South Street, Keighley, West Yorkshire BD21 5AZ. On the A629 road
Operations Manager: Michael Cope, Hon Secretary, VCT
Operating society/organisation: Vintage Carriages Trust (a Registered Charity No 510776)
Telephone: Keighley (01535) 680425
Car Park: Yes. Also coach parking at Ingrow station
Access by public transport: By Rail to Keighley (one mile), or by Worth Valley Railway train to Ingrow West (adjacent): good bus service from Keighley town centre. Calderline bus 502 from Huddersfield and Halifax and Keighley town centre. Keighley & District buses 663, 664, 665 from Bradford, via Bingley, Saltaire and

Stock

Railway	BR or previous owner Number	Date type	built	Seats	Weight	Length
MS&LR	176	4-wheel 1st/2nd/3rd/luggage	1876	34	12T	28ft 0in
ECJS	143	6-wheel 3rd brake	1888	40	14T	34ft 11in
MR	358	6-wheel 1st/3rd/luggage	1886	32	15T	34ft 0in
Met	427	BS	1910	84	30T	54ft 0in
Met	465	S	1919	108	30T	54ft 0in
Met	509	F	1923	84	30T	54ft 0in
SR (SECR)	S3554S	BSK	1924	42	33T	65ft 3in
BR (SR)	S1469S	TSO	1951	64	32T	67ft 1in
GN	2856	Non vestibule composite, lav brake	1898	34	?	45ft 0in

(also two oil tank wagons: MR, c1890, and Esso, 1939)

Industrial locomotives

Name	No	Builder	Type	Built
Bellerophon	—	Haydock Foundry (C)	0-6-0WT	1874
Sir Berkeley	—	M/Wardle (1210)	0-6-0ST	1891
Lord Mayor	—	H/Clarke (402)	0-4-0ST	1893

Keighley town centre. Keighley & District buses 696 and 697 from Bradford via Denholme. Tel: 0113 245 7676 for bus and Metro Train information
On site facilities: Toilets, transport relics shop
Public opening: Daily 11.30-17.00 except 25/26 December. Special openings outside these times and dates, and school and other party bookings, are welcome: telephone (01535) 680425
Facilities for the disabled: Toilets with full access. Limited wheelchair access elsewhere. Braille leaflet and guidebook. Taped guide book for loan during visit. It is planned to install an inductive loop system and wheelchair stairlift during the summer
Special notes: Most, but not all, of the collection is displayed in the Museum at any one time which is currently having a £300,000 extension built. Visitors are welcome to browse in the shop, or visit the museum. One or more of the carriages (and also the locomotives Bellerophon and Sir Berkeley) are occasionally in passenger use on the Worth Valley Railway (3-5, 11 and 18 May) or elsewhere. Please 'phone for KWVR running dates

Cont

Membership details: Membership Secretary c/o above address (Haworth station)
Marketing names: Vintage Carriages Trust or VCT

Metropolitan Railway No 509, photographed whilst on loan to the Great Central Railway for a filming assignment. *VCT*

Wells & Walsingham Light Railway

Member: AIRPS, TT

Norfolk
Timetable Service

One man's railway, the life and love of retired naval commander, Roy Francis, this delightful line which is totally uncommercialised runs along the old Wells branch to Walsingham where the old station has been transformed into a Russian Orthodox Church by the addition of an onion-shaped dome to its roof. A must if you find yourself nearby
Location: On A149, Stiffkey Road, Wells next the Sea, Norfolk
General Manager: Lt-Cdr R. W. Francis
Operating organisation: Wells &

Walsingham Light Railway, Wells Next The Sea, Norfolk NR23 1RB
Car park: Yes
Access by public transport: Eastern Counties buses
On site facilities: Souvenir shop, toilets and tea shop
Length of line: 4 miles, 10.25in gauge
Public opening: Daily Easter to the end September
Special notes: Journey may be commenced at either end. Believed to be world's longest 10¼in gauge line. Built on the old Wells & Fakenham Railway trackbed. Old

Swainsthorpe signalbox on site at Wells. Motive power is provided by a Garratt locomotive.
  Family ticket available for 2 adults and up to 4 children.
  Life passes in form of gilt edged enamel medallion now available, please enquire for details
Membership details: Membership Secretary, Wells & Walsingham Light Railway Support Group, c/o above address
Membership journal: Newsletter — quarterly

West Lancashire Light Railway

Lancashire
Steam Centre

Location: Alty's Brickworks. Station Road, Hesketh Bank, near Preston, Lancashire
OS reference: SD 448229
Operating society/organisation:

Industrial locomotives

Name	No	Builder	Type	Built
Clwyd	1	R/Hornsby (264251)	4wDM	1951
Tawd	2	R/Hornsby (222074)	4wDM	1943
Irish Mail	3	Hunslet (823)	0-4-0ST	1903

The West Lancashire Light Railway Association, Secretary, 790 Ormskirk Road, Pemberton, Wigan WN5 8AX
Telephone: 01772 815881 or (01942) 218078 (Secretary)
Car parks: On site
Access by public transport: BR to Preston or Southport. Bus route 100 and 102. Between Preston and Southport
On site facilities: Gift shop, light refreshments, picnic tables, 2ft gauge line
Public opening: Easter weekend (not Saturday); May Day Bank Holiday Sunday and Monday; Spring Bank Holiday, then every Sunday until end of October. Opening times 12.30-17.00
Special events: Friendly Engine Day — 18 May, Gala Day — 10 August, Industrial Day — 5 October; Santa Specials — 7, 14, 21 December

Name	No	Builder	Type	Built
—	4	Hibberd (1777)	4wPM	1931
—	5	R/Hornsby (200478)	4wDM	1940
—	7	M/Rail (8992)	4wDM	1946
—	8	H/Hunslet (4480)	4wDM	1953
Joffre	9	K/Stuart (2405)	0-6-0T	1915
—	10	Hibberd (2555)	4wDM	1946
—	16	R/Hornsby (202036)	4wDM	1941
—	19	Lister (10805)	4wPM	1939
—	20	Baguley (3002)	4wPM	1937
—	21	H/Hunslet (1963)	4wDM	1939
—	25	R/Hornsby (297054)	4wDM	1950
Mill Reef	27	M/Rail (7371)	4wDM	1939
—	30	M/Rail (11258)	4wDM	1964
—	32	M/Rail (11246)	4wDM	1963
Montalban	34	O&K (6641)	0-4-0WT	1913
Utrillas	35	O&K (2378)	0-4-0WT	1907
—	36	R/Hornsby (339105)	4wDM	1953
Jonathan	37	Hunslet (678)	0-4-0ST	1898
—	38	Hudswell (D750)	0-4-0DM	1949
—	39	Hibberd (3916)	4wDM	1959
—	40	R/Hornsby (381705)	4wDM	1959
—	41	Lister (29890)	4wPM	1946
—	42	Hunslet (8917)	4wDM	1980

Note: 30 M/Rail (11258) is presently on loan to Steamport Southport

Stock
Toastrack coach built 1986 by WLLR. Semi-open coach built 1993 by WLLR. Brake van built 1987 by WLLR. Large collection various wagons

West Somerset Railway
Somerset
Timetable Service
Member: AIRPS, TT

Running for 20 miles, this is Britain's longest preserved railway and evokes all the atmosphere of a country railway from a more leisured age. The line is host to several societies and groups, and several stations have their own museum, such as the Somerset & Dorset Trust; at Washford. There are some idyllic country stations in the Quantock Hills and Dunster station serves as the model for Hornby Dublo's branch line station
Managing Director: Mark L. Smith
Headquarters: West Somerset Railway, The Railway Station, Minehead, Somerset
Telephone: Minehead (01643) 704996. Talking timetable: (01643) 707650
Main station: Minehead
Other public stations: Dunster, Blue Anchor, Washford, Watchet, Williton, Doniford Beach Halt, Stogumber, Crowcombe, Bishop's Lydeard
OS reference: Minehead SS

Locomotives and multiple-units

Name	No	Origin	Class	Type	Built
—	53808	S&DJR	7F	2-8-0	1925
—	3205	GWR	2251	0-6-0	1946
—	3850	GWR	2884	2-8-0	1942
—	4160	GWR	5101	2-6-2T	1948
—	4561	GWR	4500	2-6-2T	1924
Dumbleton Hall	4920	GWR	'Hall'	4-6-0	1929
—	5542*	GWR	4575	2-6-2T	1928
—	6412	GWR	6400	0-6-0PT	1934
Dinmore Manor	7820	GWR	'Manor'	4-6-0	1950
Odney Manor	7828	GWR	'Manor'	4-6-0	1950
Braunton	34046	SR	WC	4-6-2	1946
—	D2119	BR	03	0-6-0DM	1959
—	D2133	BR	03	0-6-0DM	1959
—	D2271	BR	04	0-6-0DM	1952
—	D3462	BR	08	0-6-0DE	1957
—	08850	BR	08	0-6-0DE	1961
—	D9526	BR	14	0-6-0DH	1964
—	D9551	BR	14	0-6-0DH	1965
—	D7017	BR	35	B-B	1962
—	D7018	BR	35	B-B	1964
—	D7523	BR	25	Bo-Bo	1963
Royal Oak	50017	BR	50	Co-Co	1967
Defiance	50149	BR	50	Co-Co	1967
Western Campaigner	D1010	BR	52	C-C	1962
—	50413	P/Royal	103	DMBS	1957
—	51663	BR	115	DMBS	1960

Cont

England

GWR 'Manor' class 4-6-0 No 7820 *Dinmore Manor* **passing through Watchet station on the West Somerset Railway.**
Robin Stewart-Smith

975463, Williton ST 085416,
Bishops Lydeard ST 164290
Car parks: Minehead, Williton,
Bishops Lydeard. Some parking at
all stations except Doniford Beach
Access by public transport:
Nearest BR station, Taunton.
Southern National Omnibus Co
(01823 272033)
Refreshment facilities: Minehead,
Bishops Lydeard (limited opening).
Wine and Dine trains, contact
01984 623873. Buffet car on most
steam trains
Souvenir shops: Minehead,
Bishop's Lydeard
Museum: Somerset & Dorset
Railway Museum Trust, Washford
(open WSR operating days March-
end October). GWR Museum at
Blue Anchor (open Sundays &
Bank Holidays WSR operating
season)
Depots: Bishop's Lydeard,
Williton, Washford, Minehead
Length of line: 20 miles
Passenger trains: Steam and diesel
trains to Bishops Lydeard
Period of public operation: SAE
for details
Special events: 25th Anniversary
Steam Gala — 21-23 March; Easter
Steam Weekend — 30/31 March;
Vintage Diesel Weekend — 16-18
May; Friends of Thomas the Tank
Engine — 5/6 July; Vintage
Vehicle Rally at Bishops Lydeard
— 2/3 August; Somerset & Dorset
Railway Trust Weekend at
Washford — 23/24 August;
Autumn Steam Weekend — 13-15
September; Friends of Thomas the
Tank Engine — 18/19 October;
Santa Specials — 6/7, 13/14,
20/21, 24; 1st Winter trains — 26

Name	No	Origin	Class	Type	Built
—	51852	BR	115	DMBS	1960
—	51887	BR	115	DMBS	1960
—	56097	M/Cam	101	DTC	1957
—	56169	P/Royal	103	DTCL	1957
—	59678	BR	115	TC	1960

*Undergoing restoration at Bridgnorth

Industrial locomotives

Name	No	Builder	Type	Built
Isabel	—	H/Leslie (3437)	0-6-0ST	1919
Kilmersdon	—	Peckett (1788)	0-4-0ST	1929
—	24	Ruston (210479)	4wDM	1941
—	—	Ruston (183062)	4wDM	1937
—	57	Sentinel (10214)	0-6-0DM	1964

Stock
22 ex-BR Mk 1 coaches; 1 ex-BR Mk 2 coach; 2 ex-BR Restaurant cars; 1
ex-BR Sleeping Car; 3 ex-S&DJR 6-wheel coaches, 7 ex-GWR camping
coaches; 1 ex-GWR Sleeping Coach; 1 ex-SR 'Ironclad' coach; 1 ex-GWR
Hawksworth coach; 1 ex-GWR 5-ton hand crane; more than 40 freight
vehicles

Owners
53808, *Isabel, Kilmersdon* the Somerset & Dorset Museum Trust
D1010, D7017, D7018, D9526 & 08850 the Diesel & Electric Preservation
Group
D2119, D3462, D7523, 50017 Dr John F. Kennedy
5542 the 5542 Fund
3205 the 2251 Class Fund
3850 and 7820 the 3850 Preservation Society
4160 the 4160 Ltd
D2271 & D9551 the WSR plc
4920 the South Devon Railway Trust

December-1 January
Facilities for disabled: Parking
space level with entrance. No steps
to shop or booking office, level
access to toilets (disabled toilets at
Minehead 100yd from station).
Special saloon *Lorna Doone*
accommodates 14 wheel chairs and
has disabled toilet. Advanced
booking essential. Catering

facilities can be reached without
difficulties. Groups can be catered
for.
Membership details: West
Somerset Railway Association, c/o
above address
Membership journal: *WSR
Journal* — quarterly

Winchcombe Railway Museum

Three miles from the
Gloucestershire-Warwickshire
railway, the diverse collection
includes signalling equipment,
lineside fixtures, horse-drawn road
vehicles, tickets, lamps, etc. Indoor
and outdoor displays set in half-
acre of traditional Victorian
Cotswold Garden. Visitors are
encouraged to touch and operate
exhibits
Location: 23 Gloucester Street,

Winchcombe, Gloucestershire
OS reference: SP 023283
Operating society/organisation:
Winchcombe Railway Museum
Association, 23 Gloucester Street,
Winchcombe, Gloucestershire
Telephone: Winchcombe (01242)
620641
Car Park: On street at entrance
Access by public transport: Bus
service from Cheltenham operated
by Castleways Ltd

On site facilities: Relic,
refreshments and souvenir shop
Public opening: Weekends and
bank holidays — Easter to end
October; daily throughout August
Facilities for disabled: Access to
all parts except toilets
Special notes: Many visitor-
operated exhibits, picnic area, pet
animals

Scotland

Alford Valley Railway

Aberdeenshire
Steam Centre

The Alford Valley Railway operates from the restored station yard which once marked the terminus of the branch line linking the villages of upper Donside with Kintore Junction, thence to Aberdeen
Location: On A944, 25 miles west of Aberdeen, adjacent to Grampian Transport Museum
Headquarters: Alford Valley Railway Co Ltd, Alford Station, Alford, Aberdeenshire, Scotland
Main station: Alford
Car park: On site
Length of line: 3km, 2ft gauge
Museum: Grampian Transport Museum adjacent
Depot: Alford station
Period of public operation: Railway operates: April, May September — weekends only

(13.00-17.00); June, July and August — daily 13.00-17.00. Trains depart at 30min intervals Alford Heritage Centre is open daily (10.00-17.00)
Special notes: Steam-operated on first Sunday of each month from

April to SeptemberSpecial bookings available, tel: 019755 62811
Membership details: Membership Secretary, AVR, Association, Greag Mawr, Main Street, Aberdeenshire AB33 8AA

Industrial locomotives

Name	No	Builder	Type	Built
Saccharine	—	Fowler (13355)	0-4-2T	1914
Hamewith	—	Lister (3198)	4wDM	c1930
—	—	M/Rail (5342)	4wDM	1931
—	—	M/Rail (9215)	4wDM	1946
—	—	M/Rail (9381)	4wDM	1948
—	—	M/Rail (22129)	4wDM	1962
—	—	M/Rail (2221)	4wDM	1964

Rolling stock

Two 24-seat coaches, 50-seat coach, 24-seat ex-Aberdeen tramcar, various wagons

Saccharine **and a steam-outline Motor Rail stand outside the shed.** *Melvyn Hopwood*

Bo'ness & Kenneil Railway

Member: AIRPS, TT

West Lothian
Timetable Service

Historic railway buildings, including the station and train shed, have been relocated from sites all over Scotland. In a purpose-built exhibition hall, the Scottish Railway Exhibition tells the story of the development of the railways in Scotland, and its impact on the people. The rich geology of the area, with its 300 million year old fossils, is explained during a conducted tour of the caverns of the former Birkhill Fireclay Mine

Operating Society/location:
Scottish Railway Preservation Society, Bo'ness Station, Union Street, Bo'ness, West Lothian, EH51 9AQ

Access by public transport:
Nearest ScotRail station — Linlithgow. Bus services from Linlithgow, Falkirk, Stirling, Edinburgh and Glasgow

OS reference: NT 003817

Telephone: Bo'ness (01506) 822298

Main station: Bo'ness

Other station: Birkhill

Car parks: At Bo'ness and Birkhill (free)

Refreshment facilities:
Unlicenced buffets at Bo'ness and Birkhill. Buffet car on some trains. Picnic tables at both stations

Souvenir shop: Bo'ness

Depot: Bo'ness

Length of line: 3.5 miles

Period of public operation:
Weekends 29 March-19 October; Good Friday 28 March; Mondays 31 March, all Mondays in May; daily (except Mondays) 4 July-17 August; October mid-week 15/16 October; school days 10-12, 17-19 June, 10/11 September

Special events: Easter Egg Specials — 28-31 March; Friends of Thomas the Tank Engine — 17/18 May, 16/17 August; Vintage Vehicle Rally — 15 June; Diesel Gala Weekend— 30/31 August; Historic Commercial Vehicle Rally — 14 September; Santa Specials weekends — 29 November-21 December

Facilities for disabled: At Bo'ness for access to exhibition hall, shop, cafeteria and trains

Locomotives

Name	No	Origin	Class	Type	Built
Sovereign	44871	LMS	5MT	4-6-0	1945
—	419	CR	439	0-4-4T	1908
Morayshire	246	LNER	D49	4-4-0	1928
Glen Douglas	256	NBR	D34	4-4-0	1913
—	42	NBR	Y9	0-4-0ST	1887
Maude	673	NBR	—	0-6-0	1891
—	80105	BR	4MT	2-6-4T	1955
—	08443 (D3558)	BR	08	0-6-0DE	1958
—	14901 (D9524)	BR	14	0-6-0DH	1964
—	D8020	BR	20	Bo-Bo	1959
—	25235 (D7585)	BR	25	Bo-Bo	1965
—	26004 (D5304)	BR	26	B0-Bo	1958
—	26024 (D5324)	BR	26	Bo-Bo	1959
—	D5351	BR	27	Bo-Bo	1961
—	27001 (D5347)	BR	27	Bo-Bo	1961
—	47643	BR	47	Co-Co	1968
Rodney	50021	BR	50	Co-Co	1968

Industrial locomotives

Name	No	Builder	Type	Built
Clydesmill	3	Barclay (1937)	0-4-0ST	1928
—	3	Barclay (2046)	0-4-0ST	1937
—	24	Barclay (2335)	0-6-0T	1953
Texaco	—	Fowler (4210140)	0-4-0DM	1958
(Lord King)	—	H/Leslie (3640)	0-4-0ST	1926
—	19	Hunslet (3818)	0-6-0ST	1954
DS3	—	R/Hornsby (275883)	4wDM	1949
DS4	P6687	R/Hornsby (312984)	0-4-0DE	1951
(Ranald)	—	Sentinel (9627)	4wVBT	1957
—	970214	Wickham (6050)	2w-2PMR	c1951
—	—	Matisa (48626)		
—	5	Hunslet (3837)	0-6-0ST	1955
—	(7)	Bagnall (2777)	0-6-0ST	1945
Borrowstounness	—*	Barclay (840)	0-4-0T	1899
—	—*	M/Rail (110U082)	4wDH	1970
—	—	Wickham (10482)	2w-2PMR	1970
—	(17)	Hunslet (2880)	0-6-0ST	1943
—	970213	Wickham (6049)	2w-2PMR	c1951
—	17	Barclay (2296)	0-4-0ST	1952
Lady Victoria	3	Barclay (1458)	0-6-0ST	1916
The Wemyss Coal Co Ltd	20	Barclay (2068)	0-6-0T	1939
—	(6)	Barclay (2127)	0-4-0CT	1942
No 1	—	Barclay (343)	0-6-0DM	1941
City of Aberdeen	—	B/Hawthorn (912)	0-4-0ST	1887
F82 (Fairfield)	—	E/Electric (1131) (244)	4wBE	1940
Kelton Fell	13	Neilson (2203)	0-4-0ST	1876
Lord Roberts	1	N/Reid (5710)	0-6-0T	1902
(Tiger)	—	N/British (27415)	0-4-0DH	1954
Kilbagie	DS2	R/Hornsby (262998)	4wDM	1949
—	—	R/Hornsby (321733)	4wDM	1952
DS6	(1)	R/Hornsby (421439)	0-4-0DE	1958
St Mirren	(3)	R/Hornsby (423658)	0-4-0DE	1958
—	D88/003	R/Hornsby (506500)	4wDM	1965
—	(DS5)	R/Hornsby (423662)	0-4-0DE	1958

Owners

80105 and (Denis) owned by Scottish Locomotive Owners Group

246 and 24 owned by Royal Museum of Scotland

256 the Glasgow Museum of Transport

44871 the Sovereign Preservation Group

27001 the Class 27 Preservation Group

26004 and 26024 the 6LDA Group

Name	No	Builder	Type	Built
(Denis)	—	Sentinel (9631)	4wVBT	1958
—	—	Arrols (Glasgow)	2w-2DM	c1966

*3ft 0in gauge

Stock

A large selection of coaching stock, many built by Scottish pre-Grouping companies, ex-BR Class 126 dmu, and an appropriate collection of early freight vehicles

Caledonian Railway (Brechin)

Member: AIRPS

Tayside
Timetable Service

During the summer season we offer a combined 'Train & Tour' ticket. This gives the public a chance to travel on the railway and also visit the nearby House of Dun, a National Trust for Scotland property built by William Adam in 1730. Our Bridge of Dun station is also very close to one of the nation's finest bird sanctuaries, the two square mile Montrose Basin. Volunteers for the Caledonian Railway are provided exclusively by members of the Brechin Railway Preservation Society

Information enquiries: Iain A. H. Smith, Publicity Director, c/o 14 Moathill East, Cupar, Fife KY15 4DT

Headquarters: Caledonian Railway (Brechin) Ltd, The Station, 2 Park Road, Brechin, Angus DD9 7AF

Telephone: (01334) 655965, after 4.30pm Mon-Fri or (01674) 81318; or 01241 860322

Talking timetable: (01356) 622992

Main station: Brechin

Other public stations: Bridge of Dun

OS reference: NO 603603

Car park: Brechin, Bridge of Dun

Access by public transport: Nearest BR station — Montrose, 9 miles. Local bus operator, Strathtay Scottish — Dundee (01382) 228054/227201, Arbroath (01241) 870646, or Montrose (01674) 672805

Refreshment facilities: Light refreshments available during steamdays at Brechin

Picnic area: Bridge of Dun

Locomotives

Name	No	Origin	Class	Type	Built
—	46464	LMS	2MT	2-6-0	1950
—	D2866	BR	02	0-4-0DM	1961
Brechin City	D3059	BR	08	0-6-0DE	1954
—	26014	BR	26	Bo-Bo	1959
—	26035	BR	26	Bo-Bo	1959
—	27024	BR	27	Bo-Bo	1962

Industrial locomotives

Name	No	Builder	Type	Built
—	16	Bagnall (2759)	0-6-0ST	1944
—	6	Bagnall (2749)	0-6-0ST	1944
Bon Accord	2	Barclay (807)	0-4-0ST	1897
—	1	Barclay (1863)	0-4-0ST	1926
Diana	1	Hunslet (2879)	0-6-0ST	1943
BAC Ltd	1	Peckett (1376)	0-4-0ST	1915
Yard No DY326	—	Hibberd (3743)	4wDM	1955
Yard No 5198	—	Hibberd (3747)	4wDM	1955
—	—	R/Hornsby (421700)	4wDM	1959
Dewar Highlander	—	R/Hornsby (458957)	4wDM	1961

Stock

4 ex-BR Mk 1 TSOs; 1 ex-BR Mk 1 BSK; 1 ex-BR Suburban; 1 ex-BR Mk 1 SO; 1 ex-BR Engineers Inspection Saloon; 1 ex-BR Full Kitchen Car; 3 ex-BR Mk 2s; 1 ex—BR diesel craneVarious items of freight stock

Souvenir shop: Brechin

Museum: Brechin

Length of line: 4 miles

Depot: Brechin

Passenger trains: Steam trains between Brechin and Bridge of Don

Period of public operation: Sundays only May to September

Special events: Easter Sunday and Santa Specials, please contact for further details

Facilities for disabled: Ramp access to both stations, disabled toilets at Brechin only. Passengers can be assisted on and off trains by railway staff

Family tickets: Available

Disclaimer: The Caledonian Railway (Brechin) Ltd reserves the right to amend, cancel or add to these events. And whilst every effort will be made to maintain the above services, the company does not guarantee that trains will depart or arrive at the time stated and reserves the right to suspend or alter any train without notice and will not accept any liability for loss, inconvenience or delay thereby caused

Membership details: Murray D. Duncan, 2 Binghill Crescent, Milltimber, Aberdeen

104

Glasgow Museum of Transport

Members: AIRPS

Glasgow's magnificent railway collection represents one of the best efforts by a municipal authority to preserve a representative collection of items appropriate to the 'locomotive builders of the Empire'. In 1989 the collection opened to view once again in its new setting at the former Kelvin Hall

Access by public transport: Strathclyde PTE Underground Kelvinhall: Strathclyde Buses 6, 6A, 8, 8A, 9, 9A, 16, 42, 42A, 44A, 57, 57A, 62, 62A, 62B, 64; Kelvin Scottish Buses 5, 5A; Clydeside Scottish Buses 17

Operating society/organisation: Glasgow Museums

Location: Museum of Transport, Kelvin Hall, 1 Bunhouse Road, Glasgow G3 8DP

Telephone: 0141-221-9600. (Fax: 0141-287-2692)

Locomotives

Name	No	Origin	Class	Type	Built
—	123	CR	123	4-2-2	1886
—	9	G&SWR	5	0-6-0T	1917
—	103	HR	—	4-6-0	1894
Gordon Highlander	49	GNSR	F	4-4-0	1920

Industrial locomotives

Name	No	Builder	Type	Built
—	1	Barclay (1571)	0-6-0F	1917
—	—	Chaplin (2368)	0-4-0TG	1888
—	—	BEV (583)	B	1927

Stock

Glasgow District Subway car 39T; Glasgow Corporation Underground cars 1 and 4; LMS King George VI's saloon 498 of 1941

Car park: Opposite Museum entrance

On site facilities: Toilets, cafeteria, shop and public telephone

Public opening: Monday-Saturday

10.00-17.00; Sunday 11.00-17.00. Closed 1/2 January and 25/26 December only

Facilities for disabled: Access to all areas but entry via separate entrance — enquire at main door

---

Leadhills & Wanlockhead Railway

Member: AIRPS

Situated in the Lowther Hills between Abington and Sanquhar the society was formed in 1983 to construct and operate a 2ft gauge tourist railway between the villages of Leadhills and Wanlockhead.

Operating society/organisation: Leadhills & Wanlockhead Railway c/o Douglas Boyd, The Saltings, Battlehill, Annan DG12 6SN

Main station: Leadhills

Access by public transport: ScotRail trains stop at Sanquhar on Nith Valley Line (approx 10 miles) every 1hr 30min-2 hours. Bus service (Western Scottish Stagecoach) to Leadhills (please check for times). Nearest motorway — M74 — J14 from south/J15 from north. From A76 take B797 to Leadhills

Industrial locomotives

Name	No	Builder	Type	Built
—	—	O&K	0-4-0T	1913
The Gulliver	1	fowler(18892)	4wDM	1931
Elvan	2	M/Rail(9792)	4wDM	1955
Luce	4	R/Hornsby(7002/0467/2)	4wDM	1966
Little Clyde	5	R/Hornsby(7002/0467/6)	4wDM	1966
Clyde	6	Hunslet(6347)	4wDH	1975
Nith	7	H/Clarke(dm1002)	0-4-0DMF	1956

Rolling stock

3 air braked passenger coaches and guard's van built at Leadhills

On site facilities: Shop, ticket office, small museum and picnic tables. Extensive country walks. Also on 'Southern Uplands Way'. Scottish Lead Mining Museum at Wanlockhead (1-mile)

Period of public operation: Easter weekend; weekends May-October. Saturdays 12.00-17.00, Sundays 11.00-17.00 — later if passenger numbers justify

Society journal: Quarterly

Mull Rail

Member: AIRPS, TT

Operating society/organisation:
Mull & West Highland (NG)
Railway Co Ltd, Old Pier Station,
Craignure, Isle of Mull PA65 6AY
Telephone: 01680 812494 (during
operating period); (01680) 300389
(out of season);
Fax: 01680 300595
General Manager: Graham E.
Ellis
Operations Manager: Michael
Jardine
OS reference: Sheet 49, 725369
Car park: At Craignure, free
Access by public transport:
Caledonian Macbrayne ferry from
Oban (40min sail)
On site facilities: Gift shop, car
park (free)
Family ticket: Available (2 Adults
& 2 children under 14)
Length of line: 1.25 miles/10.25 in
gauge
Public opening: Easter, then 21
April to 11 October
Facilities for disabled: No steps

Locomotives

Name	No	Builder	Type	Built
Lady of the Isles	—	Marsh	2-6-4T	1981
Waverley	—	Curwen	4-4-2	1948
—	—	Alcock	4w-4PM	1973
Glen Auldyn	—	Davies	8wDH	1986
Victoria*	—	Vere	2-6-2T	1993

*Largest tank engine built for 10.25in gauge

Rolling stock
11 coaches (two with wheelchair accommodation); 3 bogie wagons;
1 4-wheel wagon

on railway, two compartments for
wheelchairs
Membership details: Friends of
Mull Rail, David Crombie,
1 Mulberry Drive, Dunfermline,
Fife KY11 5BZ. Tel: 01383
728652
Membership journal: *Crankpin
Journal* — annual
Special notes: First island railway
in Scotland, runs to Torosay Castle
and 12 acres of gardens, superb
panoramic views of mountains and
sea. Joint discounted sail/rail
tickets only from Caledonian
Macbrayne, Oban. Group discount
available for 20+ pre-booked
passengers. Special trains can be
chartered within and without
timetable hours. Special Mull Trail
tickets for families, from Glasgow
to Torosay station and return;
phone: ScotRail 0345 212282 for
details

Paddle Steamer Preservation Society

The Paddle Steamer *Waverley* was
built for the London & North
Eastern Railway in 1946; and
replaced a vessel of the same name
which was sunk off Dunkirk during
May 1940. Sold to the PSPS – a
Registered Charity – in 1974
Waverley sails on day trips and
afternoon cruises from ports and
piers in most coastal areas and river
estuaries of the United Kingdom,
from Easter until October each
year. Also in the 'fleet' is the
traditional motor cruiser *Balmoral*

and the river Paddle Steamer
Kingswear Castle which sails from
Chatham Historic Dockyard on the
River Medway
General Manager: David
Duncanson
Headquarters: Waverley
Excursions Ltd, Waverley
Terminal, Anderston Quay,
Glasgow G3 8HA
On ship facilities: Self service
reastaurants, bars, toilets (disabled
toilets on Waverley)
Membership details: Paddle

Steamer Preservation Society, PO
Box 385, Hazlemere, High
Wycombe HP11 1AE
Membership journal:
Paddlewheels — quarterly

Details of the full programme of
cruises operated by the three ships
can be obtained from the National
Booking Office, Waverley
Excursions Ltd, Gwalia Buildings,
Barry Docks CF61 5QR.
Telephone: 01446 720656.

Prestongrange Industrial Heritage Museum

Location: On the B1348 between
Musselburgh and Prestonpans.
OS reference: NT 734737
Operating society/organisation:
East Lothian Museum Service,

Library & Museum Headquarters,
Dunbar Road, Haddington, East
Lothian EH41 3PJ
Telephone: 0131-653 2904
(Prestongrange Visitor Centre),

0162-082 8203 (Museum Service)
Car park: On site
On site facilities: Once part of the
Scottish Mining Museum,
Prestongrange is being developed

as a museum which tells the story of people and industries in East Lothian — local coal deposits encouraged the growth of numerous other industries, pottery, such as pipe making, soap, glycerine, brewing and weaving
Visitor centre: Changing exhibitions of local industries: pottery, soap, glycerine, brewing, weaving. Displays of local art and craft — one-off events, demonstrations, workshops. Cornish beam engine, installed 1874 to pump water from the mine. Colliery locomotives, restored by Prestongrange Railway Society are housed here
Toilets: Visitor Centre
Refreshment facilities: Available at Visitor Centre
Public opening: 30 March to 26 October, 11.00-16.00, last tour at 15.00
Length of line: 400m (standard gauge) extension in progress

Industrial locomotives

Name	No	Builder	Type	Built
—	6	A/Barclay (2043)	0-4-0ST	1937
—	17	A/Barclay (2219)	0-4-0ST	1946
Prestongrange	7	G/Ritchie (536)	0-4-2ST	1914
Tomatin	1	M/Rail (9925)	4wDM	1963
—	—*	Hunslet (4440)	4wDM	1952
—	32	R/Hornsby (458960)	4wDM	1962
George Edwards	33	R/Hornsby (221647)	4wDM	1943
—	—	E/Electric (D908)	4wDM	1964

*2ft gauge

Rolling stock
Steam crane, Whittaker No 30, c1890, occasionally in steam

Facilities for disabled: Access and toilet at Visitor Centre. Access to powerhouse exhibition, and footpaths along the site
Special events: Steam days are held on the first Sunday of each month April to September and the last Sunday in September. Passenger rides available. Advanced notice for larger parties

Membership details: Friends of Prestongrange. Contact Peter Gray, Museums Officer — c/o operating organisation
Contact: For Prestongrange Railway Society — Charles Young, The Smiddy, Middleton, Midlothian

Scottish Industrial Railway Centre

Ayrshire
Steam Centre

Member: AIRPS, TT

The Scottish Industrial Railway Centre is based on part of the former Dalmellington Iron Co railway system which was one of the best known industrial railway networks in Britain. Steam worked up until 1978 when the system closed and it is the aim of the centre to recreate part of the railway. The Ayrshire Railway Preservation Group also owns the former G&SWR station at Waterside, 2 miles from the centre, and have access to the former NCB locomotive shed and wagon workshops at Waterside. These locations are not yet open to the general public. Working in conjunction with the Dalmellington & District Conservation Trust it is hoped to create an industrial heritage centre at Waterside based on the iron, coal and brick making industries. A passenger train service will operate between the two stations on certain Sundays
Location: Scottish Industrial Railway Centre, Minnivey

Locomotives

Name	No	Origin	Class	Type	Built
—	MP228 (12052)	BR	11	0-6-0DE	1949
—	MP229 (12093)	BR	11	0-6-0DE	1951

Industrial locomotives

Name	No	Builder	Type	Built
—	16	A/Barclay (1116)	0-4-0ST	1910
—	8	A/Barclay (1296)	0-6-0T	1912
—	19	A/Barclay (1614)	0-4-0ST	1918
Aberdeen Corporation Gas Works	3	A/Barclay (1889)	0-4-0ST	1926
—	8	A/Barclay (1952)	0-4-0F	1928
—	10	A/Barclay (2244)	0-4-0ST	1947
NCB No 23	—	A/Barclay (2260)	0-4-0ST	1949
—	25	A/Barclay (2358)	0-6-0ST	1954
—	1	A/Barclay (2368)	0-4-0ST	1955
—	118	A/Barclay (366)	0-4-0DM	1940
—	7	A/Barclay (399)	0-4-0DM	1956
Lily of the Valley	—	Fowler (22888)	0-4-0DM	1943
Tees Storage	—	N/British (27644)	0-4-0DH	1959
—	—	R/Hornsby (224352)	4wDM	1943
Blinkin Bess	—	R/Hornsby (284839)	4wDM	1950
Johnnie Walker	—	R/Hornsby (417890)	4wDM	1959
—	—	R/Hornsby (421697)	0-4-0DM	1959
—	107	Hunslet (3132)	0-4-0DM	1944
—	—	Sentinel (10012)	4wDM	1949
—	—	Donnelli (163)	4wDM	1979

Cont

Colliery, Dalmellington, Ayrshire
OS reference: NS 476074
Operating society/organisation:
Ayrshire Railway Preservation
Group
Telephone: The Secretary (01292)
313579 (evening & weekends)
Length of line: 2.25 miles
Access by public transport:
Nearest BR station, Ayr (14 miles).
Stagecoach Bus service from Ayr.
Tel: (01292) 263382
On site facilities: Steam-hauled
brake van rides. Guided tours of
centre, museum of railway relics
and photographs, souvenir shop,
buffet, locomotive shed, narrow
gauge demonstration line
Public opening: Open for static
display with limited facilities every
Saturday, June to end September
Passenger service: A steam-hauled
passenger service is expected to
operate over the 2.25-mile long
Scottish coal line to Dunaskin
(Waterside) on certain Sundays in
July and August

	Name	No	Builder	Type	Built
3ft gauge					
	—	—	R/Hornsby(256273)	4wDM	1949
	—	—	Hunslet(8816)	4wDH	1981
2ft 6in gauge					
	—	2	R/Hornsby (183749)	4wDM	1937
	—	3	R/Hornsby (210959)	4wDM	1941
	—	1	R/Hornsby (211681)	4wDM	1942

Note: Not all vehicles on public display

Stock
1 BR Mk 1 TSO, 1 BR Mk 1 BSK, 2 Wickham trolleys; 1 steam crane;
various other items

Special events: Steam open days
every Sunday in July and August,
plus last Sunday in May and
September
Membership details: Mr Frank
Beattie, 1 McKnight Avenue,
Waterside, Fenwick, Kilmarnock,
Ayrshire
Special notes: For further
information and details of special
events, telephone the Doon Valley
Heritage Office (01292) 531144
daytime, (01292) 313579 evenings
and weekends, or write to Gordon
Thomson, 8 Burnside Place, Troon,
Ayrshire KA10 6LZ (SSAE
appreciated)

Strathspey Railway
Highland
Timetable Service
Member: AIRPS, TT

Scotland's steam railway in the
highlands connects the busy tourist
resort at Aviemore to the more
traditional highland village of Boat
of Garten, famed as one of the few
nesting places of the osprey
(viewing site 3 miles from station).
The bridge at Bridge of Garten has
been replaced and three of the four
miles of track between Bridge of
Garten and Broomhill has been
laid. A great deal of work still
needs to be done but, subject to
labour and finance being available,
the railway would like to open to
Broomhill for Easter 1998
Commerical Manager: Laurence
Grant
Enquiries: Aviemore Speyside
Station, Dalfaber Road, Aviemore,
Inverness-shire PH22 1PY (SSAE
for copy of timetable brochure)
Telephone: 01479 810725. For
details of locomotives in operation
01479 831692
Fax: 01479 811022
Main station: Aviemore

Locomotives and multiple-units

Name	No	Origin	Class	Type	Built
—	5025	LMS	5MT	4-6-0	1934
—	46512	LMS	2MT	2-6-0	1952
—	828	CR	812	0-6-0	1899
—	08490	BR	08	0-6-0DE	1958
—	D5302	BR	26	Bo-Bo	1958
—	D5394	BR	27	Bo-Bo	1962
—	51990	BR	107	DMBS	1960
—	52008	BR	107	DMBS	1960
—	52030	BR	107	DMC	1960
—	54047	BR	114	DTC	1960

Industrial locomotives

Name	No	Builder	Type	Built
—	48	Hunslet (2864)	0-6-0ST	1943
Cairngorm	9	RSH (7097)	0-6-0ST	1943
—	60	Hunslet (3686)	0-6-0ST	1948
Niddrie	6	Barclay (1833)	0-6-0ST	1924
Forth*	10	Barclay (1890)	0-4-0ST	1926
Balmenach	2	Barclay (2020)	0-4-0ST	1936
—	17	Barclay (2017)	0-6-0T	1935
Inveresk	14	R/Hornsby (260756)	0-4-0DM	1950
Inverdon	15	Simplex (5763)	4wDM	1957
—	16	North British (27549)	0-4-0DM	1951
Queen Anne	20	R/Hornsby (265618)	4wDM	1948

*Not on site

(Speyside)
Other public stations: Boat of Garten
OS reference: Aviemore NH 898131, Boat of Garten NH 943789
Car parks: Aviemore and Boat of Garten
Access by public transport: BR services and express bus to Aviemore. Local service to Boat of Garten
Refreshment facilities: On train buffet car or facilities on many trains. Picnic tables at Boat of Garten (for use of ticket purchasers). No refreshment facilities on DMU services
Souvenir shop: Boat of Garten and Aviemore (Speyside)
Museum: Small relics display at Boat of Garten. Extension progress display at Aviemore (Speyside)
Depot: Aviemore (not open to public), sidings at both stations are not open to the public
Length of line: 5 miles
Journey time: 17min, return within the hour possible on most services
Passenger trains: Steam-hauled services. Boat of Garten-Aviemore.

Locomotive notes: In service 9, 828, 08490, D5394. Under restoration 60, 46512 (possibly in traffic late 1997), D5302 (possibly in service during) 1997

Stock
18 ex-BR coaches; 4 ex-LMS coaches; 1 Pullman coach; 3 ex-LMS sleeping cars; 1 ex-LNER sleeping car; 1 ex-HR coach; 1 ex-NBR coach; 1 ex-GNSR coach; Numerous examples of rolling stock

Owners
17 and 46512 the Highland Locomotive Co Ltd
828 the Scottish Locomotive Preservation Trust Fund

DMU on Saturdays June-September
Period of public operation: 23, 26, 28-31 March; 1-6, 9, 12/13, 16, 19/20, 26/27, 30 April; 3-5, 7, 10/11, 14, 17/18, 21, 24/26, 28 May; Daily 1 June-30 September; 1, 4/6, 8, 11/12, 13-19, 22, 25/26, 29 October; 14, 20/21, 26, 28, 31 December
Special events: Confirm by telephone, send SAE for details. Enthusiast's Day 24 May (steam, diesel, DMU) (members & shareholders free travel plus access to restricted areas , workshops, extension); Friends of Thomas the Tank Engine — 3-5 May, 6/7 September

Facilities for disabled: Access possible at Boat of Garten and Aviemore (Speyside). Please contact in advance for directions and if a party involved
Special notes: First and third class travel available on most trains. Family fares available for third class travel. Special rates/arrangements for parties. Luncheon on the train — Wednesdays in July and August. Bicycles carried free — groups must give prior notice
Membership details: Strathspey Railway Association at above address
Membership journal: *Strathspey Express* — quarterly

Summerlee Heritage Park

Strathclyde
Museum

Social and industrial history museum, interprets the communities in the west of Scotland in the 19th and 20th centuries. Working machinery in reconstructed workshops; miners rows, reconstructed coal mine, art gallery, working tram
Manager: Frank Little
Operating society/organisation: Summerlee Heritage Park, West Canal Street, Coatbridge, ML5 1QD
Telephone: 01236 431261
Public opening: Daily 10.00-17.00, except 25/26 December and 1/2 January
Access by public transport: BR Coatbridge Central and Coatbridge Sunnyside. Local buses
Car park: Opposite site
On site facilities: Tearoom, gift shop. Working electric tramway

Locomotives

Name	No	Origin	Class	Type	Built
Springbok	4112	SAR	GMAM	4-8-2+2-8-4	1956

(3ft 6in gauge/built by North British Loco Co)

Industrial locomotives

Name	No	Builder	Type	Built
—	—	Barclay (472)	0-4-0DH	1966
—	—	H/Clarke(895)	0-6-0T	1909
—	—	G/Hogg	0-4-0T	1898
Robin	—	Sentinel (9628)	4wTG	1957

Owner
Springbok the Springburn Museum

Stock
2 rail mounted steam cranes

with cars from Motherwell, Brussels and Graz
Special events: Organised events from April-October, details on

request
Facilities for disabled: Toilets, wheelchair available

Wales

Bala Lake Railway (Rheilffordd Llyn Tegid)

Member: AIRPS, TT

Caernarfonshire
Timetable Service

This delightful narrow gauge railway follows the route of the former Bala-Dolgellau Railway, along the shore of Wales' largest natural lake. The railway's headquarters are to be found in the fine old station building at Llanuwchllyn at the south western end of the line. Do not be deterred by the fact that the railway runs down the opposite shore of the lake to the main road — it is well worth the detour

General Manager: Roy Hardiman
Headquarters: Rheilffordd Llyn Tegid (Bala Lake Railway) Llanuwchllyn, Bala, Gwynedd LL23 7DD
Telephone: Llanuwchllyn (01678) 540666
Main station: Llanuwchllyn
Other public stations: Llangower, Bala. Request halts at Pentrepiod, Glanllyn (Flag Station) and Bryn Hynod
OS reference: Llanuwchllyn SH 880300, Bala SH 929350
Car parks: Llanuwchllyn, Llangower and Bala town centre
Access by public transport: Bus Gwynedd service No 94 to both Bala and Llanuwchllyn (from Wrexham or Barmouth)
Road access: Off the A494 Bala-Dolgellau road

Industrial locomotives

Name	No	Builder	Type	Built
Holy War	3	Hunslet (779)	0-4-0ST	1902
Maid Marian	5	Hunslet (822)	0-4-0ST	1903
Triassic	—	Peckett (1270)	0-6-0ST	1911
Meirionydd	11	Severn Lamb (7322)	Bo-Bo	1973
Chilmark	12	R/Hornsby (194771)	4wDM	1939
Bob Davies	—	YEC (L125)	4wDM	1983
Indian Runner	—	R/Hornsby (200744)	4wDM	1940
—	—	Lister (34025)	4wDM	1949
—	—	Motorail (5821)	4wDM	1934
—	—	R/Hornsby (189972)	4wDM	1938
—	—	Hibberd (FH2544)	4wDM	1941
—	—	Hunslet (1974)	4wDM	1939
Cernyw	—	R/Hornsby (200748)	4wDM	1940
Lady Madcap	—	R/Hornsby (283512)	4wDM	1949

Locomotive notes: *Holy War* and *Maid Marian* are in regular use, *Triassic* in steam for special weekends and other peak periods, remainder are on static display

Refreshment facilities: Llanuwchllyn. Large picnic site with toilet facilities by lake at Llangower
Souvenir shop: Llanuwchllyn
Depot: Llanuwchllyn
Length of line: 4.5 miles, 1ft 11.625in gauge
Passenger trains: Llanuwchllyn-Bala. Journey takes 25min in each direction
Period of public operation: 30 March-28 September
Facilities for disabled: Facilities available on most trains
Special notes: Small parties (10/12) may just turn up, but a day's notice for large parties would be helpful
Family tickets: Available for all round trip journeys
Membership details: A. V. Brassington, 39 The Crest, West Heath, Birmingham B31 3PZ
Membership journal: *Llanuwchllyn Express* — approx 4 times a year

Brecon Mountain Railway

Member: AIRPS

Merthyr Tydfil
Timetable Service

A narrow gauge passenger-carrying railway close to Merthyr Tydfil built on part of the trackbed of the former Brecon & Merthyr Railway. Gradually being extended northward, the railway has some interesting narrow gauge steam locomotives imported from East and West Germany and South Africa
General Manager: A. J. Hills
Headquarters: Brecon Mountain Railway, Pant Station, Dowlais, Merthyr Tydfil CF48 2UP
Telephone: Merthyr Tydfil (01685) 722988

Fax: 01685 384854
Main station: Pant
Car park: Pant station
OS reference: SO 063120
Access by public transport: Omnibus to Pant Cemetery — half hour frequency from Merthyr bus station. BR rail service to Merthyr

from Cardiff Central
Depot: Pant
Length of line: 3.5 miles, 1ft 11.75in gauge
Period of public operation: Daily 28-31 March, 1-5 April, 4-5 May, 25 May-4 September; Tuesdays-Thursdays & Saturdays 8 April-24 May, 6 September-2 October; Sundays 6-27 April, 31 August-26 October; Tuesdays-Thursdays 7-30 October
Refreshment facilities: Cafe at Pant, snackbar at Pontsticill
Special events: Santa Specials — December
Facilities for disabled: Facilities for disabled include ramps, toilets and carriage designed to carry wheelchairs
Special notes: There is no road access to Pontsticill

Locomotives

Name	No	Builder	Type	Built
—	2	Baldwin (61269)	4-6-2	1930
Sybil	—	Hunslet (827)	0-4-0ST	1903
Graf Schwerin-Lörwitz	—	Arn Jung (1261)	0-6-2WT	1908
—	—	O&K (12722)	0-4-0WT	1936
Pendyffryn	—	de Winton	0-4-0VBT	1894
Redstone	—	Redstone	0-4-0VBT	1905
Rhydychen	—	Simplex (11177)	4wDM	1961
—	77	Hanomag (10629)	2-6-2+2-6-2	1928
—	—	Brecon MR (001)	0-6-0DH	1987

Stock
2 balcony end 39-seat coaches; 2 balcony end 40-seat coaches; 1 19-seat Caboose Miscellaneous rail carrying and ballast wagons; Wickham petrol trolley

Conwy Valley Railway Museum — Aberconwy Museum

Conveniently situated alongside British Rail's Betws-y-Coed station, the Museum presents some well-displayed distractions to pass the time including model train layouts to delight both adult and child
Location: Adjacent to Betws-y-Coed station
OS reference: SH 796565
General Manager: Mr C. M. Cartwright
Operating society/organisation: Conwy Valley Railway Museum, The Old Goods Yard, Betws-y-Coed, Gwynedd
Telephone: (01690) 710568
Car park: On site
Access by public transport: Betws-y-Coed BR station
On site facilities: Refreshments in buffet car. Bookshop and model/gift shop in museum foyer, operating train layouts, miniature railway (1.25-miles, 7.25in gauge) steam-hauled. Picnic area.
  15in Tramway (operates daily) with 1989-built single-deck bogie tram
Public opening: Daily Easter-end of October, 10.00-17.30
Facilities for disabled: Access to museum and toilets

Locomotives

Name	No	Builder	Type	Built
Britannia	70000	TMA Engineering (1ft 3in gauge)	4-6-2	1988
Old Rube*	—	Milner Eng	2-8-0	1983
Sian*	—	Humphries	0-4-2T	1989
Shoeshone*	—	Simkins/Milner	2-8-0	1975
Union Pacific*	—	R. Greatrex	Bo-Bo	1991
Crocodile*	—	—	0-6-0+0-6-0	1985
Princess Elizabeth*	—	Barton (Lewis Shaw)	4-6-2	1960

*7.25in gauge

Stock
1 GWR fitter's van; 1 LMS 6-wheel van; 1 LNER CCT van; 1 BR Mk 1 coach; 2 SR luggage vans; 1 Pullman coach; 15in bogie tramcar

Corris Railway Museum

Member: AIRPS

In the heart of Wales 'narrow gauge country', the Corris Railway Museum, situated in the remaining buildings of Corris station, display of relics and photographs of mid-Wales' first public narrow gauge railway

Location: In Corris village off A487 trunk road. Turn opposite Braichgoch Hotel, five miles north of Machynlleth and 11 miles south of Dolgellau

OS reference: SH 755078

Operating society: The Corris Railway Society, Corris Station Yard, Gwynedd (postal address: Corris, Machynlleth, Powys SY20 9SH)

Car park: Adjacent

Access by public transport: Central train services to Machynlleth. Bus Gwynedd services 2 (Aberystwyth-Dolgellau-Machynlleth), 30 (Machynlleth-Tywyn) and 34 (Machynlleth-Aberllefenni); Dyfi Valley service 530 (Tywyn-Machynlleth-Abergynolwyn)

Catering facilities: Snacks, teas and light refreshments

Locomotives

Name	No	Builder	Type	Built
Alan Meaden	5	M/rail (22258)	4wDM	1965
—	6	R/Hornsby (51849)	4wDM	1966
—	7	Winson	0-4-2ST	19—

Locomotive notes: 5 and 6 operational on works trains. 7 under construction at Winson Engineering, based on Corris No 4 (now Talyllyn No 4 *Edward Thomas*)

Stock

Two carriages, brake van, 17 works wagons and 4 historic wagons

On site facilities: Souvenir shop, toilets and children's playground; close to Corris Craft Centre and King Arthur's Labyrinth; two miles from Centre for Alternative Technology

Length of line: Three quarter-mile, 2ft 3in gauge track between Corris and Maespoeth has been reinstated, and subject to, legal process, passenger services will recommence in late 1997 or 1998. Planning permission for a further two miles of track has been granted

Public opening: Easter, May Day and Spring Bank Holidays, June-September. Half term week in October, other times by prior arrangement. Times as advertised locally. Please write for full details

Special events: As advertised locally, please write for details

Facilities for disabled: Access to display area of Museum and shop

Internet address: http//www.apricot.co.uk/hosts/corris/corris.htm

Membership details: Membership Secretary, c/o above address

Fairbourne & Barmouth Steam Railway

Since 1986 this railway has been regauged from 15in to 12.25in and has been transformed by the introduction of new locomotives and rolling stock, a tunnel through the sand dunes, signalboxes, new workshops, a cafe overlooking the Mawddch estuary. Under new ownership since April 1995, there has been a big investment in the rolling stock maintenance so that all four steam locomotives are now in service. During the main season a two-train service is in operation. A new indoor nature attraction is scheduled to open at Fairbourne in 1997

Headquarters: North Wales Narrow Gauge Railway Co Ltd,

Locomotives

Name	No	Builder	Type	Built
Beddgelert	—	Curwen	0-6-4ST	1979
Yeo	—	Curwen	2-6-2T	1978
Sherpa	—	Milner	0-4-0STT	1978
Russell*	—	Milner	2-6-4T	1985
Lilian Walter	—	FLW	A1-1AD	1985
Gwril	—	FLW	4wBE	1987

FLW — Fairbourne Locomotive Works
*Built as Leek & Manifold *Elaine*, rebuilt to present form 1985 at FLW

Stock

12.25in gauge — 28 coaches (1st, 2nd class); 15 freight. New 1st class wheelchair coach under construction, anticipated to enter service in 1997

Note: The railway offers a range of driver experience courses (when no public trains are running), please write for details

Fairbourne & Barmouth Steam Railway, Beach Road, Fairbourne, Gwynedd LL38 2PZ
Telephone: 01341-250362
Fax: 01341 250240
Main station: Gorsaf Newydd (Fairbourne)
Other public stations: Gorsafawddacha'qidraigddanhed-dogleddolonpenrhynareudraeth-ceredigion, Porth Penrhyn (Barmouth Ferry Station)
OS reference: SH 616128
Car parks: Gorsaf Newydd
Access by public transport: Fairbourne railway station. Bus Gwynedd service (No 28)
Refreshment facilities: Porth Penrhyn cafe, tea shop on platform at Gorsaf Newydd (Fairbourne)
Souvenir shop: Gorsaf Newydd (Fairbourne)
Depot: Fairbourne
Length of line: 2.5 miles, 12.25in gauge
Passenger trains: A 2.5-mile journey connecting with ferry at Porth Penrhyn to Barmouth. 20min single journey. Through tickets to Barmouth (including ferry)

available
Period of public operation: Daily Good Friday and Easter week, then weekends only. Daily service 3 May to 28 September. Santa Specials operate 13/14 December
Membership details: Fairbourne Railway Volunteers Association, contact Hon Sec at above address
Special notes: During inclement weather the service may be restricted or cancelled. Extra trains and special parties by arrangement with the manager

Russell, Beddgelert and *Sherpa* **triple head a train during a 'Steam Day'.** *NWNGR*

Ffestiniog Railway
Member: AIRPS

Caernarfonshire
Timetable Service

In many ways, evocative of the early Swiss mountain railways as it climbs high above Porthmadog with some breathtaking views, the railway still operates an interesting variety of locomotives including some unusual Victorian survivors. Passengers have replaced slate as the principal traffic over this former quarry line
General Manager: Alan Heywood
Headquarters: Ffestiniog Railway Co, Harbour Station, Porthmadog,

Gwynedd, LL49 9NF
Telephone: Porthmadog (01766) 512340
Main stations: Porthmadog Harbour, Blaenau Ffestiniog
Other public stations: Boston Lodge, Minffordd, Penrhyn, Plas Halt, Tan-y-Bwlch, Dduallt, Tanygrisiau
OS reference: SH 571384
Car parks: Porthmadog, Tan-y-Bwlch, Tanygrisiau, Blaenau Ffestiniog

Access by public transport: Minffordd and Blaenau Ffestiniog BR stations. Porthmadog, Minffordd, and Blaenau Ffestiniog served by local buses
Refreshment facilities: Licensed restaurant at Porthmadog, cafe at Tan-y-Bwlch (summer only), refreshments also on most trains
Souvenir shops: Porthmadog, Tan-y-Bwlch (summer only), Blaenau Ffestiniog
Museum: Porthmadog *Cont*

Depot: Boston Lodge
Length of line: 13.5 miles, 1ft 11.5in gauge
Passenger trains: Porthmadog-Blaenau Ffestiniog
Period of public operation: Daily March-November, limited winter service
Special events: Festival of Steam Gala — 3-5 May; Friends of Thomas the Tank weekends 20/21 September; Vintage Weekend — 25/26 October; Santa Specials — 13/14, 20/21 December
Facilities for disabled: Porthmadog and Blaenau Ffestiniog easily accessible for wheelchairs. Facilities on trains for disabled in wheelchairs by prior arrangement
Special notes: Reduced return rates available for journeys beginning on diesel services, shown in timetable
Membership details: Festiniog Railway Society (see above address)
Membership journal: *Festiniog Railway Magazine* — quarterly

Locomotives

Name	No	Builder	Type	Built
Princess	1	G/England (199/200)	0-4-0STT	1863
Prince	2	G/England	0-4-0STT	1863
Palmerston	4	G/England	0-4-0STT	1863
Welsh Pony	—	G/England (234)	0-4-0STT	1867
Earl of Merioneth	—	FR	0-4-4-0T	1979
Merddin Emrys	10	FR	0-4-4-0T	1879
David Lloyd George	12	FR	0-4-0T	1992
Moelwyn**	—	Baldwin (49604)	2-4-0DM	1918
Blanche	—	Hunslet (589)	2-4-0STT	1893
Linda	—	Hunslet (590)	2-4-0STT	1893
Britomart*	—	Hunslet (707)	0-4-0ST	1899
Mountaineer	—	Alco (57156)	2-6-2T	1917
Livingston Thompson†	3	FR	0-4-4-0T	1886
—**	K1	B/Peacock (5292)	0-4-0+0-4-0	1909
Harlech Castle	—	Baguley-Drewry (3767)	0-6-0-DH	1983
Ashover	—	Hibberd (3307)	4wDM	1948
Upnor Castle	—	Hibberd (3687)	4wDM	1954
Conway Castle	—	Hibberd (3831)	4wDM	1958
Moel Hebog	—	Hunslet (4113)	0-4-0DM	1955
Mary Ann	—	M/Rail (596)	4wDM	1917
Criccieth Castle	—	FR	0-6-0DH	1995
Monarch*	—	Bagnall (3024)	0-4-4-0T	1953
(Jane)	—	M/Rail (8565)	4wDM	1940
The Colonel	—	M/Rail (8788)	4wDM	1943
Diane	—	M/Rail (21579)	4wDM	1957
Stefcomatic	—	Matisa (48589)	2-2-0DH	1956
—	—	Funkey	Bo-Bo	1968
Castell Caernafon	—	Funkey	Bo-Bo	1968

*Privately owned
** Not on Site
†On loan to National Railway Museum

Stock

32 bogie coaches; 6 4-wheel coaches; 2 brake vans, plus numerous service vehicles

---

Great Orme Tramway

Member: AIRPS

Aberconwy
Timetable Service

A cable-hauled street tramway to the summit of the Great Orme is operated as two sections involving a change half-way. Opened throughout in July 1903, it involves gradients as steep as 1 in 3.9
Location: Great Orme Tramway, Victoria station, Church Walks, Llandudno
OS reference: SH 7781
Operating society/organisation: Contract Services, Maesdu, Llandudno LL30 1HF

Telephone: Llandudno (01492) 574187
Car park: Approximately 100yd from Lower Terminal or adjacent to Summit Terminal
Access by public transport: Good
On site facilities: Shop
Period of public operation: Easter to end of October (daily) 10.00-18.00
Special notes: The only remaining cable-hauled street tramway in Britain. 1-mile long rising to 650ft

(3ft 6in gauge)
Stock: 4 tramcars each seating 48, built 1902/3
Family tickets: Available, along with joint tickets for Great Orme Mine — Bronze Age Heritage Centre

114

South Wales' first standard gauge passenger-carrying railway. Running alongside the River Gwili on part of the former Carmarthen-Aberystwyth line. Attractions include a fully restored signalbox and historic station building. Extension to Conwil Elfed in progress. A 7.25in gauge miniature railway operates at Llwyfan Cerrig.

Headquarters: Gwili Railway Co Ltd, Bronwydd Arms station, Bronwydd Arms, Carmarthen, SA33 6HT

Telephone: Carmarthen (01267) 230666

OS reference: Bronwydd Arms SN 417239

Llwyfan Cerrig SN 405258, Conwil SN 386263

Main station: Bronwydd Arms

Other public stations: Llwyfan Cerrig, also Conwil under restoration

Car park: Bronwydd Arms (free)

Access by public transport: Carmarthen BR station, then Bus Dyfed service No 460, 461

Refreshment facilities: Bronwydd Arms, Llwyfan Cerrig (picnic site). Bar on train

Souvenir shop: Bronwydd Arms

Depot: Llwyfan Cerrig, stock also kept at Bronwydd Arms and Conwil

Length of line: 1.5 miles

Passenger trains: Bronwydd Arms-Llwyfan Cerrig, regular hourly service

Period of public operation: 28-31 March; 1/2 April; 4/5, 11, 14, 18, 21, 25-30 May; 1, 4, 7/8, 11, 15, 18, 22, 25, 29 June; 2, 5/6, 9, 12/13, 16, 19-31 July; Daily — August; 7, 14, 21, 28 September; 21-23, 26 October; 6/7, 13/14, 20-24 December

Public opening: Trains leave Bronwydd Arms at 11.00, 12.00, 13.30, 14,30, 15.30, 16.30 on most operating days

Special events: Easter Egg Hunt — 28/29 March; Gala Weekend — 7/8June. Santa Specials in December — details: Booking Officer, Bronwydd Arms Station, Carmarthen SA33 6HT (Tel: 01276 230666)

Locomotives

Name	No	Origin	Class	Type	Built
—	12061	BR	11	0-6-0DE	1949†
—	D2178	BR	03	0-6-0DM	1962**

Industrial locomotives

Name	No	Builder	Type	Built
—	1	H/Clarke (1885)	0-6-0ST	1955
Idris	—	R/Hornsby (207103)	4wDM	1941
Trecatty	—	R/Hornsby (421702)	0-6-0DM	1959
Olwen	—	RSH (7058)	0-4-0ST	1942
Welsh Guardsman	71516	RSH (7170)	0-6-0ST	1944
Nellie	02101	YEC(2779)	0-4-0DE	1960
Rosyth No 1	—	A/Barclay (1385)	0-4-0ST	1914*
Victory	—	A/Barclay (2201)	0-4-0ST	1945**
Sir John	—	Avonside (1680)	0-6-0ST	1914†
—	3	H/Clarke (D1246)	0-4-0DM	1961†
Gunby	68067	Hunslet (2413)	0-6-0ST	1941
Swansea Vale No 1	—	Sentinel (9622)	4wVBTG	1958*
Swansea Jack	—	R/Hornsby (393302)	4wDM	1955*
Dylan Thomas	—	N/British (27654)	0-4-0DH	1956*
Folly	—	R/Hornsby (183062)	4wDM	1937
—	114	N/British (27878)	0-4-0DH	1962
—	21	H/Leslie (3931)	0-6-0ST	1938
Haulwen	—	V/Foundry (5272)	0-6-0ST	1945†*

Stock

8 ex-BR Mk 1 coaches; 1 ex-BR suburban coach; 1 ex-BR griddle car; 1 ex-BR Mk 3 sleeper; 1 ex-TVR coach (built 1891); Coles diesel rail crane; 1 ex-GWR Mink van; 1 ex-GWR Fruit D; 1 ex-GWR Monster; 1 ex-GWR Crocodile; 1 ex-GWR Loriot D; 4 tank wagons; 2 GWR Toad brake vans; 1 GWR Tube C; 1 LMS 20ton brake van; 17 open wagons; 1 BR Loriot; 8 covered wagons; 1 bogie bolster; 1 Minifit; 1 SR bogie parcels van; 1 SECR Parcels Van; 2 SR Parcels vans. Stothert & Pitt diesel crane

Owners

*The Railway Club of Wales
** Caerphilly Railway Society
†Vale of Neath Railway Society
†*National Museum of Wales Industrial & Maritime Museum in care of Caerphilly Railway Society

Special notes: Family tickets available. Disabled access to stations and trains

Llanberis Lake Railway (Rheilffordd Llyn Padarn)

Member: AIRPS

A narrow gauge passenger-carrying railway starting at the historic Dinorwic Quarry workshops (now part of the National Museum of Wales) and running along the shores of the Llanberis lake using the trackbed of the former slate railway line to Port Dinorwic. Excellent views of Snowdonia and good picnic spots along the line
General Manager: Mr B. Yarborough
Headquarters: Llanberis Lake Railway, Gilfach Ddu, Llanberis, Gwynedd LL55 4TY
Telephone: Llanberis (01286) 870549
Main station: Llanberis (Padarn station/Gilfachddu)
Other public stations: Cei Llydan
OS reference: SH 586603
Car park: Llanberis (Padarn station)
Refreshment facilities: Padarn station
Souvenir shop: Padarn Station
Length of line: 2 miles, 1ft 11.5in gauge
Passenger trains: Llanberis-Penllyn-Llanberis

Industrial locomotives

Name	No	Builder	Type	Built
Elidir	1	Hunslet (493)	0-4-0ST	1889
Thomas Bach/Wild Aster	2	Hunslet (849)	0-4-0ST	1904
Dolbadarn	3	Hunslet (1430)	0-4-0ST	1922
—	7	R/Hornsby (441427)	4wDM	1961
Twll Coed	8	R/Hornsby (268878)	4wDM	1956
Dolgarrog	9	M/Rail (22154)	4wDM	1962
—	—	R/Hornsby (425796)	4wDM	1958
Garrett	11	R/Hornsby (198286)	4wDM	1939
Braich	10	R/Hornsby (203031)	4wDM	1942
—	18	M/Rail (7927)	4wDM	1941
Llanelli	19	R/Hornsby (451901)	4wDM	1961
Una*	—	Hunslet (873)	0-4-0ST	1905

*Not part of the railway's motive power stock. Housed at the adjacent slate museum and can sometimes be seen working demonstration freight trains

Stock
13 bogie coaches; 20 wagons

Journey time: 40min round trip
Period of public operation: Mondays to Thursdays in March and October. Monday to Friday in April. Sundays to Fridays, May through September. Saturdays July and August. Family tickets available, under 5s free
Facilities for disabled: Level approaches throughout shop, café and to train. Special toilet facilities provided. All disabled visitors welcomed
Marketing names: Rheilffordd Llyn Padarn Cyfyngedig (Padarn Lake Railway Ltd); Llanberis Lake Railway

Elidir heads out of Llanberis. *Melvyn Hopwood*

Llangollen Railway

Member: AIRPS, TT

Denbighshire
Timetable Service

The line, which is presently 7.5 miles long, is the only preserved standard gauge line in North Wales. Situated in the Dee Valley, it follows the course of the River Dee for much of its route, and affords good views of the surrounding countryside between Llangollen and Carrog. It is the eventual aim to reach Corwen, some 10 miles from Llangollen where a new terminus will be built. The line's extension towards Carrog opened on 2 May 1996. The railway was the winner of the Ian Allan Independent Railway of the Year Award in 1996
Location: Llangollen station, A542 from Ruabon, A5 from Shrewsbury/Betws y Coed
Commercial Manager: Mr C. Keyse
Traffic Manager: Mr C. Wilson
Operating organisation: Llangollen Railway plc
Supporting organisation: Llangollen Railway Trust Ltd, The station, Abbey Road, Llangollen, Denbighshire LL20 8SN (both organisations)
Telephone: Answerphone (24hr): Llangollen (01978) 860951. Other enquiries: (01978) 860979 (office hours only). Llangollen Railway Trust Ltd (24hr answerphone) (01978) 861143
Main station: Llangollen
Other stations: Berwyn, Deeside Halt (by request), Glyndyfrdwy, Carrog
OS reference: SJ 214422
Car park: Llangollen (Market St) and Mill St (Lower Dee Mill), also at Carrog station on B5437 on A5 east of Llangollen
Access by public transport: Nearest station: Ruabon (2hr service), then hourly Bryn Melyn bus (Wrexham-Llangollen) or Crosville D94 service
Refreshment facilities: Llangollen, Berwyn, Glyndyfrdwy and Carrog
Souvenir shop: Llangollen
Length of line: 7.5 miles
Passenger trains: Llangollen-Glyndyfrdwy
Period of public operation: Weekends January to Easter; then

Locomotives and multiple-units

Name	No	Origin	Class	Type	Built
—	2859	GWR	2800	2-8-0	1918
Kinlet Hall*	4936	GWR	'Hall'	4-6-0	1929
—	5199	GWR	5101	2-6-2T	1934
—	5532	GWR	4575	2-6-2T	1928
—	6430	GWR	6400'	0-6-0PT	1937
—	7754	GWR	5700	0-6-0PT	1930
Foxcote Manor	7822	GWR	'Manor'	4-6-0	1950
—	7298	LMS	3F	0-6-0T	1924
—	4806	LMS	5MT	4-6-0	1944
—	KD6.463	USATC	S160	2-8-0	1942
Castel Dinas Bran	76079	BR	4MT	2-6-0	1957
—	80072	BR	4MT	2-6-4T	1954
—	03162	BR	03	0-6-0DM	1960
—	D3265	BR	08	0-6-0DE	1956
—	D8142	BR	20	Bo-Bo	1966
—	D7629	BR	25	Bo-Bo	1965
Chirk Castle	25313	BR	25	Bo-Bo	1966
—	46010	BR	46	1Co-Co1	1961
—	50454	BRCW	104	DMBS	1957
—	50528	BRCW	104	DMC	1957
—	51618	BR	127	DMBS	1959
—	51907	BR	108	DMBS	1960
—	53447	BRCW	104	DMBS	1957
—	53454	BRCW	104	DMBS	1958
—	54456	Cravens	105	DMBS	1958
—	54490	BR	108	DTC	1960
—	50416	Wickham	108	MBS	1958

*Undergoing restoration at Birmingham Railway Museum, Tyseley

Industrial locomotives

Name	No	Builder	Type	Built
Darfield No 1*	—	Hunslet (3783)	0-6-0ST	1953
Eliseg	—	Fowler (22753)	0-4-0DM	1939
Richboro†	—	H/Clarke (1243)	0-6-0T	1917
Burtonwood Brewer*	—	Kitson (5459)	0-6-0ST	1932
—	14	H/Clarke (D1012)	0-4-0DM	1956
—	1	YEC/BTH	0-4-0D	c1950
—	—	YEC	0-6-0DE	

*Undergoing overhaul at Bury
†On display at the Dr Who Exhibition at Lower Dee Mill, Llangollen

Stock — coaches — 17 Mk 1 coaches; 2 Mk 1 sleepers; 4 GWR coaches; 1 LNER buffet coach

Stock — wagons — 4 wagons; 1 Bolster wagon; 1 LNWR tool van; 2 GWR brake vans; 1 GWR Mink D wagon; 1 SR 'BY' parcels van; 3 tank wagons; 1 LNER parcels van; 2 BR Fruit vans; 1 ex-LNWR brake van; 1 Matisa track tamper; 1 BR ballast wagon; 1 Coles diesel/electric 5-ton crane; 1 BR generator van; 1 LMS Inspection saloon; 1 GWR Siphon G coach; 1 LMS box van; 1 GWR Mink A van; 1 BR Presflow bulk cement wagon; 1 BR CCT

Stock — maintenance — 1 Matisa Track Recording Machine; 1 BR Bridge/Viaduct Inspection Unit

daily to end of October. Weekends November/December with Santo Special extras in December. Please see timetable for details of services
Special events: Steam Gala – 24-26 May; Diesel Galas – 28/29 June, 18/19 October; Transport Extravaganza — 13/14 September. Please refer to timetable or event leaflet
Special notes: The Berwyn Belle operates midday Sunday and Saturday evening dining train, Tel: 01978 860583 for details. Driver experience courses are offered on both diesel and steam locomotives
Facilities for disabled: Special

Owners
5532 and 5952 the Llangollen Railway (GWR) Locomotive Group
5199 the 5199 Project
7822 the Foxcote Manor Society
7754 the Llangollen Railway Trust Ltd
80072 the 80072 Steam Locomotive Co Ltd
Richboro the National Coal Board
Burtonwood Brewer the Burtonwood Brewery
03162 the Wirral Borough Council

passenger coach for wheelchairs, also shop and refreshment rooms at Llangollen. Toilet available at Berwyn, Glyndyfrdwy and Carrog stations. Advance notice required for special coach

Membership details: Mr J. Short, 'Bryn Aber', Llangollen Railway Trust Ltd, c/o above address
Membership journal: *Steam at Llangollen* — quarterly

Narrow Gauge Railway Centre
Caernarfonshire
Museum

A very extensive collection of narrow gauge railway equipment from the British Isles mainly housed in a purpose-built exhibition hall at Gloddfa Ganol Slate Mine, a major tourist attraction. Close to other tourist attractions in Blaenau Ffestiniog, principally the Llechwedd Slate Caverns and the Ffestiniog Railway
Location: Off the A470 Blaenau Ffestiniog road half-mile north of the town, turn at the locomotive
OS reference: SH 693470
General Manager: Eryl Roberts

Operating society/organisation: Gloddfa Ganol Slate Mine, Blaenau Ffestiniog, Gwynedd, North Wales LL41 3NB
Telephone: (01766 830) 664
Car park: On site
Access by public transport: Blaenau Ffestiniog BR/FR station, bus connection to mine
On site facilities: Licensed restaurant, snack bar. Toilets, children's playground and playroom, slate works, craftshops, mining museum, preserved quarrymen's cottages. Extensive

underground workings, Land Rover tours and rail ride
Public opening: Easter-October, Mondays-Fridays. Also Sundays mid-July to end August
Length of line: Half-mile to mine entrance
Facilities for disabled: Toilets, shops, museums, restaurant and section of mine suitable. No advance notice required. Special party rates available

---

Penrhyn Castle Industrial Railway Museum
Caernarfonshire
Museum
Member: AIRPS

A collection of historic industrial steam locomotives, both standard and narrow gauge, displayed in Penrhyn Castle, a well known National Trust property in the area regularly open to visitors
Location: Llandegai, near Bangor. One mile east of Bangor on the A5
OS reference: SH 603720
Operating society/organisation: National Trust, Penrhyn Castle, Industrial Railway Museum, Llandegai, near Bangor, Gwynedd
Telephone: Bangor (01248) 353084

Industrial locomotives

Name	No	Builder	Type	Built
Kettering Furnaces No 3	—	B/Hawthorn (859)	0-4-0ST	1885*
Watkin	—	de Winton	0-4-0VBT	1893*
Fire Queen	—	Horlock	0-4-0	1848†
Hawarden	—	H/Clarke (526)	0-4-0ST	1899
Vesta	—	H/Clarke (1223)	0-6-0T	1916
Charles	—	Hunslet (283)	0-4-0ST	1882§
Hugh Napier	—	Hunslet (855)	0-4-0ST	1904§
—	1	Neilson (1561)	0-4-0WT	1870
Haydock	—	Stephenson (2309)	0-6-0T	1879
Acorn	—	R/Hornsby (327904)	0-4-0DM	1948

*3ft gauge
†4ft gauge
§1ft 10.75in gauge

Car park: Within castle grounds
Access by public transport:
Nearest BR station, Bangor
On site facilities: The castle is open to the public, and contains a gift shop. Light refreshments are available
Public opening: Daily 1 April-1 November, but the museum will be closed for the early part of the season due to on-going roof repairs, a section is expected to be open by

June/July 1997. Visitors are advised to phone to check before visiting
Facilities for disabled: Access to castle and museum
Special notes: For those interested in stately homes the castle is well worth a visit. The entrance fee covers both the castle and the railway exhibits housed in the castle courtyard

Pontypool & Blaenavon Railway
Member: AIRPS

Monmouthshire
Steam Centre

The historic Blaenavon site, complete with its railway installations and locomotives can easily be included in a visit to Big Pit Mining Museum
Location: Near Big Pit, Blaenavon, Gwent
OS reference: SO 237093
Operating society/organisation:
Pontypool & Blaenavon Railway Co (1983) Ltd, Council Offices, High Street, Blaenavon, Gwent NP4 9PT
Telephone/Fax: (01495) 792263
Car park: Adjacent to railway terminus
On site facilities: Light refreshments and souvenir shop
Public opening: Sundays Easter-1st weekend in September
Special events: Friends of Thomas the Tank Engine, Santa Sprecial. Please contact for details
Special notes: The railway incorporates the former mineral/LNWR passenger lines running through Big Pit. Both north and southbound extensions are being considered. Service currently operates between Furnace Sidings platform and Whistle Inn platform
Membership details: c/o above address, or phone 01873 857539

Locomotives

Name	No	Origin	Class	Type	Built
—	2874	GWR	2800	2-8-0	1918
—	3855	GWR	2884	2-8-0	1942
—	4253	GWR	4200	2-8-0T	1917
—	5668	GWR	5600	0-6-2T	1926
Bickmarsh Hall	5967	GWR	'Hall'	4-6-0	1937
—	9629	GWR	5700	0-6-0PT	1946
—	51074	GRCW	119	DMBC	1958
—	51104	GRCW	119	DMS	1958
—	51942	BR	108	DMCL	1960
—	52044	BR	108	DMCL	1960
—	54270	BR	108	DTCL	1960
—	53632	BR	108	DMCL	1960
Renown	50029	BR	50	Co-Co	1968
Repulse	50030	BR	50	Co-Co	1968
Eagle	50043	BR	50	Co-Co	1968

Industrial locomotives

Name	No	Builder	Type	Built
Nora	5	Barclay (1680)	0-4-0ST	1920
Harry	—	Barclay (1823)	0-4-0ST	1926
Menelaus	—	Peckett (1889)	0-6-0ST	1935
—	8	RSH (7139)	0-6-0ST	1944
—	104	E/Electric (D1249)	0-6-0DH	1968
—	106	E/Electric (D1226)	0-6-0DH	1971
—	1	Fowler (22497)	0-6-0DM	1938
—	170	Hunslet (7063)	0-8-0DH	1971
—	10083	R/Royce (10083)	0-4-0DH	1961

Stock
7 ex-BR Mk 1 coaches, 5 ex-GWR coaches, 2 ex-LSWR coaches, 36 other vans, china clay, coke and tank wagons

Owners
50029 and 50030 Operation Collingwood

The Welsh Highland Railway Co has been incorporated to reconstruct much of the original WHR line. The new northern terminus will be at Caernarfon, with re-opening to Portmadog in stages over the next 10 years. Stage One, from Caernarfon to Dinas, is expected to reopen in time for the summer season.

General Manager: Alan Heywood
Headquarters: Ffestiniog Railway Co, Harbour Station, Porthmadog, Gwynedd, LL49 9NF
Telephone: Porthmadog (01766) 512340
Main stations: Caernarfon
Other public stations: Dinas
OS reference: SH 481625
Car parks: Caernarfon
Access by public transport: Caernarfon is served by local buses. The station at Bangor is served by InterCity and Regional Railways North West. There is a regular bus service between Bangor and Caernarfon

Refreshment facilities: Licensed restaurant at Porthmadog, cafe at Tan-y-Bwlch (summer only), refreshments also on most trains
Depot: Dinas
Length of line: 13.5 miles, 1ft 11.5in gauge
Passenger trains: Caernarfon-Dinas
Future extensions: Dinas-Rhyd Ddu-Beddgelert-Porthmadog
Period of public operation: will be announced in railway press
Facilities for disabled, refreshments & souvenirs:. Telephone for details
Membership details: Welsh Highland Railway Society (see above address)
Membership journal: Snowdon Ranger — quarterly

Locomotives

Name	No	Builder	Type	Built
—	K1	B/Peacock (5292)	0-4-0+0-4-0	1909
—*	138	B/Peacock	2-6-2+2-6-2	1958
—*	140	B/Peacock	2-6-2+2-6-2	1958
—*	143	B/Peacock	2-6-2+2-6-2	1958
Castell Caernafon	—	Funkey	Bo-Bo	1968

*Former South African Railways NGG16 class locomotives
The above locomotives may not be on site. Ffestiniog Railway Co locomotives may operate some services

Stock
6 bogie coaches under construction. Numerous service vehicles

The only public rack and pinion railway in the British Isles, opened in 1896, this bustling line climbs up the slopes of Snowdon, often through the clouds, to the hotel at the top. The trip should not be missed

General Manager: A. P. Hopkins
Engineering Manager: M. Kressman
Headquarters: Snowdon Mountain Railway, Llanberis, Gwynedd LL55 4TY
Telephone: Llanberis (01286) 870223
Fax: (01286) 872518
Main station: Llanberis
Other public stations: Summit, also Clogwyn/Rocky Valley when Summit is inaccessible
OS reference: SH 582597
Car park: Llanberis
Access by public transport: Bangor BR station then by bus to Caernarfon and there change to

Locomotives

Name	No	Builder	Type	Built
Enid	2	SLM (924)	0-4-2T	1895
Yr Wyddfa	3	SLM (925)	0-4-2T	1895
Snowdon	4	SLM (988)	0-4-2T	1896
Moel Siabod	5	SLM (989)	0-4-2T	1896
Padarn	6	SLM (2838)	0-4-2T	1922
Ralph*	7	SLM (2869)	0-4-2T	1923
Eryri*	8	SLM (2870)	0-4-2T	1923
Ninian	9	Hunslet (9249)	0-4-0DH	1986
Yeti	10	Hunslet (9250)	0-4-0DH	1986
Peris	11	Hunslet (9305)	0-4-0DH	1991
George	12	Hunslet (9312)	0-4-0DH	1992

All steam locomotives were built by Swiss Locomotive Works, Winterthur
All diesel locomotives were built by Hunslet Engine Co, Leeds
*Curreently stored out of service (boilerless)

Stock
8 closed bogie coaches; 1 bogie works car; 1 4-wheel open wagon; a 3-car diesel-electric railcar set built 1995 by HPE Tredegar (fleet Nos 21, 22, 23 [Works Nos 1074/5/6])

local bus to Llanberis. There is also a limited direct service between Bangor and Llanberis in summer. Snowdon Sherpa Services to/from Beddgelert and Betws-y-Coed stop outside the station

Refreshment facilities: Llanberis, Summit

Souvenir shops: Llanberis, Summit

Depot: Llanberis

Length of line: 7.5km, 800mm gauge

Passenger trains: Llanberis-Summit. Journey time approx 60 minutes. Departures from Llanberis at 30 minute intervals during peak periods. Round trip approx 2hr 30min

Period of public operation: Daily 15 March-1 November

Special notes: All trains are subject to weather and traffic restrictions, especially before mid-May and during October. Parties welcome by prior arrangement in off peak periods. Family ticket (2 adults, 2 Children) available to Summit only on early morning trains up to and including 09.30

No 2 *Enid* is prepared for the next trip up Snowdon. *SMR*

Swansea Maritime & Industrial Museum

Swansea Museum

This Museum houses a number of relics from Swansea's industrial and maritime past one of which is stationed outside the Museum. The Tramshed Annexe houses a restored Swansea City double-deck tram (Brush Electrical Engineering 1923/24 model), and a replica of the early Mumbles railway carriage, in addition to the sole surviving example of the Mumbles Railway rolling stock, the front section of the tramcar,

manufactured by the Brush Electrical Engineering Co in 1928.

Artefacts from the Mumbles Railway are also displayed within a graphic presentation, as are

Industrial locomotives

Name	No	Builder	Type	Built
Sir Charles*	—	A/Barclay (1473)	0-4-0F	1919
—	—	Peckett (1426)	0-6-0ST	1916

Notes
*Not on public display

examples of Brunel's 'GWR' broad gauge rail track.

Location: On the south side of the town between the shopping centre and the sea in the newly created

Maritime Quarter
OS reference: SS 659927
Operating society/organisation:
City of Swansea Museum Services,
Maritime & Industrial Museum,
Museum Square, Maritime Quarter,
Swansea SA1 1SN
Telephone: Swansea (01792)
650351

Car park: Public car parks close
by
Access by public transport:
Reached on foot from shopping
centre, central bus depot or by car
On site facilities: No refreshments
in the Museum but several cafés
close by. Museum shop selling
souvenirs and produce of the

Woollen Mill which operates in the
Museum throughout the year.
Education Service available on
request to Education Officer
Public opening: 10.00-17.00 six
days a week, closed Mondays and
25/26/27 December and New
Year's Day. Last admission 16.45
Facilities for disabled: Available

Swansea Vale Railway

Member: AIRPS

Swansea
Timetable Service

Location/headquarters: Swansea
Vale Railway Upper Bank,
Pentrechwyth, Swansea, West
Glamorgan SA1 7DB
Telephone: 01792 653615
Operations Manager: Mike
Meyrick
Main stations: Six Pit Junction,
Nany-Y-Ffin Road, Llansamlet
(Swansea)
Other stations: Cwm Crossing
(planning), Upper Bank Junction
(under restoration)
OS reference: Sheet 159; Six Pit
Junction — SN 683969, Upper
Bank Junction — SN 668953
Car parks: Six Pit Junction, Upper
Bank Works
Access by public transport: To
Six Pit Junction (ask for
Llansamlet) — by train rail
Llansamlet (1-mile); by bus South
Wales Transport (from Quadrant
Bus Stn) 30B/31/31B/32/33/34.
To Upper Bank bus 34. Bus Info

Locomotives and multiple-units

Name	No	Origin	Class	Type	Built
—	4270	GWR	4200	2-8-0T	1919
—	9642	GWR	5700	0-6-0PT	1946
—	51135	BR	116	DMBS	1958
—	51148	BR	116	DMS	1958
—	55026	P/Steel	121	DMBS	1960
—	59445	BR	116	TS	1959

Industrial locomotives

Name	No	Builder	Type	Built
Llantanam Abbey	—	Barclay (2074)	0-6-0ST	1939
—	—	Hunslet (3829)	0-6-0ST	1955
—	1	Peckett (1345)	0-4-0ST	1914
—	12514	H/Clarke (D1254)	0-6-0DM	1962
—	2	N/British (27914)	0-4-0DM	1961
—	1	R/Hornsby (476143)	4wDM	1963
—	—	R/Hornsby (312433)	4wDM	1951

Owners
9642 the South Wales Pannier Group
Class 116 DMU the Llanelli & District Railway Society
Llantanam Abbey the *Llantanam Abbey* Locomotive Association

Stock — coaches: 1 BR suburban SO; 1 BR Mk 2 BSK

Peckett No 1 heads a two brake van train on the Swansea Vale Railway. *Melvyn Hopwood*

01792 580580
Refreshment facilities: On train on operating days only (snacks & drinks)
Souvenir shop: On train on operating days only
Depot: Upper Bank
Facilities for disabled: None (new Six Pit platform will have wheelchair ramp — hopefully opening 1997
Period of public operation: April-August 11.00-17.00; October-December 11.00-16.00
Operating days: Steam: 28-31 March; 4/5, 24-26 May; 8, 15, 22 June; 6, 20, 23, 27, 30 July; 3, 6, 10, 13, 17, 20, 23/-25 August;

Stock — *wagons:* 1 GWR brake van, 1 BR brake van,.3 4-wheel tar tanks (ex-NCB), 3 LMS 12ton mineral wagons, 1 BR 'Gane A' bogie bolster, 1 GWR 'Mink' 10ton van, 3 GWR 10ton vans, 1 10ton open, 2 GWR 'tunney' wagons, 1 LNER low-fit

Stock — *cranes:* Smith-Rodley 4-wheel steam crane, Cowans & Sheldon LMS rail-mounted hand crane, Jones 20ton rail-mounted diesel crane

25/26 October; 6/7, 14, 20/21 December.
DMU services: 3 May, 7, 14, 21 June, 5, 19, 26 July; 2, 9, 16 August; 13 December
Special events: Easter Bunny Specials — 28-31 March; Friends of Thomas the Tank Engine — 24-26 May, 23-25 August; Halloween Ghost Trains— 25/26 October;

Santa Specials — 6/7, 13/14, 21/21 December
Membership details: G. Fuller, Swansea Vale Railway Society, 21 Elmhurst Crescent, St Thomas, Swansea, West Glamorgan SA1 8EA
Membership journal: *Vale News* — quarterly

Talyllyn Railway
Member: AIRPS, TT

Caernarfonshire
Timetable Service

The very first railway in the country to be rescued and operated by enthusiasts, the line climbs from Tywyn through the wooded Welsh hills past Dolgoch Falls to Nant Gwernol. The trains are hauled by a variety of veteran tank engines all immaculately maintained by the railway's own workshops at Tywyn Pendre
Managing Director: M. J. Wilson
Traffic manager: David Leech
Headquarters: Talyllyn Railway Co, Wharf station, Tywyn, Gwynedd LL36 9EY
Telephone: Tywyn (01654) 710472
Fax: 01654 711755
Main station: Tywyn Wharf
Other public stations: Tywyn Pendre, Rhydyronen, Brynglas, Dolgoch Falls, Abergynolwyn, Nant Gwernol
OS reference: SH 586005 (Tywyn Wharf)
Car parks: Tywyn Wharf, Dolgoch, Abergynolwyn
Access by public transport: Tywyn BR station. Bus Gwynedd services to Tywyn
Refreshment facilities: Tywyn Wharf, Abergynolwyn hot and cold snacks available. Picnic areas at Dolgoch Falls and Abergynolwyn. Picnic site at Dolgoch Falls
Souvenir shops: Tywyn Wharf, Abergynolwyn
Museum: Tywyn Wharf
Depot: Tywyn Pendre

Locomotives

Name	No	Builder	Type	Built
Talyllyn	1	F/Jennings (42)	0-4-2ST	1865
Dolgoch	2	F/Jennings (63)	0-4-0WT	1866
Sir Haydn	3	Hughes (323)	0-4-2ST	1878
Edward Thomas	4	K/Stuart (4047)	0-4-2ST	1921
Midlander	5	R/Hornsby (200792)	4wDM	1940
Douglas	6	Barclay (1431)	0-4-0WT	1918
Tom Rolt*	7	Barclay (2263)	0-4-2T	1949
Merseysider	8	R/Hornsby (476108)	4wDH	1964
Alf	9	Hunslet (4136)	0-4-0DM	1950

Locomotive notes: In service — 1, 3, 4 , 6 and 7; 2 not currently in service
*Virtually a new locomotive rebuilt from the original at Pendre Works

Stock
13 4-wheel coaches/vans; 10 bogie coaches; 45 wagons

Narrow Gauge Museum, Tywyn

Name	No	Builder	Type	Built
Dot	—	B/Peacock (2817)	0-4-0ST	1887
Pet†	—	LNWR	0-4-0ST	1865
Rough Pup	—	Hunslet (541)	0-4-0ST	1891
—	2	K/Stuart (721)	0-4-0WT	1902
Jubilee 1897	—	M/Wardle (1382)	0-4-0ST	1897
George Henry	—	de Winton	0-4-0T	1877
—	13	Spence	0-4-0T	1895
Nutty*	—	Sentinel (7701)	0-4-0VB	1929

*Not currently on site
†On loan from National Railway Museum

Stock
Various wagons and miscellaneous equipment

Length of line: 7.25 miles, 2ft 3in gauge
Passenger trains: Tywyn-Nant Gwernol

Period of public operation:
Sundays 16 February-16 March.
Daily 22 March to 1 November.
26 December-3 January 1998

Cont

Journey times: Tywyn-Nant Gwernol — single 55min, return 2hr 15min

Special events: Rolt Vehicle Rally — 25 May; Victorian Week — 3-9 August; Annual Race the Train event — 16 August; Land Rover Rally — 24 August; Entertainment by Train — (Sundays only) 13 July-24 August; Enthusiast Weekend — 27/28 September; Santa Specials — December

Family tickets: Available

Facilities for disabled: No problem for casual visitors, advance notice preferred for groups. Access to shop and cafeteria possible at Tywyn and Abergynolwyn. Disabled toilet facilities at Tywyn and Abergynolwyn. Access possible to lower floor of museum. Limited capacity for wheelchairs on trains. New vehicle for wheel chairs now in operation

Special notes: Parties and private charter trains by arrangement. Children under 5 years of age free. Narrow gauge 'Wanderer' four- and eight-day tickets accepted

Membership details: Mr A. Johnston, 9 Reynolds Way, Croydon, Surrey CR0 5JW

Membership journal: *Talyllyn News* — quarterly

Marketing names: One of the Great Little Trains. The first preserved railway in the world

---

Teifi Valley Railway
Member: AIRPS

Pembrokeshire
Timetable Service

Operating Society/organisation: Teifi Valley Railway, Henllan Station, Llandysul, Dyfed SA44 5TD

Manager: Mr R. Sanderson

Telephone: 01559 371077

Main Station: Henllan

Other public stations: Forest Halt, Pontprenshitw, Llandyfriog

Car Park: Henllan

OS reference: SN 358407

Access by public transport: BR station — Carmarthen (14 miles). Bus service 461 to Henllan

Refreshments: Henllan

Souvenirs: Henllan

On site facilities: Children's play areas, woodland theatre and trails, crazy golf and crazy quoits, GWR library.

Industrial locomotives

Name	No	Builder	Type	Built
Alan George	—	Hunslet (606)	0-4-0ST	1894
Sgt Murphy	—	K/Stuart (3117)	0-6-2T	1918
Sholto	—	Hunslet (2433)	4wDM	1941
Simon	—	M/Rail (7126)	4wDM	1936
Sammy	—	M/Rail (605)	4wDM	1959

Depot: Henllan, engine shed open to public

Facilities for disabled: All facilities including portable steps and wide door for wheelchairs in one coach

Period of public operation: Good Friday to 31 October

Special events: Easter Sunday fair, Victorian Day (late August), Halloween, Santa Specials

Membership details: Teifi Valley Railway Society, c/o Henllan station

Membership journal: *Right Away* — quarterly

Vale of Glamorgan Railway
Member: AIRPS

Vale of Glamorgan
Steam Centre

In 1997 the company will operate at its new site at Barry Island, having transfered all operations from the previous site at Cardiff. Steam-hauled rides will be available over a short distance of track while the extension of the line to Barry Town is being worked upon. For details please 'phone 01443 432205.

Location: Barry Island Station, Barry, South Wales

Operating society: Vale of Glamorgan Railway Company

Locomotives and multiple-unit

Name	No	Origin	Class	Type	Built
—	2861	GWR	2800	2-8-0	1918
—	4115	GWR	4101	2-6-2T	1936
—	5227	GWR	5205	2-8-0T	1924
—	5539	GWR	4575	2-6-2T	1928
—	6686	GWR	5600	0-6-2T	1928
Willington Hall	7927	BR	'Hall'	4-6-0	1950
—	44901	LMS	5MT	4-6-0	1945
—	48518	LMS	8F	2-8-0	1944
—	80150	BR	4MT	2-6-4T	1956
—	92245	BR	9F	2-10-0	1958
—	54279	BR	108	DTC	1959

Locomotive notes: In store, not on public view

Car park: Large public car park near site
Access by public transport: Frequent train services from Cardiff to Barry Island. Regular bus services from Cardiff
On site facilities: Museum, shop, light refreshments
Public opening: Please telephone 01446 747171 (daytime) or 01443 294627 (evenings)
Length of line: 600yd
Further inforation: Mr D. J. Morgan, 34 Bryn Gwyn Road, Cyncoed, Cardiff CF2 6PQ

Industrial locomotives

Name	No	Builder	Type	Built
Sir Gomer	—	Peckett (1859)	0-6-0ST	1932
Menalaus	—	Peckett (1889)	0-6-0ST	1935
Pamela	—	Hunslet (3840)	0-6-0ST	1956
—	52/001	Barclay (1966)	0-4-0F	1929
—	107	North British (27932)	0-6-0DM	1959

Stock
BR Mk 1 coaches, TVR coach No 153, various freight vehicles

Vale of Rheidol Railway
Member: AIRPS

Cardiganshire
Timetable Service

This narrow gauge railway offers a 23-mile round trip from Aberystwyth to Devils Bridge providing spectacular views which cannot be enjoyed by road. At Devils Bridge there are walks to the Mynach Falls and Devils Punch Bowl. Many artists have been inspired by the magnificence of Devils Bridge and the Rheidol Valley
General Manager: N. Thompson
Headquarters: Vale of Rheidol Railway, The Locomotive Shed, Park Avenue, Aberystwyth, Dyfed SY23 1PG
Telephone: 01970 625819
Main station: Aberystwyth (adjacent to BR station)
Other public stations: Devils Bridge, Rhiwfron, Rheidol Falls, Aberffrwd, Nantyronen, Capel Bangor, Glanrafon, Llanbadarn
OS reference: SN 587812
Car parks: Aberystwyth, Devils Bridge

Locomotives

Name	No	Origin	Ex-BR Class	Type	Built
Owain Glyndwr	7	GWR	98	2-6-2T	1923
Llywelyn	8	GWR	98	2-6-2T	1923
Prince of Wales	9	GWR	98	2-6-2T	1924
—	10	Brecon MR (002)	98/1	0-6-0DH	1987

Stock
16 bogie coaches including one Vista coach; 1 4-wheel guards van; 11 wagons for maintenance use; 1 inspection trolley

Access by public transport: Aberystwyth BR station: and bus services to Aberystwyth
Refreshment facilities: Aberystwyth (not railway-owned), Devils Bridge (not railway operated)
Souvenir shop: Aberystwyth
Depot: Aberystwyth (not open to the public)
Length of line: 11.75 miles, 1ft 11.75in gauge
Journey time: Single 1hr, return 3hr

Passenger trains: Aberystwyth-Devils Bridge
Period of public operation: Daily 28 March-3 April, 24 May-11 September; Saturday, Sundays, Tuesday-Thursday 5 April-1 May, Saturday-Thursday 3-22 May, 13 September-2 October; Saturday, Sundays, Tuesday-Thursday 4-30 October

Welsh Highland Railway

Caernarfonshire
Steam Centre

The Welsh Highland Railway Ltd operates services over a short section on the south western end of the old Welsh Highland line.

The company are in the process of developing an exciting new project to transform the existing site at

Gelerts Farm in Porthmadog into an all-weather tourist attraction based around an interpretative Railway Heritage Centre. The railway is a family orientated attraction offering bargain fares and a range of events in 1997

Location: Tremadog Road, Porthmadog, Gwynedd, adjacent to Cambrian Coast station
OS reference: SH 571393
General Manager: Stuart Weatherby
Operating society/organisation:

Welsh Highland Light Railway (1964) Ltd, Gelert's Farm Works, Madoc Street West, Porthmadog, Gwynedd LL49 9DY

Telephone: Porthmadog (01766) 513402 (weekends and operating days); this is a 24hr information line

Car park: At terminus

Catering facilities: Station buffet — 'Russells' supplying hot meals, cold buffet, sandwiches and light refreshments

Access by public transport: Rail service to Porthmadog station. Bws Gwynedd service 1 and 3 to Porthmadog

On site facilities: Souvenir shop, information boards, toilet facilities, taped commentary on coaches, extended shed tours on each journey

Length of line: Three quarter-mile, 1ft 11.5in gauge

Passenger trains: Porthmadog-Pen-y-Mount. Return journey time 40min approximately, steam-hauled bank holidays, every weekend and every day (except Fridays and Mondays from mid-July to end of August)

Family tickets: Available, 2 Adults + 2 children

Period of public operation: Easter, then May-October

Special events: Please contact for details

Facilities for disabled: Disabled passengers can be accommodated without prior notice — except in parties

Membership details: Membership Secretaries, R. & P. Hughes, Cil-y-nant, Gladestry, Kington, Herefordshire HR5 3NR

Membership journal: *The Journal* — quarterly

Locomotives

Name	No	Builder	Type	Built
Moel Tryfan	—	Bagnall (3023)	0-4-2T	1953
Gelert	—	Bagnall (3050)	0-4-2T	1953
Russell	—	Hunslet (901)	2-6-2T	1906
Pedemoura	—	O&K (10808)	0-6-0WT	1924
Karen	—	Peckett (2024)	0-4-2T	1942
Glaslyn	1	R/Hornsby (297030)	4wDM	1952
Kinnerley	2	R/Hornsby (354068)	4wDM	1953
Cnicht	36	M/Rail (8703)	4wDM	1941
Katherine	9	M/Rail (605363)	4wDM	1968
—	4	M/Rail (605333)	4wDM	1963
—	5	Hunslet (6285)	4wDM	1968
—	3	R/Hornsby (370555)	4wDM	1953
Jonathon	6	M/Rail (11102)	4wDM	1959
—	7	Hunslet (7535)	4wDM	1977
—	10	R/Hornsby (481552)	4wDM	1962
—	11	Hunslet (3510)	4wDM	1947
—*	NG120	S. F. Belge	2-8-2	1950
Prospecton	—	Bagnall (2819)	4-4-0T	1946
Edward Saunders	—	Bagnall (2287)	4-4-0T	1926
Snowdonia/Eryri†	—	Buch (23389)	0-6-0DM	1977
—†	—	Buch (2405)	0-6-0DH	1980
—	—	Barclay (554)	4wDH	1970
—	—	Barclay (555)	4wDH	1970
—	—	M/Rail (22237)	4wDM	1965

*Ex-South African Railways Class NG15
†Ex-Polish State Railways class LYD2

Locomotive notes: 1997 steam service will be worked by the sole surviving locomotive from the old Welsh Highland, 91 year old *Russell* assisted by *Gelert*

Stock
Passengers will have the opportunity to travel in the restored 'Gladstone' coach used by William Gladstone during a visit to Snowdonia in the 1890s

---

Welshpool & Llanfair Light Railway

Member: AIRPS

Mid Wales
Timetable Service

There is a decidedly foreign atmosphere to the trains over this line. The steam locomotive collection embraces examples from three continents, and the coaches are turn-of-the-century balcony saloons from Austria or 1960s bogies from Africa. The line follows a steeply graded route (maximum 1 in 24) through very attractive rolling countryside, and is rather a gem in an area too often missed by the traveller heading for further shores

General Manager: Andy Carey

Headquarters: Welshpool & Llanfair Light Railway Preservation Co Ltd, The Station, Llanfair Caereinion, Powys SY21 0SF

Telephone: Llanfair Caereinion (01938) 810441

Fax: 01938 810861

Main station: Welshpool (Raven Square)

Other public stations: Castle Caereinion, Sylfaen, Llanfair

Caereinion

OS reference: SJ 107069

Car park: Llanfair Caereinion, Welshpool (both free)

Access by public transport: BR station at Welshpool, one mile from Raven Square. Cambrian Midland Red buses from Shrewsbury, Oswestry and Newtown to Welshpool

Refreshment facilities: Light refreshments at Llanfair Caereinion. Picnic areas at Welshpool & Llanfair

Souvenir shops: Welshpool, Llanfair Caereinion

Depot: Llanfair Caereinion

Length of line: 8 miles, 2ft 6in gauge

Passenger trains: Welshpool-Llanfair Caereinion

Period of public operation: Weekends and Bank Holidays Easter to 28 September. Daily 12 July-7 September

Special events: Santa trains on three weekends before Christmas; Friends of Thomas the Tank Engine — 5/6 July; narrow gauge steam gala — 30/31 August

Family tickets: Available

Facilities for disabled: Specially adapted coaches for wheelchairs now available. Easy access to shops. Disabled toilet facility at Welshpool

Locomotives

Name	No	Builder	Type	Built
The Earl	1	B/Peacock (3496)	0-6-0T	1902
The Countess	2	B/Peacock (3497)	0-6-0T	1902
Chattenden	7	Drewry (2263)	0-6-0DM	1949
Dougal	8	Barclay (2207)	0-4-0T	1946
Sir Drefaldwyn	10	Franco-Belge (2855)	0-8-0T	1944
Ferret	11	Hunslet (2251)	0-4-0DM	1940
Joan	12	K/Stuart (4404)	0-6-2T	1927
SLR 85	14	Hunslet (3815)	2-6-2T	1954
Orion	15	Tubize (2369)	2-6-2T	1948
Scooby	16	Hunslet (2400)	0-4-0DM	1941

Locomotive notes: Locomotives expected in service 1997 — *Countess, Sir Drefaldwyn,* SLR No 85. The remainder can be seen at Llanfair station, No 12 is displayed with access to the footplate.

Stock

1 Wickham trolley; 6 W&LLR wagons; 8 ex Admiralty wagons; 2 ex Bowater wagons; 5 ex Zillertalbahn coaches; 4 ex-Sierra Leone coaches

Membership details: John Parkinson, 124 London Road, Long Sutton, Spalding, Lincolnshire PE12 9EE

Membership journal: *The Journal* — quarterly

Marketing name: Llanfair Railway

Special notes: New buildings at Raven Square largely a reconstruction of the 1863 station from Eardisley in Herefordshire. Restored station at Llanfair. Access to No 12 at Llanfair, steps up to footplate. Children can see how an engine works. Open balcony coaches — travel right next to the engine at the front of the train. Or see the line rolling away behind the back end!

A contrast in styling as Beyer Peacock and Franco-Belge creations stand side-by-side.
John East

Channel Islands/ Ireland/Isle of Man

Alderney Railway

The Alderney Railway will be 150 years old, having opened on 14 July 1847. Queen Victoria was the only passenger until 1980. A Alderney 150 event is planned for 13/14 July. Free rides and drinks will feature as part of the celebrations
Location: Alderney, Channel Islands
Operating society/organisation: Alderney Railway Society, PO Box 75, Alderney, Channel Islands
Telephone: 01481-823260
Car park: Yes
Access by public transport: Aurigny Air Services from Southampton
On site facilities: Station at Braye Road (tickets & souvenirs; teas (Sundays) at Mannez Quarry
Public opening: Weekends and Bank Holidays, Easter to September

Industrial locomotives

Name	No	Builder	Type	Built
Elizabeth	—	Vulcan (D2271)	0-4-0DM	1949
Molly 2	—	R/Hornsby	0-4-0DM	1958

Stock
4 Wickham trolleys
2 Goods wagons
2 ex-London Underground 1938 Stock tube cars, Nos 10177/11177 (locomotive-hauled)
2 Wickham Flats
NB: all Wickhams privately-owned

Special events: Alderney Week August. Easter Egg Specials on Easter Saturday. Santa Specials, Saturday before Christmas
On site Facilities: Miniature railway (7.25in gauge), quarter-mile circuit operates at Mannez in connection with standard gauge line
Length of line: 2 miles

Facilities for disabled: Yes
President: Roger Warren
Chairman: Bruce Nightingale
Hon Sec: Mike Taylor
Membership journal: Issued infrequently.
Notes: New shed at Quarry. Three Wickham 'trains' to operate 1995 low season; *Elizabeth* and tube cars high season and Easter

Cavan & Leitrim Railway

Restoration work commenced in June 1993 and to date some half-mile of line has been rebuilt, water tower and engine shed refurbished and new workshops and carriage shed constructed. The ultimate objective is to rebuild a further 5.75 miles of line to Mohill.
Location/headquarters: The Narrow Gauge Station, Dromod, Co Leitrim, adjacent to the Irish Rail station
Telephone: 00 353 78-38599 (from UK)
General Manager: David Parks
Running Superintendent: Michael Kennedy

Locomotives

Name	No	Builder	Type	Built
Dromod	1	K/Stuart (3024)	0-4-2ST	1916
Dinmor	F511	Fowler (3900011)	4wDM	1947
–	LM87	R/Hornsby (329696)	4wDM	1952
–	–	H/Hunslet (2659)	4wDM	1942
–	9	Motorail (115U093)	4wDH	1970
–	LM350	Simplex (60SL748)	4wDM	1980

Railcars

Name	No	Builder	Type	Built
–	C11	Bord Na Mona	2w-2wPHR	–
–	C42	Wickham (7129)	2w-2wPHR	1955
–	C42	Wickham (7681)	2w-2wPHR	1957
–	C47	Bord Na Mona/ Southern Motors	4wPHR	1958
–	W6/11-4	Wickham (9673)	2w-2wPHR	1963

Main station: Dromod
Other stations: Clooncolry Halt
Car park: At Dromod terminus
Access by public transport: Rail service to Dromod (Irish Rail) on the Dublin/Sligo line
Refreshment facilities: At nearby 'Railway Bar'
Souvenir shop: Dromod
Length of line: Half-mile (3ft gauge)
Museum: Large collection of Irish and British narrow gauge locomotives and rolling stock
Period of public operation: Daily all year round. Steam-hauled 1 May/31 October
Special events: Annual Vintage Rally — second weekend in May; Ghost Trains — 31 October; Santa Specials — weekends in December
Contact address for operating Co: Cavan & Leitrim Railway Co Ltd, Dromod, Co Leitrim, Republic of Ireland
Membership journal: *Cavan & Leitrim News* – quarterley, and an annual handbook

Rolling stock
Includes West Clare railway trailer 47c, Tralee & Dingle coaches 7 and 10, Isle of Man carriage F21

Kerr Stuart 0-4-2T No 1 and ex-GNR(I) bus conversion AU345 on a service train in August 1996. *Joe St Leger*

Downpatrick Steam Railway

Members: AIRPS

County Down
Timetable Service

Location: Downpatrick Station, Market Street, Downpatrick, Co Down BT30 6LZ
OS reference: J483444
Operating society/organisation: Downpatrick & Ardglass Railway Co Ltd, with the support of the Downpatrick Railway Society
Telephone: 01396 615779
Car park: Available adjacent to station in Downpatrick
Access by public transport: A regular service is operated by Ulsterbus from Belfast Europa bus centre Tel: (01232) 320011
Refreshment facilities: Buffet carriage open on operating days
On site facilities: Souvenir shop, toilets
Length of line: 1.75-miles. King Magnus' Grove built. Track is extending southwards towards Ballydugan Mill and northwards to Inch Abbey
Public opening: St Patricks Day (17 March); Easter Sunday, Monday and Tuesday; Sundays in July and August; August Bank Holiday; plus some dates in *Cont*

Locomotives

Name	No	Origin	Class	Type	Built
W. F. Gillespie OBE	E421	CIE	421	C	1962
—	E432	CIE	421	C	1962
—	G611	CIE	611	B	1962
—	G617	CIE	611	B	1962

Industrial locomotives

Name	No	Builder	Type	Built
Guinness	3BG	H/Clarke (1152	0-4-0ST	1919
—	1	O&K (12475)	0-4-0T	1934
—	3	O&K (12662)	0-4-0T	1935

Rolling stock
1 CIE Brake open standard; 1 CIE Brake open standard generating steam van; 1 CIE Buffet open standard; 4 NCC parcels vans; 1 NIR brake open standard; 1 NIR brake open standard driving trailer; 2 NCC open wagon; 1 LMS (NCC) brake van; 1 GNR(I) brake van; 1 CIE closed van; 1 GS&WR ballast hopper; 1 GSR ballast hopper; Belfast & County Down Railway 'Royal Saloon' No 153; 1 B&CDR 1st/2nd composite (No 152); 1 B&CDR 3rd open (ex-railmotor); 1 B&CDR 6 wheeled brake 3rd (No 39); 1 B&CDR 6 wheeled 2nd (No 154); 1 GS&WR 3rd open (No 836); 1 GS&WR ballast plough van (on loan from Westrail [Tuam] Ltd); 1 Ulster Railway Family Saloon (No 33, built 1862); 1 GSWR 6-wheeled full brake (No 69); selection of carriage and wagon underframes for internal use

Owners
1 and 3 the Irish Sugar Locomotive Group
3BG on loan from the Railway Preservation Society of Ireland
G611 and G617 the Irish Traction Group

September and October.
Period of public operation:
14.00-17.00
Journey time: 30min return
journey to Quoile marshes
Special events: Ghost Trains —

October; Santa Specials —
December
Facilities for disabled: All station
facilities at Downpatrick accessible
for disabled
Membership details: The

Secretary, Downpatrick Railway
Society, The Railway Station,
Downpatrick, Co Down BT30 6LZ

Foyle Valley Railway

Members: AIRPS

Londonderry
Steam Centre

The Foyle Valley Railway Centre
is a museum of narrow gauge
railways in the northwest of
Ireland, adjoining and associated
with an operating pleasure railway.
The centre houses a number of
items and rolling stock from the
former County Donegal and Lough
Swilly Railways. The centre is
housed in a modern building in an
attractive, newly developing,
riverside park. Plans exist for the
line to run along the former Great
Northern Railway (Ireland)
formation to Carrigans, and then on
towards St Johnston, a total
distance of 8 miles.
Location: Foyle Valley Railway
Centre, Foyle Road, Londonderry
BT48 6AQ
Main station: Waterside Railway
station
Car park: Adjacent to the station
Access by public transport: By
NI Railways to Londonderry
station (quarter-mile). By Ulsterbus
from various centres (three-quarter-
mile)
Souvenir shop: Operated by North
West of Ireland Railway Society at
railway museum
Operating group: A combined
project operated by Derry City
Council and the North West of
Ireland Railway Society
(responsible under Council control
for the rail service)

Locomotives and railcars

Name	No	Origin	Class	Type	Built
Meenglas	4	CDRJC	5	2-6-4T	1907
Columbkille	6	CDRJC	5	2-6-4T	1907
—	12	CDRJC	—	Diesel Railcar	1934
—	18	CDRJC	—	Diesel Railcar	1940

Industrial locomotives

Name	No	Origin	Type	Built
—	—	Simplex	0-4-0DH	1974

Rolling stock
1 ex-CDRJC carriage No 12, 1 ex-Londonderry & Lough Swilly Railway
carriage, 1 ex-Ballymena & Larne Railway carriage, 1 ex-Clogher Valley
Railway Box wagon No 19, 2 ex-CDRJC goods wagons

Museum: At Foyle Valley Railway
Centre
Facilities for disabled: Yes
Operating society: North West of
Ireland Railway Society, 8
Letterkenny Road, Londonderry
BT48 9XG
Telephone: (01504) 265358 or
(01504) 264865
Membership details: Secretary, D.
W. Mason, 7 Nicholson Terrace,
Londonderry BT48 7LW
General Manager: R. Gallagher,
telephone (01504) 265234
Society Journal: *The Starter*
published once a year

Refreshment facilities: None on
site but City Centre quarter-mile
away
On site facilities: Souvenir shop,
museum, toilets, and 3ft gauge
railway
Period of public operation: April-
September, Tuesday-Saturday and
public holidays 10.00-17.00,
Sunday 14.00-18.00. October-
March, Tuesday-Saturday 10.00-
17.00. Special opening times Easter
and Christmas
Length of line: 2.5 miles operated
by diesel railcars of the former
County Donegal Railways

Groudle Glen Railway

Isle of Man
Steam Centre

Location: Groudle Glen Railway,
Isle of Man
Officer in charge: Tony Beard
Operating company: Groudle
Glen Railway Ltd (managed by the
Isle of Man Steam Railway
Supporters' Association) of 29

Hawarden Avenue, Douglas, Isle of
Man IM1 4BP
Telephone: (01624) 622138
(evenings)
Car park: Yes
Access by public transport: Manx
Electric Railway (Groude Hotel)

On site facilities: Sales shop
Length of line: Three-quarter-mile,
2ft gauge
Public opening: Easter Sunday
and Monday, Sundays and Bank
Holidays May to September
(11.00-16.30), Wednesday evening

services July/August (19.00-21.00);
Santa Trains 14, 21 December
(11.00-15.30); 26 December
(12.00-15.30)
Facilities for disabled: Due to the
line's location, those who are
disabled will have some difficulty.
It is suggested that they telephone
for advice
**Further information and
membership details:** From above
address
Membership journal: *Manx
Steam Railway News* — quarterly

Locomotives

Name	No	Builder	Type	Built
Dolphin	1	H/Hunslet (4394)	4wDM	1952
Walrus	2	H/Hunslet (4395)	4wDM	1952
Sea Lion	—	Bagnall (1484)	2-4-0T	1896
Annie	—	GGR	0-4-2T	*

*Under construction, Bagnall look-a-like

Irish Steam Preservation Society

County Laois
Museum

Members: AIRPS

1996 was the Diamond Jubilee year
for *Nippy*, Ireland's oldest working
diesel locomotive
Location: Stradbally Hall, eight
miles from Athy, six miles from
Portlaoise.
Telephone: 00 353 502 25444
(from UK)
Access by public transport: Irish
Rail train to Athy or Portlaoise.
Kavanagh's Bus Portlaoise-
Stradbally-Athy also Portlaoise-
Stradbally-Kilkenny (both routes
twice daily Monday-Saturday)
On site facilities: 3ft gauge
railway
Catering facilities: None on site

Industrial locomotives

Name	No	Builder	Type	Built
—	2	Barclay (2264)	0-4-0WT	1949
—	—	Hunslet (2281)	4wDM	1941
Nippy	—	Planet (2014)	4wDM	1936
—	4	R/Hornsby (326052)	4wDM	1952

Stock
1 Passenger coach; 2 Ballast wagons; 1 Brake van

but town centre quarter-mile away
Length of line: 1km
Public opening: Please contact for
details
Special notes: This is the longest
established steam railway in
Ireland, now in its 29th year —
please contact Secretary, ISPS,
Bunnacrannagh, Timahoe Road,
Stradbally, Co Laois

Irish Traction Group

Co Tipperary
Museum

Member: AIRPS

Location: The former goods store
adjacent to Carrick-on-Suir railway
station
Operating society/organisation:
Irish Traction Group, 31 Hayfield
Road, Bredbury, Stockport,
Cheshire SK6 1DE, England
Telephone: 0161 285 5836 (Mon-
Fri 18.00-21.00 only)
Car park: Available in station
goods yard
Access by public transport:
Sparse train service. Services
operated by Bus Eireann from
Dublin, Limerick and Waterford
Cont

Locomotives

Name	No	Origin	Class	Manufacturer	Type	Built
—	1	NIR	DH	E/Electric (D1266)	4wDH	1969
—	2	NIR	DH	E/Electric (D1267)	4wDH	1969
—	3	NIR	DH	E/Electric (D1268)	4wDH	1969
—*	A3ᴿ	CIE	001/A	M/Vickers (889)	Co-Co	1955
—*	A39	CIE	001/A	M/Vickers (925)	Co-Co	1956
—	B103	CIE	0101/B	BRCW (DEL22)	A1A-A1A	1956
—	226	CIE	201/C	M/Vickers (972)	B0-B0	1957
—*	C231	CIE	201/C	M/Vickers (977)	B0-B0	1957
—	G601	CIE	601/G	Deutz (56119)	4wDH	1956
—*	G611	CIE	601/G	Deutz (57225)	4wDH	1962
—	G616	CIE	601/G	Deutz (57227)	4wDH	1962
—*	G617	CIE	601/G	Deutz (57229)	4wDH	1962
—*	712	CIE	–	Wickham (8919)		1962

*Not on site

Facilities: Toilets on Ei station. Site is located quarter-mile from town centre
Special events: Operation of railtours over EI/NIR sysytems
Opening times: Premises open most weekends throughout the year, although most locomotives are stabled outside. Please telephone above number before visiting.

An 'A' or '001' class diesel-electric No A3ᴿ is currently stored at Limerick, with IE No E428 hiding behind.
A. Marshall/ITG

Isle of Man Railway
Members: AIRPS, TT

Isle of Man
Timetable Service

The 3ft gauge Isle of Man Railway is a survivor of a system which covered the whole island. Almost continuous operation since 1873 makes it one of the oldest preserved railways in the British Isles. The railway has changed little since the turn of the century and retains much of its Edwardian atmosphere. It runs for over 15 miles between Douglas and Port Erin through the island's rolling southern countryside

Director of Public Transport: R. H. Smith
Operations Superintendent: M. G. Warhurst
Engineering Superintendent: G. F. Lawson
Headquarters: Isle of Man Railways, Strathallan Crescent, Douglas, Isle of Man IM2 4NR
Telephone: Douglas (01624) 663366

Locomotives

Name	No	Builder	Type	Built
Sutherland	1	B/Peacock (1253)	2-4-0T	1873
Loch	4	B/Peacock (1416)	2-4-0T	1874
Peveril	6	B/Peacock (1524)	2-4-0T	1875
G.H. Wood	10*	B/Peacock (4662)	2-4-0T	1905
Maitland	11*	B/Peacock (4663)	2-4-0T	1905
Hutchinson	12*	B/Peacock (5126)	2-4-0T	1908
Kissack	13	B/Peacock (5382)	2-4-0T	1910
Caledonia	15*	Dubs & Co (2178)	0-6-0T	1885
Viking	17*	Schottler (2175)	0-4-0DH	1958
—	19*	Walker (GNR (I))	diesel railcar	1950
—	20*	Walker (GNR (I))	diesel railcar	1951
—	—*	M/Rail (22021)	4wDM	1959
—	—	Wickhams	4wPM	1956
—	—*	Wickhams	4wPM	1961

*Operational, Nos 1, 4, 6 and 13 stored out of use

On display in museum at Port Erin

Name	No	Builder	Type	Built
Mannin	16	B/Peacock (6296)	2-4-0T	1926

Fax: 01624 663637
Main station: Douglas
Other public stations: Port Soderick, Santon, Castletown, Ballasalla, Port St Mary and Port Erin
Car parks: Douglas, Ballasalla, Castletown, Port Erin
Access by public transport: Isle of Man Transport bus to main centres
Special events: Enthusiasts Week — 19-27 July
Refreshment facilities: Port Erin and Douglas
Souvenir shops: Douglas and Port Erin stations and Douglas – Lord Street Travel Shop
Museum: Port Erin
Depot: Douglas
Length of line: 15.5 miles, 3ft gauge
Passenger trains: Douglas-Port Erin

Owned by IoM Railway & Tramway Preservation Society Ltd (not on display)

Name	No	Builder	Type	Built
Mona	5	B/Peacock (1417)	2-4-0T	1874
Tynwald*	7	B/Peacock (2038)	2-4-0T	1880
Fenella†	8	B/Peacock (3610)	2-4-0T	1894
Douglas	9	B/Peacock (3815)	2-4-0T	1896

*Chassis only
†Undergoing restoration to working order.

Rolling stock
Gibbons crane (on display at the former Union Mills station/owned by IoMR&TPS), 41 coaches, 3 vans, 2 'M' type wagons, 1 well wagon

Period of public operation: Daily Easter-end September
Facilities for disabled: Level access throughout Douglas and Port Erin stations including refreshment area. Carriages able to carry wheelchairs, ramps provided. Advance notice helpful

No 11 *Maitland* stands at Douglas with the 10.10 departure to Port Erin. *Nigel Hunt*

The 3ft gauge Manx Electric Railway is a unique survivor of Victorian high technology. A mixture of railway and tramway practice, it was built in 1893 and was a pioneer in the use of electric traction. Two of the original cars are still in service making them the oldest tramcars still in operation in the British Isles. After leaving Douglas, the railway passes the Groudle Glen Railway before reaching the charming village of Laxey, home of the Snaefell Mountain Railway. The line continues over some of the most breathtaking coastal scenery in the island before reaching its terminus at Ramsey nearly 18 miles from Douglas

Director of Public Transport: R. H. Smith

Operations Superintendent: M. G. Warhurst

Engineering Superintendent: G. F. Lawson

Headquarters: Isle of Man Railways, Strathallan Crescent, Douglas, Isle of Man IM2 4NR

Telephone: Douglas (01624) 663366

Fax: 01624 663637

Main station: Douglas (Derby Castle)

Other public stations: Laxey, Ramsey, Groudle, Dhoon Glen, Ballaglass and numerous wayside stops

Car parks: Douglas, Laxey, Ramsey (nearby)

Access by public transport: Isle of Man Transport buses to main centres

Special events: Enthusiasts Week — 19-27 July

Depots: Douglas, Laxey, Ramsey

Refreshment facilities: Laxey

Museum: Ramsey

Souvenirs shops: Ramsey and Douglas – Lord Street Travel Shop

Length of line: 17.5 miles, 3ft gauge

Passenger service: Douglas-Ramsey

Period of public operations: Daily Easter-October

Special notes: Folded wheelchairs can be carried. Please notify in advance. One trailer (capable of carrying wheelchais) with built-in lift. Please notify in advance

Motor Cars

Nos	Type	Seats	Body	Built
1, 2	Unvestibuled saloon	34	Milnes	1893
5, 6, 7, 9	Vestibuled saloon	32	Milnes	1894
14, 15, 17, 18	Cross-bench open	56	Milnes	1898
16	Cross-bench open	56	Milnes	1898
19-22*	Winter saloon	48	Milnes	1899
23†	Centre-cab locomotive	—	IOMT & EP6	1900
25-27	Cross-bench open	56	Milnes	1898
28-31	Cross-bench open	56	ERTCW	1904
32, 33	Cross-bench open	56	UEC	1906

*22 re-bodied 1991, McArd/MER

†owned byIoM Railway & Tramway Preservation Society Ltd

Trailers

Nos	Type	Seats	Body	Built
13	Cross-bench open	44	Milnes	1893
36, 37	Cross-bench open	44	Milnes	1894
40, 41, 44	Cross-bench open	44	EE Co	1930
42, 43	Cross-bench open	44	Milnes	1903
45-48	Cross-bench open	44	Milnes	1899
49-50, 53, 54	Cross-bench open	44	Milnes	1893
52	pw flatcar (ex trailer)	—	Milnes	1893
55, 56*	Cross-bench open	44	ERTCW	1904
57, 58	Saloon	32	ERTCW	1904
59	Special Saloon	18	Milnes	1895
60	Cross-bench open	44	Milnes	1896
61, 62	Cross-bench open	44	UEC	1906

*rebuilt as invalid carriage in 1993

MER Nos 2 and 27 near Howstraks on a Laxey-Douglas service. *C. I. Quiggin*

Railway Preservation Society of Ireland

Members: AIRPS, TT

Steam Centre

The RPSI was formed in 1964, making it one of the older preservation societies in these islands. It has always specialised in main line steam operations, and runs an intensive summer programme of trips out of both Belfast and Dublin. The main maintenance base is situated at Whitehead, 15 miles north of Belfast on the NIR route to Larne Harbour. Here not only are the traffic locomotives shedded, but the locomotive shed is also used for heavy maintenance. Currently the society is completing the full rebuilding of its fifth boiler 'in-house'. A large carriage shed is also on site where traffic vehicles are maintained and coaches are fully rebuilt. There are also heavy lifting facilities on site, and access may occassionally be limited for safety reasons when these are in use. Annual operations commence with 'Easter Bunny' trains out of Belfast, usually on Easter Monday. In May the 'International Railtour' is the main event, a three day steam extravaganza, which in 1997 will visit Tralee. During June there are main line trips out of both Belfast and Dublin, including a Midsummer Barbecue and a Jazz Special. July and August see the 'Portrush Flyers' from Belfast to Portrush and back, around 180 miles of main line steam, as well as the 'Sea Breeze' excursions from Dublin to Rosslare and back, covering 205 miles. During July and August there are often steam train rides on site at Whitehead on Sunday afternoons. The season usually ends with further excursions in September, giving the Society a breather before the 'Santa Specials' out of both capitals

Location: Whitehead Excursion station, Co Antrin, Northern Ireland

Operating society: Railway Preservation Society of Ireland,

Locomotives

Name	No	Origin	Class	Type	Built
Merlin	85*	GNR (I)	V	4-4-0	1932
Slieve Gullion	171	GNR (I)	S	4-4-0	1913
—	4	LMS (NCC)	WT	2-6-4T	1947
—	184†	GS&WR	J15	0-6-0	1880
—	186†	GS&WR	J15	0-6-0	1879
—	461**	D&SER	K2	2-6-0	1922
Lough Erne	27	SL&NCR	Z	0-6-4T	1949

Industrial locomotives

Name	No	Builder	Type	Built
Guinness	3§	H/Clarke (1152)	0-4-0ST	1919
R. H. Smyth	3	Avonside (2021)	0-6-0ST	1928
—	23	Planet (3509)	0-4-0DM	1951
—	4	R/Hornsby	0-4-0DM	1954

*On loan from Ulster Folk & Transport Museum
**Currently based in Dublin for regular operations
†Awaiting restoration, hopefully to commence soon
§On loan to Downpatrick & Ardglass Railway Society

Stock

The Society also owns some 20 operational coaches, normally divided between Whitehead and Dublin. A further 10+ coaches are awaiting restoration and a small number of freight wagons are also preserved, as well as a steam crane. Some coaches are stored at the Society's secondary maintenace base at Mullingar, Co Westmeath, but there is **No** public access

Castleview Road, Whitehead, Carrickfergus, Co Antrim BT38 9NA

Telephone/fax: Whitehead (01960) 353567

Car park: Public car parking is readily available adjacent to the Society premises, with a further large car park 5min walk away on the sea front. Both car parks are normally free

Access by public transport: Northern Ireland Railways or Ulstersbus to Whitehead

On site facilities: Souvenir shop (operating days only)

Public opening: Visitors welcome most weekends. Site not open during the week or when main line trains are operating from Whitehead of Belfast. Special opening for parties, or in the evening, may be arranged by telephoning in advance

Special notes: The RPSI is noted for its main line excursions and traditional rolling stock. For details: RPSI Railtours, c/o 22 Town Lane, Islandmagee, Larn, Co Antrim BT20 3SZ (9x4 SAE please)

Operations Officer: Heather Boomer

Membership details: Membership Secretary, 148 Church Road, Newtonabbey, Co Antrim BT36 6HJ

Future developments: A new heavy engineering workshop is planned, with further site development projects in the pipeline. Additional locomotive and coach restoration will hopefully take place.

The 3ft 6in gauge Snaefell Mountain Railway is unique. It is the only electrically-driven mountain railway in the British Isles. Almost all the rolling stock is original and dates back to 1895. The railway begins its journey at the picturesque village of Laxey where its terminus is shared with the Manx Electric Railway. The climb to the summit of Snaefell (2,036ft) is a steep one and the cars travel unassisted up gradients as steep as 1 in 12. From the summit, the views extend to Wales, Scotland, England and Ireland.

Director of Public Transport: R. H. Smith

Operations Superintendent: M. G. Warhurst

Engineering Superintendent: G. F. Lawson

Headquarters: Isle of Man Railways, Strathallan Crescent, Douglas, Isle of Man IM2 4NR

Trams

Nos	Type	Seats	Body	Built
1-4, 6	Vestibuled saloon	48	Milnes	1895
5 (rebuild)	Vestibuled saloon	48	MER/ Kinnin	1971

Telephone: Douglas (01624) 663366

Fax: 01624 663637

Main station: Laxey

Other public stations: Bungalow, Summit

Car parks: Laxey, Bungalow (nearby)

Access by public transport: Manx Electric Railway or Isle of Man Transport bus to Laxey

Special events: Enthusiasts Week — 19-27 July

Depot: Laxey

Refreshment facilities: Laxey, Summit

Museum: Ramsey

Souvenirs shops: Summit and Douglas – Lord Street Travel Shop

Length of line: 5 miles, 3ft 6in gauge

Passenger service: Laxey-Snaefell summit

Period of public operation: Daily May-September

Special notes: No special facilities for disabled

No 6 makes its way down Snaefell.

South Donegal Railway Restoration Society

Members: AIRPS

County Donegal
Museum

Location/Headquarters: Old Station House, Donegal Town, Ireland
Telephone: (010353-73 [from UK]) (073 [from Ireland]) 22655
General Manager: Patrick Stewart
Public opening: Old Station House to open as a permanent Railway Museum & Heritage Centre from Easter 1995
Membership details: From above address
Membership journal: *The Phoenix*
Special notes: Unfortunately, the development of the track at Barnesmore had to be abandoned due to unforseen and severe planning restrictions, but the group is now in the process of developing a very scenically attractive 3-mile section between Rossnowlagh and Ballintra

Locomotives

Name	No	Origin	Class	Type	Built
Drunboe	5	CDRJC	5	2-6-4T	1907

On loan from the Foyle Valley Railway

Stock

1 CDR brake/third coach
1 CDR railcar No 14
1 CDR trailer No 5
1 CDR combined goods/cattle and horse van (247 of 1893)
1 goods van

Viewing of all rolling stock is by arrangement only

Ulster Folk & Transport Museum

Members: AIRPS

County Down
Museum

45 acres are devoted to the Transport Galleries. Permanent exhibitions include the earliest forms of transport, horse-drawn vehicles, bicycles, motor cars and the Museum's *Titanic* exhibition.

The Irish Railway Collection is displayed in an award-winning purpose-built gallery — the largest Transport Museum gallery in Ireland.

The collection features *Maedb* — the largest locomotive run in Ireland. The display includes narrow gauge and standard gauge rolling stock; locomotives; carriages; goods wagons; railcars and railbuses along with new, previously undisplayed material and memorabilia
Location: Ulster Folk & Transport Museum, Cultra, Holywood.
Operating organisation: Ulster Folk & Transport Museum, Cultra, Holywood BT18 0EU

Locomotives (5ft 3in)

Name	No	Origin	Class	Type	Built
—	93	GNR(I)	JT	2-4-2T	1895
—	30	BCDR	I	4-4-2T	1901
Dunluce Caste	74	LMS(NCC)	U2	4-4-0	1924
Maedb	800	GSR	B1A	4-6-0	1939
—	1	R/Stephenson (2738)	—	0-6-0T	1891
Merlin	85	GNR(I)	V	4-4-0	1932
—	85	GNR(I)	—	Railbus	1932

Locomotives (narrow gauge)

Name	No	Origin	Class	Type	Built
Blanche	2	CDRJC	5A	2-6-4T	1912
Kathleen	2	CLR	—	4-4-0T	1887
Phoenix	11	CVR	—	4wD	1928
—	20	Industrial	—	0-4-0	1905
—	2	Industrial	—	0-4-0	1907

Stock

1 Dublin, Wicklow & Wexford Railway coach; 1 Dundalk, Newry & Greenore Railway coach; 1 Midland & Great Western Railway director's saloon (ex-private vehicle); 1 Electric tramcar of Bessbrook-Newry Tramway; 2 trams from Giant's Causeway Tramway, 1 Cavan-Leitrim Railway coach; 2 County Donegal Railway railcars; 1 County Donegal

Telephone: 01232 428428
Fax: 01232 428728
Access: By car or bus the museum is about 7 miles from Belfast City Centre on the A2 Belfast-Bangor Road. You can also reach the museum by train from any station on the suburban line.
Car park: Extensive
On site facilities: Shops, toilets, tea room, 7.25in line
Opening times: All year round. Opening times vary with season, check with the museum for details

Railway director's coach; 1 County Donegal Railway trailer coach (bodywork ex-Dublin & Lucan Railway coach); 1 Giants Causeway (P&BVR) saloon trailer; 1 Castleder & Victoria Bridge Tramway 1st/3rd coach; 1 County Donegal Railway 7ton open wagon, 3 Belfast trams, 1 Belfast trolleybus, 1 Belfast double-deck bus. Extensive collection of cars, motorcycles, bicycles, commercial vehicles and fire fighting equipment

Blanche from the County Donegal Railway as on show in the Ulster Folk & Transport Museum. *UFTM*

Westrail   County Galway

Location: Tuam, Co Galway, Ireland
OS Reference: Lat 42, Long 52
Operating society/organisation: Westrail (Tuam) Ltd, The Railway Station, Vicar Street, Tuam, Co Galway
Telephone: (093) 25400, (091) 91039, (093) 49253. Fax: (091) 25111
Car park: On site
Catering facilities: On train, licensed snack bar. Platform shops at Athenry
Length of line: Athenry-Tuam, 15 miles or Galway-Athenry 13 miles
Period of public operation: At the time of writing it was uncertain

Locomotives

Name	No	Origin	Class	Type	Built
—	90	GSWR	J30	0-6-0T	1875
—	E428	CIE	421	C	1962
—	3	CSET	—	0-4-0DM	1960

Rolling stock
3 ex-CIE coaches

what, if any, services would be operated during 1997. *If* services are operated they will be on Saturdays in July and August, departing Galway at 12.00 and 15.30, Athery at 14.00 and 17.05
Journey time: 1-3hr return (see

timetable for details)
Memberships details: Contact above address for details
Note: Prospective travellers are advised to check before their visit.

Channel Islands / Ireland / Isle of Man

Miniature Railways

Audley End Railway, Essex

Audley End, Saffron Walden, Essex. Tel: (01799) 541354 or 541956

General Manager: Donald Saggers

Opening details: Daily — Easter week, summer half-term, summer school holidays; Saturdays, Sundays and bank holidays April-October (from 14.00)

10sin gauge; 1.5-miles long; 4 steam, 3 diesel locomotives

Public access: BR Audley End (1-mile), free car park

Site facilities: Light refreshments on ex-London Transport RT-type double-deck bus, toilets, large picnic area

Note: (Postal address) Audley End Estate Office, Brunketts, Wendens Ambo, Saffron Walden, Essex CB11 4JL

Dobwalls Family Adventure Park

Dobwalls, Nr Liskeard, Cornwall PL14 6HD. Tel: (01579) 320325/321129. Infoline (01579) 320578. Fax: (01579) 21345

General manager: J. B. Southern

Opening details; Daily Easter-30 September. 10.00-18.00 (last admissions 16.30)

7.25in gauge; two 1-mile long routes; 6 steam and 4 diesel locomotives

Public access: By train: BR Liskeard — 3 miles; By Bus — National Express coaches to/from Cornwall via Plymouth stop in Dobwalls village; By car — signposted off A38

Site facilities: Refreshments, toilets inc disabled, mother & baby facilities, picnic area, souvenirs, radio-controlled boats and trucks, crazy golf, children's adventure playground, wildlife gallery

Facilities for disabled: Wheelchair access throughout (free loan, subject to availability), toilets

Great Cockcrow Railway, Surrey

Hardwick Lane, Lyne, Chertsey, Surrey. Tel: Mon-Fri (01932) 228950; Sun (01932) 565474

Opening details: Every Sunday May to October inclusive, 14.00-17.30

7.25in gauge; normal run 1-mile; 16 steam locomotives, 1 electric, 2 petrol (nine normally in service)

Public access: BR Chertsey (1.25 miles); London Buslines 561, 586 Holloway Hill (half-mile), free car park

Site facilities: Toilet; light refreshments

Special note: Sponsored by Ian Allan Group

Kerr's Miniature Railway

West Links Park, Arbroath, Angus. Tel: (01241) 879249

(Along the seafront to the west of town)

General Manager: Mathew B. Kerr

Opening details: Easter-end of September — weekends (14.00-17.00). All of July and first half of August — daily 11.30-13.00/14.00-17.00. All times weather permitting

10.25 in gauge; 400yd (alongside br line); 3 steam, 2 diesel, 2 petrol

Public access: BR Arbroath station 1.5 miles; Strathtay Buses route A92

Site facilities: None, but park has toilets, snack bar etc

Lightwater Valley Theme Park, North Yorkshire

North Stainley, Nr Ripon, North Yorkshire. Tel: (01765) 635368 (24 hours), 635321 (administration/party bookings)

Opening details: Easter-October (daily in June/July/August). Telephone for details

Chief Engineer: Chris Bulmer

15in gauge; 1-mile long; 6 steam, 1 diesel, 1 petrol locomotives

Public access: BR Harrogate (12 miles), BR Thirsk (9 miles), free car park

Site facilities: 125 acres of country park featuring unique white knuckle rides including the world's biggest rollercoaster, live family entertainment, leisure pursuits, skill-testing activities. Wide range of catering facilities and themed shopping malls

Moors Valley Railway, Dorset

Moors Valley Country Park, Horton Road, Ashley Heath, Nr Ringwood, Dorset. Tel: (01425) 471415

General Manager: Mr J. A. W. Haylock

Opening details: Sundays all year; Saturdays March-October; daily all school holidays and Spring Bank Holiday to mid-September. Santa Specials in December.

  Steam Gala — 7/8 June

7.25 in gauge; 1-mile long; 10 steam locomotives

Public access: Wilts & Dorset bus X2, from Bournemouth/Ringwood to Ashley Heath

Site facilities: Picnic areas, lakeside walks, adventure playground, railway shop and refreshments all set in the beautiful Moors Valley Country Park. Car park toilets (including disabled)

Association of Independent Railways & Preservation Societies Ltd

Company Secretary & General Administrator
Raymond Williams, 16 Woodbrook, Charing, Ashford, Kent
TN27 0DN. Tel/fax: 0123 3712130

Company Limited by Guarantee and not having a share capital.
Registered in England No 2226245
(Registered Office: 21 Market Place, Wednesbury, West
Midlands WS10 7AY)
President: Dame Margaret Weston DBE
Vice President: Allan Garraway MBE

General Membership Secretary:
Arthur Harding, 6 Ullswater Grove, Alresford, Hants SO24 9RP.
Tel/Fax: 01962)733327.

Corporate Membership Secretary:
David Woodhouse MBE, 8 Ffordd Dyfrig, Tywyn, Gwynedd
WQ16 8BX.

Journal Editors:
Jackie and Michael Cope, 30 Gledhow Drive, Oxenhope,
Keighley, West Yorkshire BD22 9SA.

Members of the Association of Independent Railways & Preservation Societies Ltd

UK Affiliate Members
Britt Alcroft (Thomas) Ltd: 3
Grovenor Square, Southampton,
Hampshire SO1 2BE
Friends of Tynemouth Station:
Ylana First, 20 Hotspur Street,
Tynemouth, Tyne & Wear
NE30 4EL
Guild of Railway Artists: Mr F. P.
Hodges, 45 Dickens Road,
Warwick, Warwickshire
CV34 5NS
Locomotive Club of Great Britain:
Mr R. L. Patrick, 8 Wolviston
Ave, Bishopgate, York YO1 3DD
*London Transport Museum
Library:* 39 Wellington Street,
Covent Garden, London WC2E
7BB
Transport Trust: Mr D.
Muirhead, 202 Lambeth Road,
London SE1 7JW
Westinghouse Signals: Mr J. Mills
PO Box 79, Pew Hill,
Chippenham, Wiltshire SN15
1ND
Winson Engineering: Miss Gill

Watkins, Units 3 Faraday Close,
Drayton Fields, Daventry,
Northants NN11 5RD

Overseas Affiliate Members
AJECTA: M Phillippe Tomatis,
Depot des Machines, Boite
Postale No 1, F-77650,
Longeville, Franmce
APPEVA: Secretariat, BP 106-
80001, Amiens Cedex 1, France
*Association of Tourist Railways
Inc:* 8 Tristania Street, Doncaster
East, 3109 Victoria, Australia
*Australian Railway Historical
Society:* Mr R. Jowett, New South
Wales Division, 67 Renwick St,
Redfern, NSW 2016, Australia
CFM Blonay-Chamby: PO Box
366 CH 1001, Lausanne,
Switzerland
Febelrail: Mr J. van Olmen,
Holle, Eikaard 45, B-2250
Kontitck, Belgium
Locomotive & Railway Press: PO
Box 95, Richmond, VT, 05477,
USA

*National Museum of Science &
Technology:* The Librarian, PO
Box 9724, Ottawa Terminal,
Ottawa, Ontario K1G 5A3,
Canada
Puffing Billy Railway: PO Box
145, Belgrave, Victoria 3160,
Australia
Stoomscentrum Maldegem: Rik
Degruyter, De Streep 19, B-B340
Damme-Sysele, Belgium
*Stoompoorlijn Dendermonde-
Puurs:* Mr Jaak Serckx, Station
Baasrode Noord, Fabrieksstraat
118, B-9200, Baasrode, Belgium
Swedish Railway Museum: Kjell
Palen, Box 571, S801 Gavle,
Sweden

Additional Corporate Members not listed in the main part of the book
Bahamas Locomotive Society: Mr
K. J. Tait, 73 Derby Road, Heaton
Moor, Stockport, Cheshire SK4
4NG

Battle of Britain Locomotive Preservation Society: Mr R. J. Tanner, 317 Cardington Road, Bedford MK42 0DU

Britain's Great Little Railways: M. Gaunt, 28 South View, Holton le Clay, Grimsby DN36 5BW

Britannia Locomotive Society: Mr A. Sixsmith, 6 Vermont Grove, Peterborough PE3 6BN

Bulleid Society Ltd: Mr D. A. Foale, Namron, South Chailey, Lewis, East Sussex BN8 4AD

Butetown Historic Railway Society Ltd (Vale of Glamorgan Railway)

Camelot Locomotive Society: Mr P. W. Gibbs, 54 Latimer Gardens, Pinner, Middx HA5 3RA

Class 45/1 Preservation Society: P. Crumpton, 34 Alexander Road, Handsworth, Birmingham B21 0PL

Cornish Steam Locomotive Preservation Society Ltd: Mr M. Orme, 3 Jubilee Terrace, Goonhavern, Truro, Cornwall TR4 9JY

Cotswold Steam Preservation Ltd: Mr F. G. A. Leach, Kelso, Vicarage Lane, Brockworth, Glos GL4 3EZ

Diesel and Electric Group: Mr R. Jones, 32 Ty Wern Road, Rhiwbina, Cardiff CF4 6EB

Diesel Units Preservation Associates Ltd: Mr M. Cornell, 24 Ashbury Drive, Marks Tey, Colchester, Essex SS6 9AR

Eastleigh Railway Preservation Society: Mr K. P. Horn, 1 Merry Tree Close, West Wellow, Romsey, Hants SO51 6RB

Errol Station Museum Trust: David Tough, 48 Moyness Park Drive, Blairgowrie, Perthshire PH10 6LX

Forest Pannier Tank Fund: Mr J. S. Metherall, 15 Sudbrook Way, Gloucester GL4 4AP

Foxcote Manor Society: Mr I. W. N. Evans, 183 Delamere Street, Winsford, Cheshire CW7 2LY

GWR 813 Preservation Fund: Mr P. Goss, 23 Hatchmere, Thornbury, Bristol BS12 3EU

Hampshire & Sussex Units Preservation Society: Mr C Dann, 48 Hollybrook, Bordon, Hants GU35 0DL

Hastings Diesels Ltd: Mr G.

Smith, 15 Orchard Glade, Headcorn, Nr Ashford, Kent TN27 9SS

Hull & Barnsley Railway Stock Fund: Mr A. Halman, 6 Chequerfield Court, Chequerfield Avenue, Pontefract, West Yorkshire WP8 7TQ

Irchester Narrow Gauge Railway Trust: Mr R. Kingston, 'Lysander', 71 Bedford Road, Cranfield, Bedfordshire MK43 0EX

Irish Traction Group: Mr Peter Jones, c/o 31 Hayfield Road, Bredbury, Stockport, Cheshire SK6 1DE

Keighley & Worth Valley Preservation Society

Lambton No 29 Syndicate: Mr J. M. Richardson, 5 Ravine Hill, Filey, North Yorkshire YO14 9EU

Lancashire & Yorkshire Railway Preservation Society: Mr E. Ring, 111 Huddersfield Road, Elland, West Yorks HX5 0EE

Lincolnshire Coast Light Railway Historical Vehicles Trust: Mr H. L. Goy, 12 Giles Street, Cleethorpes DN35 8AE

Liverpool Locomotive Preservation Group: Mr K. Soper, 90 Brick Kiln Lane, Rufford, Lancs L40 1SY

Lloyds Railway Society: Mr Peter Wood, 30 Beechwood Road, Caterham, Surrey CR3 6NA

Locomotive Owners Group (Scotland) Ltd: Mr J. L. Stevenson, 4 Queens Road, Blackhall, Edinburgh EH4 2BY

London & North Western Society: Mr J. C. James, c/o Westlands Hotel, 30 Trinity Ave, Llandudno LL15 2TQ

Lynton & Barnstable Light Railway: Mr D. Tooke, 3 Torrs Walk Ave, Ilfracombe, Devon EX34 8AU

Maid Marian Locomotive Fund: Mr R. Mason, Bodnolwyn Wen, Llantrisant, Anglesey LL65 4TW

Manston Locomotive Preservation Society: T. L. Mann, 41 Crow Hill Road, Garlinge, Margate, Kent CT9 5PF

Maunsell Locomotive Society: Mr R. Packham, Chairman, 132 Church Road, Swanscombe, Kent DA10 0PH

Merchant Navy Locomotive Preservation Society Ltd: Mr R. Abercrombie, 12 Inglewood Avenue, Heatherside, Camberley, Surrey GU15 1RJ

Modern Railway Society of Ireland: Mr M. A. McFerran, 54 Prince's Drive, Newtownabbey, Northern Ireland BT37 0AZ

North British Locomotive Society: Mr E. M. Pepperell, 5 Perry Court, South Place, Surbiton, Surrey KT5 8RZ

North Eastern Locomotive Preservation Group: Mr P. Hutchinson, 57 Millview Drive, Tynemouth, Tyne & Wear NE30 2QD

North Gloucestershire Railway Co Ltd: Mr R. H. Wales, 'Wellesbourne', Oakfield Street, Tivoli, Cheltenham, Gloucestershire GL33 8HR

North London Locomotive Preservation Society: Mr R. T. Moore, 7 Woodbine Grove, Enfield, Middlesex EN2 0EA

North West Ireland Rly Soc: D. W. Watson, 7 Nicholson Ter, Londonderry NI BT49 7LW

Ongar Railway Preservation Society: Mr B. Ayton, 75 Highland Road, Nazeing, Essex EN9 2PU

Railworld: Mr J Jeffery, 42 North Street, Oundle, Peterborough PE8 4AL

Rother Valley Railway(East Sussex) Ltd: Mr G. S. Crawley, Penny Cottage, Yelsted, Sittingbourne, Kent ME9 7UT

Redditch Steam Locomotive Preservation Society: Mr A. Marsden, 72 Longhurst Croft, West Heath, Birmingham B31 4SQ

Salisbury Steam Locomotive Preservation Trust: Mr E. J. Roper, 33 Victoria Road, Wilton, Salisbury, Wiltshire SP2 0OZ

Somerset & Avon Railway: Mr D. J. Hill, 8 Long Lakes, Willington, Taunton, Somerset TA4 4SR

Somerset & Dorset Railway Trust: M. J. Palmer, The Haven, Chandlers Lane, Edington, Bridgwater, Somerset TA7 9JY

South Wales Pannier Group: Mr J. Melhuish, 74 Loychurch Road, Bridgend, Mid Glamorgan CF31 2AP

South West Main Line Steam Co: Mr D. Cloke, Church Cottage, Burton Cross, East Coker, Yeovil, Somerset BA22 2AP

Southern Electric Group: Mr J. M. Cousins, 51 Primrose Walk, Shortcroft Road, Ewell, Surrey KT17 2EZ

Stanier 8F Locomotive Society Ltd: Mr D. R. McIntosh, 1 The Hawthornes, Comberton Road, Kidderminster, Worcs DY10 3DH

Steam Power Trust '65: Mr A. R. Thompson, The Station House, Penshaw, Houghton le Spring, Tyne & Wear DK4 7PQ

Stephenson Locomotive Society: Mr B. F. Gilliam, 25 Regency Close, Chigwell, Essex IG7 5NY

The Gresley Society: Mr G. Goslin, 8 Pevensey Grove, Flitwick, Bedford MK45 1SD

Tunbridge Wells & Eridge RPS: General Manager, Eridge Station, Eridge Green, Tunbridge Wells TN3 9LE

Underground Railway Rolling Stock Trust: Mr D. C. Alexander, 13 Irvine Drive, Stoke Mandeville, Aylesbury HP22 5UN

Urie Locomotive Society: Mr A. Ball, 'Lavenham', Adams Lane, Selbourne, Alton, Hants GU34 3LJ

Wainwright 'C' Preservation Society: Mr I. DeMaid, 69 Bromley Gardens, Bromley, Kent BR2 0ES

Weardale Railway Society: Mr G. Chatsfield, Stanhope Station,

Bondisle, Bishop Aukland Co Durham DL13 2YS

Welsh Industrial & Maritime Museum: Bute Street Docks, Cardiff CF1 6AN

Western Locomotive Association: Mr D. H. Tompkins, 9 Queens Court, Ledbury, Herefordshire HR4 9DN

Worcester Locomotive Society Ltd: Mr A. T. Dowling, 23 Belle Orchard Close, Ledbury, Herefordshire WR14 1HR

1708 Locomotive Preservation Trust Ltd: Mr G. W. Kingham, Registered Office, 106 Stanford Road, Luton, Beds LU2 0QA

1857 Society: Mr K. R. Bowen, 18 Lochmore Close, Hollycroft, Hinckley, Leicestershire

45428 Stanier Class 5 Locomotive Society Ltd: Mr J. B. Hollingsworth, 'Creua', Llanfrothen, Penrhyndeudraeth, Gwynedd LL48 6HS

48624 Locomotive Soc: G. Robb, 26 Old Gardens Close, Tunbridge Wells, Kent TN2 5ND

6024 Preservation Society Ltd: Mr C. K. Hargreaves, Spencer Lodge, Back Lane, Chapel Brampton, Northampton NN6 8AJ

6201 Princess Elizabeth Society Ltd: Mr E. J. Whitlock, 4 Lypiatt View, Bussage, Stroud, Glos GL6 8DA

71000 Duke of Gloucester Steam Locomotive Trust Ltd: Mr F. Reid, 2 Bodmin Avenue, Marthside, Soutport PR4 9TU

8E Association: Mr A. Ashurst, 149 St Mary Street, Latchford, Warrington, Cheshire WA4 1EL

9462 Preservation Group: Mr R. Melhuish, 74 Coychurch Road, Bridgend, Mid Glamorgan CF31 2AP

A1 Steam Locomotive Trust Ltd: PO Box 282, Doncaster, Yorks DN8 7LF

A4 Locomotive Society Ltd: Mr G. R. Pope, Secretary, Keeper's Cottage, Muntham Farm, North End, Findon, Worthing BN14 0RQ

LM2MT 46464 Trust: Mr D Fraser, 6 Westbury Lodge Close, Pinner, Middx HA5 3FG

Applicant Organisations

Alne Valley Railway
Barrow Hill Engine Shed Society
Birmingham Railway Museum Trust
Bredgar & Wormshill Light Railway
Eden Valley Railway Society
Great Yorkshire Railway Preservation Society
Grimsby Louth Railway Preservation Society
Market Drayton Railway Preservation Society
Port Road Railway Society
Southwold Railway Society

Late Information

The Co-Bo, No D5705, has moved from Peak Rail to the **East Lancashire Railway**.

Great Gable is returning to the **Midland Railway Centre** following two years on the Great Central Railway.

The **East Lancs Railway** has acquired Class 03 No D2062.

The **Mid-Norfolk Railway** services between Dereham and Wymondham are expected to start in August subject to HM Railway Inspectorate authorisation.

The sale of track to the **Nottingham Heritage Centre** has been 'postponed' by Railtrack pending the outcome of consultation with potential freight operators.

The East Anglian Railway Museum's *Gunby* is on a five year loan to the **Gwili Railway.**

Three Class 03s, Nos 03027/084/158 have moved to **Peak Rail** from a private location.